Hope with Depression

To Kevin, Charlotte and Samantha
and
to all my family and friends, thank you for loving me.

Acknowledgements

First and foremost, I would like to say a BIG thank you to my wonderful husband Kevin, who has always given me his unconditional love and support. His unquestioning belief in me has given me the strength to achieve all I have so far... I love you more with every new day.

To our beautiful twin daughters, Charlotte and Samantha; I am so proud of the gorgeous young ladies you have become and love you both very much.

A big thank you to Callum and Jay for loving our girls unconditionally and making my family complete; love you both loads.

Much love to my mum and dad, who have always been there for me with the kettle on and ready to listen, with their constant love and support.

My brother Steve and sister-in-law Sue, thank you for being there.

A special thank you to Kate, Wendy, Gill, Gerry, Leanne, Hannah, Dionne, Kyra, Michelle, Shauna, Neil and all my friends who continue to love me unconditionally, your friendship is a rare and valued gift.

A warm thank you to our wonderful GPs, past and present, John Dalzell and Sarah Benney, who over the years have given us as a family and me as a professional their unreserved support.

Thank you to all my clients both past and present who have put their trust and belief in me and my work, which has enabled me to help and support them to make the positive changes needed in their lives and, in doing so, changed mine.

A huge thank you to Mel Hunter, who has been my writing hand to help create *Hope with Depression*.

And special thanks to Stephen Mallen for all his support throughout the writing of this book and for honouring the pledge he made to his son, to bring about lasting change for all those affected by mental illness.

I have been incredibly privileged to have been supported by so many wonderful people from all walks of life, who have all trusted and believed in me enough to make a contribution to this book; for that I thank you all.

Lastly, and by no means least, thank you to my lovely publisher Georgina Bentliff (Hammersmith Health Books) for being so supportive, open minded and a total pleasure to work with.

Once again, a big thank you to all the mentioned above and the many others who have championed, helped and supported me over the years; without each and every one of you, I know I would not be who and where I am today, both personally and professionally; for this I will always be grateful.

Foreword

Depression is one of mankind's most prevalent and most pernicious diseases. According to the World Health Organization (WHO), approximately 300 million people, representing 4.4% of the world's population, are suffering from depressive illness.[1] Depression is a leading factor in suicide, which accounts for more than 800,000 deaths worldwide and more than 6000 in the UK every year.

WHO data in 2015 also showed that depression is the single largest cause of global disability, accounting for 7.5% of all years lived with a disability or illness. Depression is quite simply one of humanity's greatest burdens, impacting on the lives of untold millions who endure profound misery and despair on a daily basis.

Perversely, however, depression – like many other psychological disorders – remains poorly appreciated and mired in stigma and misunderstanding. This is intensely problematic. Millions of people suffer in silence, afraid to reach out for the care and support they so desperately need. Policy makers and economists struggle to formulate plans and investments which might start to address the problem. Employers remain unsure how to properly address mental health in the workplace and the school system has become the unwitting crucible of a crisis in adolescent mental illness.

We also remain largely illiterate as a society with regard to depression and mental illness. This leaves vast numbers of parents, spouses, relatives, colleagues and friends unable to provide care and support for those they love. Our attitudes towards and understanding of mental illness are decades behind our knowledge of physical illness. In the UK, 'Parity of Esteem' between mental and physical health was enshrined in the Health & Social Care Act (2012).[2] For the vast majority of those suffering from depression, however, parity remains little more than empty rhetoric and a distant dream.

Parity will only be achieved via structural reform. Within the UK, less than 6% of the total medical research budget is spent on mental illness.[3] Each year, we spend approximately £8 per capita on mental health research. This compares with £110 on dementia and £178 on cancer.[4] In recent years, society, celebrities, the media, employers and multiple organisations have worked together to destroy stigma and raise awareness. And we have come a long way. The persistent and profound imbalances in spending and resource allocation for those afflicted by mental illness nevertheless remind us of the enormity of the challenge still before us.

Within this context, *Hope with Depression* provides an invaluable resource which greatly improves our under-standing of this terrible condition. Drawing upon scientific reference, expert advice and the poignant and powerful lived experience of both suffers and carers, this comprehensive, accessible and honest book is designed to not only assist anyone with an interest in the subject, but to also provide crucial and detailed advice to those either living with or affected by depression.

The selfless and dedicated work of the Crilly family in this field is nothing short of exemplary, turning adversity and tragedy into informed analysis and positive action. When I lost my dear son to depression four years ago, I dedicated myself to improving the mental health system. Much progress has been made, but there is a long journey ahead. This publication represents another significant step on that journey.

Stephen Mallen
Bereaved father
Co-founder, Zero Suicide Alliance
National Suicide Prevention Action Group, Department of Health &
Social Care
Chair, The MindEd Trust

June 2019

References

1. World Health Organization. Depression and other Common Mental Disorders.: Global Health Estimates. 2017. https://apps.who.int/iris/bitstream/handle/10665/254610/WHO-MSD-MER-2017.2-eng.pdf (accessed 18/06/2019)

2. Mental Health Foundation. Parity of esteem. www.mentalhealth.org.uk/a-to-z/p/parity-esteem (accessed 18/06/2019)

3. Centre for Mental Health. The NHS Mandate and mental health. 09 April 2018. www.centreformentalhealth.org.uk/nhs-mandate-and-mental-health (accessed 18/06/2019)

4. www.theguardian.com/mental-health-research-matters/2017/jan/20/12-statistics-to-get-you-thinking-about-mental-health-in-young-people (accessed 18/06/2019 – no longer available)

To cut a long story short...

Anyone looking at us 15 years ago would have assumed from the outside that we were a perfectly 'normal' family: my husband Kevin and I and our beautiful twin daughters Charlotte and Samantha seemed to have everything anyone could possibly wish for, and more. We were in a really good place in our lives, glued together by the strong foundations of our marriage and two happy, healthy girls. Of course, we had our ups and downs, like most couples, and life threw challenges our way, but we always worked together to overcome them and move forward, trying carefully to balance our scaffolding business and family life, just like any other working parents. We were doing okay... Or so we thought.

Our picture-perfect little world fell apart when Samantha was diagnosed with the early stages of anorexia nervosa at the start of her teenage years. Her battle with this particular mental illness tested our family to its limits and, just when we thought we had come through the worst, she was then diagnosed with obsessive compulsive disorder (OCD). We had no knowledge at all of eating disorders or OCD when the girls were young and tackling these two illnesses, one following the other, was akin to climbing a mountain without a map, a guide or any of the right equipment.

As a fellow sufferer of mental illness, the main thing as a mother I was armed with was love and empathy. I had faced my own struggle in the years before Samantha's problems became apparent. For me, the diagnosis was depression, and for three years I tried to shift the black cloud that permanently overshadowed my life. With the unconditional love of my family and close friends, and a supportive GP who prescribed antidepressants, I was finally able to pull myself free, but I can now see that I too am predisposed to mental ill health and I have since had to be alert to and act on the tell-tale signs that those dark and threatening clouds could once again be gathering. I now realise it is something I will probably have to be aware of for the rest of my life.

Along with my personal experience of depression, it is also the battle we faced with Samantha that ultimately led me to where I am now, writing this book... *Hope with Depression*.

Like any parent, I wanted to do the best I could to help my daughter to recover. We tried everything we could to get her the help she so desperately needed, from our local (very supportive) GP to both NHS and private clinics and therapists, but sadly nothing appeared to be working for Samantha. I read many books and scoured the internet for as much information and guidance as I could get my hands on but could not find anything that I or my family could truly relate to or which gave me any real hope that there was a light at the end of the tunnel, for Samantha and for us as a family.

Every website, book or support group I found seemed to focus mainly on the actual person experiencing the illness and not the family, friends or carers, who I felt needed help and support just as much as the sufferer. I desperately needed answers and was keen to reach out to others, anybody with a genuine understanding of what was happening to us, to help us stop Samantha's condition in its tracks, but there was nothing available.

In a moment of desperation, with my family falling apart, I let my intuition guide me and took the decision to rehabilitate her myself. Thankfully, with the full support of our GP, the girls' school and our family and friends, I was able to dedicate myself completely to Samantha, injecting positive thinking, love and hope, whilst trying to show her a life outside of the eating disorder, and later the OCD, never giving up on my belief that she would get better no matter how difficult the situation became.

I slowly encouraged her to start communicating with me. She began sharing her distorted, and at times very irrational, views of her world and her innermost thoughts, her head engaged in a constant battle with itself. Patience, love and open-mindedness were paramount, not just with Samantha but for the family as a unit. It was the steepest learning curve I could have ever imagined, but, step by step, Samantha slowly found her way back to us.

Despite Sam's illnesses and my own experience of depression, Kevin, my husband, has never really understood mental illness, and has never pretended to. At the height of Samantha's illness the pressure and enormity of it all took its toll on us briefly, to the point that I once asked him to leave. Thankfully, he ignored my request and stayed, continuing to provide his powerful and unconditional love and support, without which we could never have survived. He used to think Samantha was intentionally behaving as she did for attention but now he readily accepts things for what they are, supporting Samantha unconditionally, even though, sometimes, he struggles to get his head around her quirky ways of thinking.

Samantha's twin sister Charlotte has also been pivotal in her recovery and now works alongside me at my practice, with an empathy that can only come from first-hand experience. She has forfeited pieces of her own life so that Samantha could be given the full-on care that she needed and the bond between my two girls is now unbelievably strong. Their mutual respect for one another, as a result of the journey they have shared, is testament to that.

I have learnt through all of this the importance of constant communication, patience, non-judgement, unconditional love and most of all HOPE and that in fact there is no such thing as the 'perfect' family. Trying to be perfect is not only unrealistic, but can be dangerous.

Some time into Samantha's recovery, I was contacted by the mother of a 17-year-old girl who was suffering from an eating disorder. She asked me if I could help them as they were finding, as we had, that none of the conventional routes was making any difference. Encouraged by my husband, I approached their situation just as I had approached Samantha's, looking beyond her illness to the person within and giving her the unconditional and non-judgemental support that I realised from our experience had been so beneficial. Having been able to help her, and her family, successfully, I made the decision to build my own counselling practice based on everything I had read, learnt and experienced from our own journey with Samantha. I then went on to do some studying of my own, including training as a Master of NLP (Neuro-linguistic Programming) and as a Psy-Tap practitioner. I was keen to work with other sufferers and their families, giving them the unreserved support and complete lack of judgement that my own experience had taught me were both vital and necessary. I tentatively opened my doors to people from all walks of life, struggling to deal with mental illness, be it the sufferer or a supportive loved one. My little successes were never shouted from the rooftops but from then on people seemed to find me through recommendation and word-of-mouth. I am now contacted on a daily basis by frantic and frightened parents, carers and siblings from all over the world, all of whom have concerns about loved ones, some as young as eight years old, most just wanting to talk to me, desperate for a glimmer of hope. I now help people suffering from eating disorders, OCD, depression anxiety, self-harm and low self-esteem. The way I interact with my clients may seem a little unorthodox to some; however, I feel it is important to get to know the person as a whole rather than just seeing them through the lens of their illness, and working alongside the family rather than just the sufferer helps to build a united front against the illness. No two people who enter my office are ever the same and they all experience the issues in a way that is unique to them; hence, the way I approach their treatment is similarly unique to each client. I am learning about each individual case as it naturally unfolds so I can give as much time and attention as we need both in and outside our sessions to build a mutual trust within our relationship which enables me to be one step ahead of the illness, in turn facilitating a quicker and more effective recovery for all concerned; we may do puzzles together while we chat, or make jewellery or other arts and crafts projects. The atmosphere tends to be much less intense than the traditional image of the patient-therapist relationship, and can at times even be fun! I have certainly learnt a lot from working with people in this way, and I focus on maintaining a positive environment, so from the minute they walk in they feel comfortable and at ease and from the very start they know they can get better and that they are in control of their own recovery.

I also respond on an emotional level rather than a clinical one to the things they tell me. I do not always get it right, and I do not pretend to; sometimes, on the odd occasion, there may be the need for additional assistance and input from other avenues but my practical and down-to-earth approach has earned me the endearing handle of 'Fairy Godmother'!

So here I am, many years later. If you had told me over 10 years ago that I would be doing what I am doing today I would not have believed you! Nor could I have foreseen that our future as a family would be so much healthier and happier; our dynamics have changed in a way I did not think possible. During these rewarding years I have had the privilege of working with some wonderful people and their families, each and every one of them unique. Whilst I have been able to support and guide them through their journeys, I too have learnt from them. My clients have said that they find my practical and down-to-earth approach really refreshing and have even compared me to the therapist in the film *The King's Speech* on more than one occasion. His methods were unconventional and unorthodox – but they got results. I never expected my practice to expand to the scale it has but through this I have been able to share my ever-growing knowledge of all kinds of mental illness and help clients to find the best route towards recovery, not just for the sufferer but for those close to them.

My ever-increasing client list highlighted just how little emotional support or real empathy there was available for the carers, friends and families of those suffering from mental illness, and having had first-hand experience of the destruction it can cause within the family unit I felt compelled to write my first book (*Hope with Eating Disorders*, published in 2012). I was keen to share what I had learnt from our journey with Samantha in the hope that it would bring some guidance, comfort, strength and hope to others. Outwardly it was impossible to identify families who were going through similar experiences, yet when I spoke openly about what we had experienced within our family, I learnt that most people I knew were struggling with something behind closed doors. They had been too afraid to talk about it for fear of the stigma or judgement which sadly still surrounds mental health issues, even in today's society when a staggering one in four of us will experience or suffer from some form of mental illness at any one time. It was then I realised how widespread issues like self-harm, anxiety, depression, OCD and eating disorders are and how confusing the wealth of information available on these subjects can be to the reader. Despite many high-profile initiatives by the Government and various celebrities making mental health awareness a target, there are still countless people of all ages suffering in silence, in need of help and support, and many loved ones, friends and carers confused and unsure of how to help them.

Looking back, although Samantha had left most of her issues

behind, she never truly felt comfortable in her own skin until the last few years, when she reignited her love for drama and the arts. Consequently, we have watched her grow into a beautiful, confident and vibrant young lady, pursuing a passion that allows her to express herself. Her passion and desire for life have been strengthened by the encouragement of her supportive and loving fiancé, Jay. Charlotte also has a wonderful, understanding husband, Callum, who has been on this journey with us since the beginning, so I am hugely relieved – being happy and healthy is all I have ever wanted for both of my girls.

This brings us to *Hope with Depression*...

My main aim in writing this new book is to help you understand depression and identify the symptoms of this destructive mental illness as early as you possibly can, allowing you to intervene swiftly and with more insight into the different treatments available (mainstream and alternative), all of which are paramount for a quicker and more effective long-term recovery.

After the first edition of *Hope with Eating Disorders* was published in 2012, which I am proud to say was very well received by sufferers, carers and those who work in the eating disorder world, I went on to write more books: *Fundamentals, A Guide For Parents, Teachers and Carers on Mental Health and Self-Esteem*, with co-author Natasha Devon; *Hope with OCD* with the publisher of this edition, Hammersmith Health Books; and then the second edition of *Hope with Eating Disorders*, again published by Hammersmith Health Books, in 2019.

In the eight years since I wrote my first book, the first edition of *Hope with Eating Disorders*, many things have moved on and changed in the way mental illness is portrayed and understood. The wider public's understanding of these complex conditions has in many ways grown but at the same time the pressures that society faces are evolving at such a pace that it can be difficult to keep up. The media landscape has altered, with the internet and social media exerting a stronger influence than ever before – and this is something we do our best to influence positively with our YouTube channel, *Hope with Mental Health*.

In the chapters that follow, I will try to answer some of the questions that I am asked frequently, and my objective is to give you, the reader, the hope and belief that you have the strength and courage not only to support and guide your child/friend/loved-one through these turbulent waters but to be able to see them safely to the other side, where they and, indeed, everyone closely involved with them will be able to move forward with their lives. I would like this book to act as a road map not only for those who simply do not know where to turn for help, but also for those who would like to have a clearer understanding of depression in general.

I hope to relieve you of some of the burden, confusion and pain you may be feeling, as you enter the unknown, and to arm you with as much knowledge, guidance and strength as I can, to enable you to continue your journey with courage, trusting in your own personal skills and instinct, just as I did, remembering always that communication is the key, along with unconditional love, perseverance, non-judgement, patience and hope.

This book emphasises that there is no 'right' or 'wrong' path to recovery. My own experience demonstrates that each family or support network must take whatever action is right for them: if one option proves ineffective, try another – never buy into the myth that people with depression cannot recover. Never give up hope and never give up trying.

With hope, perseverance, love and a lot of effort from us all, my family has reached a very positive place. Samantha has recently graduated with a 2:1 in performing arts, and is now writing her own book, *Hope Through Poetry* (some poems from which are in this book) due to be published May 2020. She has become engaged to Jay, who I know will continue to love and support her through any difficult times that may lie ahead. And above all she is happy and healthy – bubbly, funny and waking with a smile on her face. Her sister, Charlotte, is forging her own path with a loving partner, Callum, and a bright future ahead, and my husband and I can look forward to the next phase in our lives, finally content that our girls are happy and surrounded by love. Our experiences of mental illness have brought us to where we are now: wiser, more appreciative of each other, and with more understanding of others. I never stopped hoping we would one day reach this point, and now we have, I am able to hand that hope on to you. Anything is possible... my family is living proof of that.

Please note:

Over the pages that follow you will share the experiences of other carers and sufferers, and realise that some of the emotions you may be experiencing are natural and normal. You will be given an insight into how your loved one is thinking and feeling, with the aim of providing you with a genuine understanding of their condition. I have also included an unbiased guide to some different types of treatment available, both mainstream and alternative. All the contributors and therapists are real people, but some have changed their names to protect their identity.

Behind the mask
By Samantha Crilly

People sometimes ask me why I feel this way
And for the life of me I can never think of what to say
It can be mistaken for a feeling of sadness, but this couldn't
be less true
Although don't get me wrong, I can feel sad too
I can even feel streaks of happiness run through my mind
But it's always the clarity I can never seem to find
Like an emotionless fog running through my head space
Always keeping me in exactly the same place
An intense crippling timeless dimension
Where everything I do requires constant attention
It sounds crazy, but the biggest struggle for me is getting out
of bed
It's never out of laziness, it's pure dread for the day ahead
An on-going battle which continuously waits at my feet
The same one as yesterday I crawled my way through to
defeat
The only escape I encounter is when I'm sleeping
Yet so often I still feel the depression creep in
I can occasionally be persuaded to venture out for a walk
But I pray I don't bump into anyone and have to talk
Sometimes I catch familiar faces I haven't seen in a while
But I never set loose the truth, I just stand there and smile
I do wonder if they can ever tell,
Then again I know my mask hides me well
My home is now my safe place, I feel somewhat secure
Nowadays I never really feel curious as to what's outside the
door
I don't seem to hold a connection to the world anymore
When I am in my moments of darkness
I always remember that time moves on regardless
I know this present moment won't last after today
And maybe, just maybe, one day I will feel okay

Chapter 1

What is depression?

Depression, in its clinical sense, is defined as a 'low mood disorder'; however, in reality it is much more than that. It is a deep-rooted, debilitating and destructive mental illness that affects both the sufferers and their carers alike. Once well established, the severity of this dreadful illness and the tormented misery it rains down on the sufferer can destroy relationships and ruin the lives of not only the person suffering but also everyone around them. Some may describe depression as 'feeling like they are stuck under water'; others as though they are 'looking at their life through a frosty window'. For me, it was like having a black cloud following me around wherever I went from the minute I woke up to the minute I went to sleep.

Depression changes a person's way of thinking, their feelings and/or their behaviour. This can cause the person distress, and can make it difficult to function on a psychological and sometimes on a physical level too. Individuals with depression may not always look ill, particularly if their symptoms are mild. However, some sufferers may show more obvious and explicit physical signs.

Together, anxiety and depression are two of the most common mental illnesses and are thought to affect around one in five of the British population at some point in their lifetime.[1] Like all mental illnesses, depression does not discriminate and can affect anyone, regardless of age, gender, sexuality, ethnicity or social background. However, evidence also shows that certain groups in society may be more vulnerable to depression than others.

Everyone's experience and journey with depression is unique to them. It can present itself in many different guises and can be an illness of extremes. For some, its control can deprive them of sleep, while others may find themselves sleeping for days at a time. Similarly, some may find themselves emotionally eating to excess, while others may find their appetite has been totally demolished. Equally, some sufferers may find themselves frantic with excess energy, while others may struggle just to get out of bed. For me, the depression caused extreme fatigue. I felt constantly exhausted, making it a struggle to function on a daily basis.

Depression is a serious mental illness and deserves the same attention and respect as any physical illness, yet sadly, as it is essentially invisible, it is still often woefully misunderstood, feared and trivialised. If we were to break one of our arms or legs, not only would a doctor know exactly how to fix it, but we would probably receive a lot of sympathy and support from the people around us.

With depression, there is no such obvious response. Fearing what they cannot see, people around the sufferer may draw away or worry that they will say or do the wrong thing. This can be frustrating for someone experiencing depression, as they might feel that their condition has not been recognised, or that the people close to them do not care.

Emma, who suffers from depression, says:

> I don't think that people fully understand how I feel. My husband certainly doesn't. No one talks to me about it and sometimes I feel that I want to talk about it but that it's pointless.

To be brutally honest I didn't understand mental health issues before I was diagnosed with depression. I feel I was very dismissive of it, like it didn't exist. Like people made it up. And I wonder if that's how other people feel about me.

For someone suffering in silence it can take an act of great courage and strength to admit to a loved one or a medical professional that there could potentially be something wrong. Once it is all out in the open, it can be such a relief for the sufferer to know they are not going mad and that what they are experiencing is, in fact, a very common mental health issue suffered by millions of people across the globe.

The duration for which someone can suffer from depression differs from person to person; in some cases, as it was for me, it can take root and manifest itself for months or even years at a time; in other cases, it can pass through like a succession of rainstorms.

You may turn to the internet hoping it may help you to understand a bit more, or you may scour articles in the press on the condition, but this could leave you even more confused and frustrated. As there is so much varied information available through different channels, it is very difficult to know what applies to you and your own situation.

Clare O gives us her advice from her own experience as a carer:

The internet has good advice on what not to say to someone who has depression and how to support someone, but it's not as connected as sitting across from someone who is completely neutral. Hearing someone talk back to you instead of just reading off a screen seems more connected to the situation, more human.

Within this book I aim to provide the information that I think really matters, with no agenda other than helping you to

understand some of the different types of depression, the signs
to look for, and some of the various options going forward that
are available to you, the sufferer or carer.

How is depression different from feeling low?

One of the most common misconceptions surrounding
depression is that it is comparable to feeling a little sad or down.
Many people who suffer from depression do feel sadness, but
true depression is very different from just feeling low.

Bernice explains how depression is more than just having the
blues:

> I became aware of my depression when I suddenly lost my job.
> I knew it was more than just a case of feeling down. It persisted
> for a long period of time, weeks turning into months. After
> realising a year had gone by and i still felt no different, I knew
> something had to be done.

Sadness and low feelings generally resolve themselves after a
relatively short period of time, usually a matter of weeks. Feeling
this way is a normal reaction to things that happen in life, and
when hard times hit, it is absolutely natural to be plunged into
a bleak mood. Similarly, it is normal to be anxious about challenges in life and feeling worried or nervous is a sign that our
body's natural stress response is working properly.

Depression, on the other hand, extends beyond sadness. It
persists and deepens, seeping into many, if not all, areas of life
and may leave those with this debilitating and draining mental
illness struggling to cope on both a mental and a physical level,
often losing interest in the world around them.

Claire, who is in recovery from clinical depression and anxiety,
describes how her depression was more than feeling low:

Completely empty and numb. It is the only way I can describe it. The lack of reasoning, interest in your surroundings and family, kids, jobs etc. The feeling of hopelessness, that you are a failure, that you are no good at anything. A waste of space, ugly, like a big black cloud is constantly sitting with you, holding you tightly and not letting you escape.

Depression is a serious mental illness, which you cannot simply 'snap out of', or 'cheer up' by trying to think positively. The feelings of despair, lethargy, anxiety and emptiness that may characterise someone's depression are very real and should be acknowledged as such rather than dismissed or glossed over.

How does it feel?

A pervasive feeling of unhappiness coupled with a loss of interest in the things they used to love doing is fairly common to many sufferers. They may feel anxious or tearful, hopeless or wracked with guilt. Things they used to love doing may no longer bring them pleasure, and they may feel removed from other people, isolated and trapped within their own thoughts. For me, I constantly felt sad, drained and distant. Everything was all too much effort – all of which was very out of character for me.

There are also likely to be some physical symptoms. Those with depression may struggle to sleep or sleep too much. They may feel constantly lethargic, suffer with aches and pains, lose their sex drive and/or have issues with food. They may find it hard to concentrate, battle with making decisions and/or be weighed down by poor self-esteem and self-worth.

Pete, who is in recovery from major depressive disorder, shares how he felt:

The guilt and shame can be unbearable – partly because of the stigma that we associate with mental health problems. I lose all energy and can struggle to get up and do even the most basic day-to-day tasks. I struggle to concentrate and can become forgetful and unreliable, causing myself more guilt. I've had periods when I've felt so ashamed of myself and how I have looked that I've been unable to look at myself in a mirror for even a fraction of a second. I've also had physical symptoms, such as mystery aches and pains, tingling in my arms and hands, and headaches. All of these feelings have led to me having significant periods where I've had consistent suicidal thoughts.

In severe cases, these feelings of worthlessness and hopelessness may be so acute that sufferers may struggle to see the meaning of their existence, to the point where they may consider taking their own life.

I have briefly mentioned the black cloud that constantly followed me around, as that is how my depression felt to me, but it will vary from person to person. Many are familiar with the phrase 'The Black Dog', which, it is said, is how Winston Churchill described his own depressive spells. The idea of a dark companion who stays bleakly by your side, snarling and growling, will be familiar to many people with depression. To others it can feel different, perhaps causing a feeling of numbness or detachment from everyday life. Some will say they feel like they are suffocating and struggling for breath; others, that they have a heavy weight pressing down on them. They may even say it as if life is a rollercoaster with the fall approaching but the sufferer powerless to stop it. Each individual with depression will have their own interpretation

Jamie Day, who is in recovery from severe depression, says:

At its worst, it was like wearing blinkers. All I could see was a dark tunnel with immense, frenzied noise attacking me as I tried to make my way through. There was no clarity to my thinking, just sadness, panic and loss of hope, which always resulted in suicidal thoughts. Dark thoughts became my norm and were like a (very dangerous) coping strategy, knowing I'd be ending it soon. Thankfully, I didn't.

Katie says of how her depression makes her feel:

> Depression made me feel like I was in a bubble. I could see normality around me but I couldn't feel it and I couldn't pop that bubble. I would watch my family and friends smiling and interacting but I couldn't pop the bubble and come out of it and be the real Kate. I would often remind myself of the real Kate and couldn't understand why I couldn't be that person again. I felt like a shell of my former self, almost like an out-of-body experience.

Sheila describes how she puts on a mask when she is out and how it makes her feel:

> When I do go out, I put on an act, with a smile, and pretend all is okay with me. Which in itself I find totally exhausting! As soon as I get back home I feel a sense of relief, I can take the mask off and go back to how I really feel – depressed!

What depression is not

In the hope of arming you with as much knowledge and understanding of this dark and destructive mental illness as I can, I thought it might be helpful to cover a few points on what I think depressions is *not*.

Depression is NOT:

Something you can just 'snap out of'

For most people, it is not possible to 'out-think' depression. A sufferer cannot simply paint a smile on their face and forget how they are feeling. I know this from my own experience and, believe me, I tried. However much I 'put on a brave face' and pretended everything was okay, the black cloud continued to follow me around and was constantly present.

For carers and loved ones who have never suffered from or

had any personal experience with depression, it can be hard not to tell someone to just 'look on the bright side' or 'count your blessings'. But it is much more helpful to try to acknowledge their feelings and to understand what they are going through as this could be the validation they need that will encourage them to seek help.

Howard says of how people around him thought it was a phase he would snap out of:

> When I was at my lowest and I couldn't hide the depression any longer, my friends just really did not understand. They kept saying I would just wake up and not feel like this anymore. Every day I woke up and felt the exact same, if not worse. It is definitely something I could not just snap out of.

A sign of weakness

Depression is not a sign that someone simply cannot cope, that they should 'man up' and be strong enough to resist the negative thoughts. However, it is misconceptions like this that can actually prevent people from getting help because they fear that society (including family, friends and work colleagues) could judge them.

In fact, the opposite is true. Fighting through the turmoil of depressive illness is truly a testament to someone's strength. Like a powerful storm, depression can mentally batter a sufferer. To be strong enough to face that onslaught, while at the same time making efforts to gain an understanding of the illness they are suffering from, shows a person should be respected and admired.

Janet, whose husband is now recovered from depression, says:

> It took a good year or so for my husband to start feeling like himself again after struggling with depression for quite a long

time. Honestly, I think it took more courage and strength for him to start the recovery journey and get himself on track than it did for him to stay with the depression. I am so proud of where he is now and he has said that he is so happy that he took that difficult journey.

Something everyone goes through

Most people experience extreme sadness at some point in their life, perhaps through a traumatic event, such as the death of a loved one, or a major upheaval, such as redundancy, divorce or illness. This may even make them 'feel depressed', but that sadness is often a feeling, whereas depression itself is an illness.

The difference is that people who 'feel depressed' will find that their sadness is temporary and is generally linked to something that has happened to them. Depression, on the other hand, which according to the charity Mind around 3% of the population are experiencing at any one time, can be exacerbated or even triggered by life events.

For those who do not suffer from depression, their black clouds can be chased away by sunshine. For those who battle through this mental illness, the cloud stubbornly lingers, no matter how bright the world outside is looking.

Something that lasts forever

The idea that depression could last forever, that it could plague someone for the rest of their life, can make the illness seem even more overwhelming and distressing. It may even prevent sufferers from seeking help as they believe and worry that there is no way out of it. In fact, for around half of those who suffer a depressive episode, it will be a one-off. Though the other half will suffer from depression more than once, they may also have many long periods when they are well. They can often find ways other than medication to manage the illness, and those tools they learn may also benefit other areas of their life. Furthermore, they will come to recognise when they might be vulnerable or susceptible to another period of depression, which will enable them to get the right help and support more quickly and recover faster.

Arun inspires us when he says:

> Recovery is like being born again. Another opportunity within life, to be able to be yourself and no longer fear what others may think of you and not to fear that you are a monster. You are entitled to be you.

Causes of depression

It is clear that depression can have a range of complex factors at its root, including biological and psychological causes, as well as issues linked to society and the knocks and challenges that life can throw at us.

Although there are various theories surrounding its development, it is currently thought to be a combination of biological, genetic, cognitive and environmental factors acting together, or individually, as a trigger.

Genetics and family history

While depression can often be linked to someone's experiences in life, it is also now known that genetics can play a part and if you have a close family member with depression, you are more likely to develop it yourself. Research is ongoing to identify the genes that make people more susceptible to certain types of depression, although it is worth bearing in mind that the link may also be due to the fact that we learn behaviour from those closest to us as we are growing up.

Ella shares her experience:

> Both of my parents have suffered with mental illness at one point in their life. I definitely think I was 'born' with it in my blood. No matter how much I try to fight it sometimes it just still comes at me. I am able to live my life, but just know it is part of me and my family and we all have to stay strong for each other.

Personality type

The way someone views the world and how they react to the things that happen to them in their life can also influence their chance of developing depression. Our perspective is shaped early by events in our childhood and the models we are shown by those closest to us, leading us to develop certain personality types. Some of these personalities place us more at risk of developing depression. For example, those who are prone to worrying or are easily rattled may have a higher risk, while those who fear social situations or who are wary of getting too close to others can be more sensitive and less resilient when faced with stressful life events.

Elaine shares her experience of how her depression emerged:

> I believe it was my internalisation of things and feeling that everything was my fault and that I was not good enough. I never put myself first. Low self-worth and low self-esteem. My parents were very strict and always said you can do better so now I am a perfectionist and try to strive for perfection which is unattainable, so everything I do is never up to the standards I have so this leads to feeling a failure.

Brain chemistry

For the non-scientists among us, brain chemistry can remain pretty mystifying. Even the experts are not entirely sure what happens in the brain that causes depression. The most likely answer is thought to lie with neurotransmitters, the chemicals that carry signals from one part of the brain to another. In people with depression, the signals that relate to happiness are thought to weaken or become disrupted as they move between nerve cells, with the movement of serotonin – a chemical in the body that helps regulate mood – most likely to be affected.

Childhood experiences

It is now thought that going through difficult experiences in childhood may leave a person more susceptible to depression later in life. Abuse, neglect, an unstable family life, bereavement or another traumatic event can have an impact that lasts a lifetime. It is possible that a succession of challenges may have a bigger impact than one single traumatic event.

Battling through painful emotions and situations as a child can lead to low self-esteem, and this could impact someone's chances of developing depression.

Charliee, who suffers from bipolar disorder, shares her experience:

> I had quite a challenging childhood with my family. My father also has a bipolar diagnosis and would self-medicate with alcohol. Sadly, this made him physically violent to me, my mum and my eight siblings. I've had no contact with him for 12 years so I'm guessing that probably had something to do with causing depression!

Stressful life events

Often a stressful event can be the precursor to depression developing. This may be because self-esteem, which when strong can be an important defence against mental illness, is compromised. Without support to help someone cope with the emotional fallout caused by stressful chapters in their life, it is all too easy for a low mood to spiral into depression.

People who have experienced a relationship breaking down, redundancy, bereavement, or even a stressful 'positive' event such as moving to a new house or getting married, may also find their depression is triggered.

Mary shares her experience of when she feels her depression started:

> I think it was the stressful life event of someone you are very close to, who has always been there for you, being ill and not knowing if they are going to get better. Even when my mum got better, I was still unable to lift myself back out of depression for a long time, which made me feel guilty and I didn't understand it. I should have been happy she had recovered. In the last few years my dad has suffered ill health and when he is in hospital etc I get the feelings of panic and anxiety back again that I had before and I can almost feel it creeping up on me.

Another stressful life event is something known as 'empty nest syndrome', affecting parents. This can be described as feelings of grief and/or loneliness when a child leaves home for the first time, either to attend university, live on their own or move away. A parent can be left feeling bereft and with a lack of purpose or of being needed. As this life stage is a very normal and common event, the emotional and mental repercussions could go unrecognised or even just be taken as the norm. However, these could progress into something deeper if left unspoken about or not addressed.

Tania, whose empty nest syndrome escalated into severe depression, tells us more below:

> I was very much looking forward to my son moving out. I wanted more time to myself and quality time with my husband. Once my son moved out I suddenly felt a massive void in my life; I was completely not expecting it. I did speak to a few

friends who just said it would pass and it was normal to feel that way, but for some reason the void just wouldn't shift; it got bigger and bigger until I found myself deep into depression. My husband got really worried about me and took me to the doctors; from that point I found ways to bring myself back up. It was a very dangerous time in my life and I am so grateful that my husband looked after me.

Life stages

If we consider the path of life, there are certain times and stages that may make people more vulnerable to depression, either because of changes in their bodies that may alter the way their brain processes things, or because of external factors which are more likely to cause stress in their lives.

Biological changes can occur throughout life but are most recognised during the teenage years and pregnancy. It is also recognised that in older age, changes can occur to brain function which may be related to physical illness, which could make these people more vulnerable to depression. Coupled with social isolation and loneliness that is often experienced by older members of society, depression may take hold.

Frances says:

For many years I so looked forward to the day I retired, having lots of dreams and ambitions to cover when I finally had the time. I came from quite a stressful job, and then just one day I stopped. It was actually very difficult for me, and having been around lots of people daily, and being busy, to then being pretty much on my own or with my husband caused me to sink into depression for a while. Thankfully now I am enjoying retirement and am volunteering part time.

Physical illness

Physical illness can play a part in depression in different ways. Depression (or low mood) can be triggered by illness in another part of the body, while someone with depression is also more prone to developing another illness.

Someone who has an illness may experience anxiety or depression linked to their feelings and fears about their condition, especially if the illness is a long-term one and is compromising a person's quality of life. Depression can also be a symptom of a particular illness. For example, people who have Parkinson's disease, stroke, cancer or thyroid disorders may be at higher risk of developing depression (for more information see Chapter 6).

If it is the depression that came first, the risk of developing certain illnesses is thought to be higher for those who have the mental illness. For example, research suggests that adults who have experienced depression may be at a higher risk of heart disease than those who have not.[2] Furthermore, depression can affect the life-choices that people make. It may lead to a less healthy lifestyle and it is well documented that obesity, smoking and/or heavy drinking, for example, can have a huge impact on a person's health.

Natalie shares her experience:

> When I was a teenager, I had numerous spontaneous pneumothoraxes and seven surgeries in two years. It's a lot to deal with. A lot physically and emotionally. I missed school and had to try and catch up on homework and things. I just felt really down all the time and was struggling so my parents took me to the doctor, and he said I had clinical depression. I don't think I fully realised what was going on with me, just that I felt 'different'.

Caring for someone else

Being a carer increases the risk of depression significantly. It is thought that nearly three-quarters (72%) of carers in England have suffered mental ill health, such as stress and depression.[3] This is due to a number of factors. There is the understandable stress and anxiety of looking after a loved one, the financial worries that may be connected with that, often coupled with fears about the future. By the nature of their role, carers also have little time for themselves, with their own health and well-being often put on the back-burner. They may also feel isolated and alone, which has a knock-on effect on their self-esteem and resilience. These are all factors that can make someone more vulnerable to depression.

Clare O, who now suffers from situational depression as a result of caring for her partner with depression, tells us more of her experience:

> I think being around someone you love, you can't help but to go through the motions with them.
>
> For me, although I understood that someone with depression can become a different person, at times it still was hard not to take it personally. I felt like I was a sponge to my partner's depression. There's only so many times you can listen to someone say they no longer wish to live before it puts you yourself at risk mentally, which is why I sought support in therapy, for my own well-being, without feeling guilty about putting my family and friends in the middle of the negative emotions. I never realised how little help there was for partners of people with depression; a good group would have been ideal.

Other mental illnesses

There is a very strong link between depression and other mental illnesses. For example, people with an eating disorder or obsessive-compulsive disorder may find their illness interlinks with depression. This can be something of a chicken and egg situation; it can be really difficult to determine which illness originated first, the depression or the other illness. Research clearly shows that those who suffer with one of these mental illnesses can be very vulnerable to another.[4]

For example, with eating disorders, there is evidence that a significant number of those diagnosed also have a history of depression, with persistent low mood contributing to the onset of an eating disorder. However, that connection can also work in reverse, with the undernourished brain and body of an eating disorder sufferer having a negative and debilitating effect on their mood and outlook.

For sufferers themselves and those close to them, it is therefore important to come to terms with this reality, to be vigilant to persistent changes in their mood and outlook and to understand that they need to be fore-armed against mental illness in all its guises.

Having that knowledge will give them power. It will allow them to prioritise looking after their physical and mental health and building their self-esteem and self-worth to help them deal with the mental health challenges that may come their way (for more information see Chapter 6).

Hope with depression

I know the above paints a pretty bleak picture, but I cannot reiterate enough that, from my own experience, both personally and professionally, and contrary to popular belief, full and lasting recovery from depression is possible, remembering always that, as every individual sufferer is unique, so is their experience and in turn their recovery.

The most common question I am asked by concerned friends and relatives of sufferers of depression is simply 'What can I do?' The most crucial step is to develop a better understanding of depression – not just the physical symptoms, but the state of mind which infuses them. Furthermore, the earlier you can both recognise the signs for concern and in turn act on them, the quicker your loved one may be able to receive help, stopping the illness from becoming hard-wired and taking over their life.

If you notice something is amiss, try not to adopt a 'wait and see' approach, remembering that early intervention can be key to a quicker and more effective recovery. Even if they are not ready to seek help, acknowledging your loved one's struggle and showing that you are there for them can be the first crucial step on their journey to recovery.

One thing I do not want carers to do is feel guilty. It is all too easy for the people around sufferers of depression to blame themselves. Not only is this blame often misplaced, it can actually delay recovery, potentially placing an obstacle in the way of your loved one's journey back to health. Guilt is a destructive and ultimately pointless emotion, and one I hope to rid you of.

All carers – whether they be family, friends, colleagues or professionals – if possible, need to work together as a team, not only to support the sufferer but each other, too.

Carol, whose friend is in recovery from severe depression, says of how her group of friends worked together to help Paula into recovery:

> Paula and I are part of a small group of friends, we have known each other for a long time and when Paula opened up about her depression, we all pulled together to get her the help she needed and support her through it. I do feel this is what made the difference.

Sadly, there is no miracle cure for depression. You cannot, as a carer, simply wave a magic wand to make your loved one better. You can give all the love, support and understanding in the world, but ultimately the only person that can really make that change is the sufferer. The greatest thing you can do is be right beside them as they take the difficult steps on that journey.

Depression can be contradictory and confusing, making it difficult to see a clear path ahead. No two cases are the same, which makes every treatment journey unique to the sufferer and their carer(s). I hope this book will help to give you the clarity you need to provide consistent and coherent support to both sufferers themselves and their wider family and friends. It is said that 'knowledge is power' and I hope that, by passing on many of the lessons I have learnt, you will feel armed to deal with the journey ahead.

One of the most dangerous and depressing myths surrounding depression is that it is a life sentence. It is distressing to see people 'managing' their condition, learning to cope with their illness on a day-by-day basis, with both the sufferer and their carers resigned to the fact that this is as good as it gets. Although for some, being able to manage their condition may be a huge achievement in itself, others will want to rid themselves of the illness completely.

Often it will feel like you are getting nowhere. Sometimes the situation may seem to get worse. But please do not give up. Even then, your love and support will be setting down foundations for recovery in the future. With communication, perseverance, positive thinking, love and, most importantly, hope, there is always a way through the maze of depression and a path back to health and happiness for both the sufferer and their carers – myself and my wonderful family are proof of this.

Hope with Depression will show you that full and lasting recovery is possible, and that there is no right or wrong way to recover; just as a person's journey with depression is unique to them, so is their recovery.

Below is a summary of the familiar 'facts' which are often quoted in relation to depression; many of them are, as we will discover in the rest of the book, myths which can prevent people from getting to grips with, and really being able to understand, this illness.

Myths and truths

Myth 1: It is obvious when people have depression.

Truth: Many people with depression hide it very successfully, or at least they try their very hardest to. They may be so good at concealing how they really feel that only the most alert loved ones are able to see what is really happening behind that smile. This is where knowing someone well and being aware of what is normal for them are vital. If they start showing unusual behaviour, perhaps sleeping or eating in a way that causes concern, dig deeper to see if depression or another mental illness could be the cause.

Myth 2: Antidepressants are the only way to treat depression.

Truth: Some people see antidepressant medication as something to be feared (and often avoided), because of the concerns about its side-effects and whether it could lead to an addiction. Those concerns should certainly not be ignored, but neither should they put people off seeking medical help for depression.

The best person to advise a patient about whether medication is suitable for them and what the effects of taking that medication might be is their GP. However, that is not to say that all responsibility should be handed to a medical practitioner. The patient themselves, along with their loved ones and carers, should ask about side-effects and remain alert to any potential problems they may cause.

Medication is also only one line of treatment. It is not always needed and therapy or counselling can also be very effective, while other alternative therapies may also be helpful. (See Chapters 4 and 5 for more information).

Myth 3: Depression affects mainly women.

Truth: While the number of women known to be suffering from depression is greater than the number of men, we also know that men are much less likely to come forward to seek help for their symptoms and, in our 'macho' society, perhaps find it harder to talk about their state of mind. However, the shocking fact that the biggest cause of death among men under the age of 50 is suicide clearly shows that men are also suffering with mental illness, and they need to be right at the centre of the conversation about it.

Another myth, that 'real men don't get depression' must also be scotched. Unfortunately, many men still believe that depression is a kind of weakness and should not be acknowledged. This makes the illness even more dangerous for men than women, as again they are less likely to ask for help.

Myth 4: The taboo over depression is well and truly broken these days.

Truth: Make no mistake, huge strides have been made in the way depression is recognised and understood. The younger generation of British Royals have led their own campaign, Heads Together, to help to break the stigma around mental illness and to change how wider society understands depression and other related illnesses; when they started this, suddenly it seemed that awareness about these conditions had been placed firmly under the spotlight; since then a real shift does seem to have occurred in how mental illness is viewed at work, by the media and in wider society.

However, the battle is not won. People are still wary of admitting they have a mental illness, worried that they will be judged, excluded and even potentially find they have put their careers at risk. There are still misconceptions about what mental illness really feels like, and there is still a long way to go in society's understanding of the issues.

Myth 5: You cannot help people with depression.

Truth: You cannot wave a magic wand and make the depression disappear, but you can support and care for someone with the illness and show them acceptance and understanding, and in doing so you will help to make their journey through depression easier to bear. By increasing their own knowledge about depression, the close circle of people around the sufferer can understand better how their own actions can make a difference. Furthermore, appropriate professionals, teachers, youth workers and employers can play a very important part in ensuring they deal with a mental illness such as depression appropriately, just as they would a physical illness. Society as a whole can help and support people with depression, by showing tolerance, acceptance and true understanding to those who suffer from it.

To conclude

Depression is recognised by the professional medical community and can be treated successfully with time, perseverance, determination, the right kind of therapy and, in some cases, medication. No two cases are ever the same; they are all unique to the individual sufferer, which is why treatment techniques and recovery journeys can be so varied. Sadly, there is no magic bullet, and whilst acceptance, understanding, support and patience are paramount to the sufferer's recovery, the only person who can really make the change is them. It is not an easy journey, but it is definitely one worth taking; it was for me.

Dave Davies, manager of Frank Bruno and whose own mother and mother-in-law have both had and still have depression, seconds the above:

> Working alongside Frank Bruno, who now is a mental health advocate and goes round the country giving talks on the subject, I have come to realise just how many people suffer from depression and the amount of people looking for different ways to recover. In my own experience and talking to hundreds of sufferers, I have learnt that recovery is only possible if they really want it and are prepared to put the work in to make it happen.

Chapter 2

Types of depression

Suffering from depression can be compared to being locked away in solitary confinement – isolated, dark and lonely. As time progresses, the depression begins to wreak internal havoc, until the sufferer feels like their mental space is not their own anymore, leaving them feeling helpless and trapped within their own mind, as it continues to build a powerful mountain of mental torment and chaos inside their head. Sadly, there is no escaping this jail sentence without the sufferer's own determination and willpower to break free, alongside the right kind of help and support, be it from a professional or a loved one(s), or both. For the sufferer, they are fighting an internal war with themselves, with no clear resolution. This can be utterly exhausting, and the more tired the person who has the depression becomes, the more space the head creates for the depression to occupy. Being at war with any part of yourself can never bring peace, whether it be for the sufferer or their loved ones.

Sheila, who has suffered from depression on and off for the last 20 years and is supported unconditionally by her husband Paul, says:

> I constantly feel unwell, both mentally and physically. My head is always full, I am always tired. It has got to the point where I cannot go out on my own – so I am very reliant on my husband at the moment. I have a lovely home, a wonderful husband,

> a caring family, enough money, I have everything – but I have
> nothing!

Paul, Sheila's caring husband, says:

> I accept it for what it is but cannot understand why the medical
> profession cannot sort it out! My life revolves around what
> Sheila wants to do and I am okay with that!

For anyone closely connected to depression, be it the sufferer, a carer or a loved-one, it can be a very lonely and isolating experience.

If you are the sufferer, I have the greatest compassion for you; I have felt and seen for myself how tormenting it can be for both you and the people who love and support you. You will no doubt, at some point, feel that you are losing your mind, particularly if the people around you are fearful, or dismissive about it. Or, on the other hand, you may be too frightened or embarrassed to tell anyone, so leaving you feeling utterly trapped and unsafe within your own head. Please remember, you are not alone and you are not mad no matter what the content of your thoughts are; you will not be judged by people who truly accept and understand or by those who try to. These are symptoms of a treatable mental illness, not a reflection on you as a person. And best of all, by reading material like this, you are well on the way to taking steps in a much more positive direction and expanding your understanding and knowledge.

If you are a loved-one and/or the carer, it can be not only frustrating and confusing but also very upsetting, and at times push your patience to the limit and beyond. The sufferer can sometimes seem evasive and rude, but usually they are not meaning to be or to appear so. It is often all part of the illness – their head is full of so much chaos and mess that it is a major undertaking to keep things together let alone be able to hold a half-decent conversation with anyone.

Mary says of her struggles day-to-day when her depression is bad:

> When I feel depressed, I find it hard to be motivated to do anything; it's difficult to lift myself out and it takes a real effort to do so. I don't want to talk to anyone, I don't want anyone to talk to me. I cry all the way to work, hold it together for the day then cry all the way home again. Although it doesn't make sense, I also feel bad for feeling bad.

Opportunities to communicate with someone suffering from depression about how they feel should be encouraged; the information you receive from them may prove vital in the recovery process. Do not always apply logic; accept that their mind is a confused place and that, in talking, they are providing you with an important glimpse into its inner workings.

There is so much information available now, we can often end up utterly baffled and vaguely hysterical and therein lies the problem. The term 'depression' actually covers a multitude of different manifestations, affecting people in a multitude of different ways. Some forms of depression are so well identified that they may be considered as a condition in their own right, such as postnatal depression or seasonal affective disorder (SAD), while others, such as dysthymia or cyclothymia, may be less well known.

With the hope of trying to understand this multi-faceted illness, it can be useful to be aware of the many different types of depression. At this point, it is also important to stress that these 'labels' can often have blurred boundaries. Your loved one may show signs of more than one of them or may exhibit different behaviours altogether. So, while labels can be helpful, it is important to keep in mind that everyone displays their signs and symptoms differently.

Perhaps, you have heard a number of terms used to describe

depression. In this section I will endeavour to explain what some of these mean. It is important to remember that this is by no means an exhaustive list and there will be types of depression that express themselves differently, that are not included here.

Mild, moderate or severe depression

There are varying levels of depression; these can be classified as mild, moderate or severe. The precise classification can be based on many aspects, which can include:

- the types of symptoms displayed,
- how they are experienced and
- the level of impact they have on someone's day-to-day living.

Someone with **mild depression** may find themselves less interested in doing the things they used to enjoy, lack motivation and sometimes turn their back on social activities. They may be able to continue to function on a day-to-day basis and may not even consider seeking help for their feelings. However, it can help to prevent the illness from escalating further when depression is diagnosed at this stage. Seeking help from your GP at this point is vital as there also tend to be more treatment options available, including lifestyle changes and/or natural therapies, at this early stage.

Leanne says of how her son developed mild depression after a period of bullying at school:

It seemed to have happened over night; one day he woke up and refused to go to school. After giving him a little space, I approached the subject, knowing something was wrong. He seemed quite relieved that I had asked him and he said he just didn't want to face the day. Thinking about it, a few weeks before he had withdrawn from after-school activities and seeing his friends. In the end we moved him to a different school and he became a different person, much happier and content within himself. I do think, if we hadn't acted quickly and spoken together about it, he could have got worse quite quickly.

For those with **moderate depression**, day-to-day functioning can become a real struggle. Their interest in things that they once enjoyed may dip significantly, if not altogether, so making it hard to find the motivation to carry on with normal everyday activities. This change in outlook may be made worse by a plummeting sense of self-confidence and self-worth. Again, lifestyle changes may help and make a difference; however, a doctor is also likely to consider talking therapies, such as cognitive behavioural therapy (CBT), and may, in some cases, suggest medication.

Having suffered from moderate depression myself, I can honestly say that it affected every part of my everyday living. From the minute I woke up, all I wanted to do was to go back to sleep. It was agonising just having to get through each day. The longer I suffered, the harder it became to keep pretending everything was 'normal' and I was 'okay'. My self-confidence and self-esteem lowered; it was like one big vicious cycle – until with the right help and support I found the strength to challenge and break that cycle.

Severe depression is likely to have a major impact on someone's work, school, social and/or home life. It makes daily functioning nearly impossible. People with severe depression will find it hard to successfully mask their illness and, for some, may start to see suicide as the only way out of their feelings of hopelessness and despair, believing that others may be better off without them. It is vital, at this point, that they seek help from a doctor or, in an emergency, A&E at your local hospital, and maintain the treatment path that is prescribed.

Hayley shares her experience with severe depression:

I was diagnosed with severe depression when my partner took me to the doctors after about two weeks of refusing to get out of bed. I am so pleased he did, looking back on it now. Severe depression is like being broken down piece by piece from the inside out until you cannot think straight anymore. I could not even think about if I was hungry, if I needed a shower or even what I wanted to say. It has been a very difficult recovery path for me, but I am now, finally, in a much better place.

Situational versus clinical depression

While 'mild', 'moderate' or 'severe' describes the depth of someone's depression, other labels may be given that could relate to the potential root of a person's illness. Situational and clinical depressions are similar, but not the same; being able to recognise the difference between the two can be the first step towards getting the right kind of help.

Situational or reactive depression

Situational depression can be known as an 'adjustment disorder with depressed mood'. This is often short term and usually very responsive to therapy.

Clinical depression can also be known medically as 'major depressive disorder'. This can be a more severe mental health condition.

Knowing some of the main differences between situational depression and clinical depression can help to decide the type of treatment the person requires and the severity of their illness. No kind of depression is more 'real' than another. They both can cause significant challenges and threats to the sufferer's well-being.

If a depressive episode has been triggered by a specific event, such as bereavement, divorce or the loss of a job, it could be classed as reactive or situational. The feelings of lethargy, sadness and hopelessness are very real and can really affect and interfere in the life of someone who is battling this kind of depression.

They may show a wide range of symptoms, which can include anxiety or panic attacks, being very emotional or angry, eating more or less than usual, sleeping more or less, behaving irrationally or dangerously and, in some cases, cutting social ties and withdrawing into themselves.

As the condition is in response to a specific occurrence or event, it typically improves with talking therapy, time and, in some cases, medication. Nevertheless, receiving the right support and treatment can really help the sufferer deal with their depression and help prevent it from escalating further into another type of mental illness, such as clinical depression. Many people with reactive depression respond well to cognitive behavioural therapy or another type of talking therapy (see Chapter 4), where they can address the underlying cause of the depression and find ways to alter, challenge and change their behaviour and thinking patterns in relation to it.

Donna describes when she first felt her depression start:

> I had been with my husband since I was 18. We had a very happy life together or so I thought. One day he just turned round to me and told me he wanted a divorce. I had not seen it coming and it was just heart-breaking. I stayed strong for a while so my children had security. However, when everything died down, I couldn't hold on anymore. I sought help via a local therapist who helped me work through my feelings surrounding my divorce. It was exactly what I needed and with time I learnt to move on.

Clinical depression

'Clinical depression' is often the term used to describe depression that cannot be clearly linked to a life event or situation. It may also be known as 'major depression' or 'major depressive disorder'. This can be a longer lasting illness that may call for long-term help and support. A traumatic life event may play a part, but other factors are also likely to be involved, including someone's biological and genetic make-up.

Luke shares his experience:

> I sometimes think I was born with something wrong. My life has not had any particular major events happen whereby I can link the start of my depression to them. I just started to feel really groggy and then it was like a wave that took over me. No rhyme or reason to it. This was the hardest part to accept for me – where did it come from? I think it just came from me.

There are a huge number of symptoms associated with depression and those with the illness are likely to suffer with a range, rather than all, of them. Although it does not capture the complexity and variety of the illness, it might be helpful to look at how *The Diagnostic and Statistical Manual of Mental Disorders* (DSM) classifies major depression. The DSM is the handbook used by healthcare professionals in the United States and much of the world as the authoritative guide to the diagnosis of mental disorders.

The manual says that patients can be diagnosed with the illness if they suffer from five of the symptoms out of the following during the same two-week period. The symptoms must cause the individual significant distress and/or affect the way they function on a day-to-day basis, and must also not be a result of substance abuse or another medical condition.

According to the DSM, one of the five symptoms of major depression must be:

- Low mood most of the day, nearly every day, or marked loss of interest or pleasure.

And then the sufferer must have at least four of these symptoms:

- Significant change in appetite and marked weight loss or gain.

- Sleep disturbance.
- Agitation or feelings of being slowed down in thoughts or physical movement that others can notice.
- Loss of energy or feeling fatigued every day.
- Feelings of worthlessness or inappropriate guilt nearly every day.
- Loss of the ability to concentrate.
- Thoughts of death and suicide.

Once diagnosed with major or clinical depression (or major depressive disorder), the recovery process can begin. Some will find the correct treatment path quickly and will respond well. Others may find it much harder to piece together the correct 'puzzle' of medication, therapy and lifestyle changes that can have a real and lasting positive impact on their lives. I cannot pretend that there is a quick fix for everyone, but I do know personally that there is always hope with depression and that with love, understanding, patience, communication, support and the right kind of professional help, this type of depression need not be a life sentence for sufferers and their carers.

Becky says of how her depression seemed to just come out of the blue:

One morning I woke up and just didn't feel quite right. I was going through a bit of stress at work but nothing more than I could handle, but this time it just seemed I couldn't. Every little thing that happened seemed to make me stressed and sad. As time went on, the feelings got deeper and deeper and I couldn't shake myself out of it. The strange thing is, when I look back now, there was nothing really that I could put my finger on that caused it. I got to a point where I visited the GP and they diagnosed me with clinical depression, I went on medication and am still on it now, but I feel so much better.

Prenatal and postnatal depression

Pregnancy and birth can often be a rollercoaster ride emotionally for any woman. It is a time when their identity can often feel re-defined and, particularly after the baby is born, they may feel a real sense of being under scrutiny, by friends, family, strangers and even themselves. They may feel they do not measure up as a parent, that they cannot cope with the pressure, that they are physically and emotionally exhausted, and that the 'old' version of themselves has completely disappeared. All these feelings, tough as they are, are pretty normal. Some call it the 'baby blues'. This is a time, usually three to 10 days after giving birth, when it is thought that more than eight in 10 new mothers feel highly emotional and overwhelmed. With all the new demands they face, these feelings really are quite natural and understandable.

For around 10-15%,[5] however, those feelings can run much deeper. They may start during the pregnancy (known as prenatal or antenatal depression) or after the birth (postnatal depression). However, in both cases, this illness can have a huge impact on new mothers and their partners, as well as their wider support network and their new baby.

At what is generally perceived as a time of great joy, those suffering from pre- or postnatal depression could feel even more acutely that they are somehow failing. They may feel ashamed and that their baby would be better off without them. Their self-esteem could hit rock bottom and they might shy away from activities that they would normally enjoy. Panic attacks and thoughts of suicide may plague them, and they may feel disconnected from their new baby. In very rare cases (around 1 in 1000 births[6]), postnatal psychosis could develop where the new mother appears confused and restless, with wide mood swings and possibly inappropriate or delusional behaviour.

In all these cases, women will need professional help, but many will be very nervous about seeking it. They may fear being judged as failures or even that their children could be taken away from them. It is important, at this point, that they know they have the unconditional love and support from those around them. Family and friends who can step up with emotional, non-judgemental and practical support will be able to help their loved one weather this difficult time, guiding them to seek the professional help they so desperately need.

Elsa says of how she struggled to ask for help:

> As I was a qualified primary school teacher, everyone naturally assumed that I would be able to cope with my own baby, including me. It wasn't until my son had arrived that I realised it was harder than I had thought, as my husband worked away and I was on my own a lot. At first, I was afraid to ask for help from my family as it made me feel a failure, but when I eventually broke down in a supermarket with my mum, when my son wouldn't stop crying, I told her everything. Then it changed. My family stepped in and gave me breaks on a regular basis.

Many assume that depression associated with childbirth must be rooted in the hormonal changes that occur around this time. Indeed, hormones can and do have a role to play. However, every woman experiences those changes and not all of them develop depression, so it is important to understand that other factors are also involved. Someone who has previously had a mental illness may be more at risk of developing depression around childbirth, as may someone who has suffered trauma during childhood or has been through a stressful life experience. For women who have little or no support around pregnancy and childbirth, or perhaps live in very challenging conditions, it may make it harder to cope with this time in their life, with all the extra anxieties and pressures that it brings.

Women who experience pre- or postnatal depression will benefit greatly from love, support and understanding, from family and friends as well as professionals. Like other types of depression, keeping a mood diary can help, as can sticking to a routine (as much as a new baby allows). For any new mother, getting up, dressed and out of the house can often feel as daunting as running a marathon. As a carer or loved one, being aware of this and providing a supportive network is particularly important for those who could be more vulnerable to mental health issues at this time.

Nikki talks of her experience with postnatal depression:

> I developed antenatal and postnatal depression with my first son in 2010. I was completely unaware of what was happening in my mind and blamed my mood swings, tiredness, excessive crying and strange thoughts all on pregnancy hormones. It was only when my baby was 5 months old and I was having severe suicidal thoughts, that I realised something was very wrong. The concept of leaving my children now seems foreign, but at the time I felt like such a complete failure as a mother. Everyone seemed better off without me. It was at that point that I went to the GP and asked for help. I was diagnosed with postnatal depression, which was terrifying, but also relieving to know I wasn't mad.

Seasonal affective disorder

The NHS estimates that approximately one in 15 people in the UK, between September and April, are affected by seasonal affective disorder (SAD), a form of depression. This is an incredibly large number of people, although of course the symptoms will vary in severity from person to person.

All of us will probably be affected by the seasons in some way. Who would not say that they feel more cheerful when the sun is shining or that they crave their duvet and comfort food during the darker winter months? But those with SAD will feel these seasonal changes much more acutely. The shorter, darker days will not simply alter their mood; they will transform it. At its most extreme, SAD can lead to the symptoms of depression that make it very hard for the sufferer to function during the winter months, at least until they find an effective treatment.

It is not clear exactly what causes SAD, although it is thought to be an interplay between the effect of light on the body's own natural 'circadian' rhythms (or internal body clock) that can be challenged by the huge swing in seasons that we experience. Those with SAD may have been found to have lower levels of the mood-regulating hormone and neurotransmitter serotonin and higher levels of melatonin that helps us sleep. Coupled with all these are the usual risk factors for depression, including a genetic predisposition to suffering the condition, as well as an individual's capacity for processing traumatic life events.

Someone may be diagnosed with SAD after suffering common symptoms for at least two winters, including sleep problems, lethargy, overeating, feeling sad and even hopeless, withdrawing from social situations, struggling to cope with stress, loss of libido and a lack of interest in usually enjoyable activities.

In terms of treatment, some self-help measures can be useful for those with SAD. Going outside during the brightest part of the day can be effective, as can using a special light box, and decorating the home in bright, light-reflecting colours rather than darker shades. None of these will cure SAD but they may have some positive effect. Seeking help through the GP is essential. The GP may be able to recommend a support group or other specialist help, as well as being able to prescribe medication or therapy where and if necessary.

Betty describes how the sun is her medication:

I have been retired for many years now. I seemed to not have a reason to make me go outside and I think this was my downfall. I have always enjoyed fresh air and the feeling of the sun on my skin. I think my body missed this and I just became a recluse over the winter periods. I actually did visit my GP in the end, who said I might be suffering with SAD. I now have a light box that helps me a little during the winter; as soon as the sun comes out, I make sure I enjoy it. The sun is like my medication; it makes me feel better.

Bipolar disorder

Bipolar disorder is a fairly common mental illness, affecting one in every 100 adults at some point in their life. Nevertheless, understanding about bipolar disorder still remains poor and the myths and misconceptions surrounding it present another challenge for those with the condition to overcome.

Formerly known as 'manic depression', it is a condition that can lead to wild swings in a person's mood, from bleak periods of depression (often characterised by feelings of lethargy, hopelessness, worthlessness and even suicidal thoughts) to mania (when they can feel very happy, excited and even incredibly creative). During the manic periods they could behave inappropriately or dangerously, their mania sometimes leading them to think they are untouchable so that they shed their inhibitions and take risks with their safety, money and/or health.

Charliee talks about her experiences of bipolar disorder, which is made more complex by also suffering with bulimia nervosa:

When my bipolar is in a manic episode, I tend to either not eat at all because I'm too busy trying to save the world (in my opinion anyway – ha ha ha!) or I'll binge on everything! I'll purge as soon as I've eaten and this will also include medication. Bipolar is a nightmare anyway, but even worse when you aren't medicated. One medicine I take is called lithium, which is a salt. I've become quite unwell on occasions due to toxicity. It's important to not allow yourself to become dehydrated or to change the level of salt in your diet. So massively abusing diuretics and laxatives really doesn't help.

Dealing with such extreme mood swings can be very hard for the sufferer themselves to handle and can be daunting for loved ones to witness and truly understand. The highs of the mania can make the lows of the depressive episode feel even more acute, and even the periods of 'normal' mood can feel strange and difficult to adjust to.

Furthermore, some – but not all – sufferers of bipolar can also experience psychotic episodes, usually during their manic phases. While these are extremely worrying for friends and loved ones, they can feel extremely real to the person experiencing the hallucinations or delusions. This can make it incredibly difficult to get through to them and to support them in seeking help.

Those with bipolar should be treated for both the depressive and manic sides to their illness and this often takes the form of different medications. There are also lifestyle changes the sufferer can make to help themselves. Learning to recognise their triggers and know their limits will help them take measures to lessen the impact on daily life. Exercise, for example, can sometimes really help someone through the depressive phases of their bipolar, while it also helps burn energy during the manic times. Also, keeping a daily routine, sticking to a regular pattern of eating, sleeping and taking medication while building in time for exercise, relaxation and/or meditation, can help to maintain a feeling of stability. Writing a mood diary could also help those with bipolar learn to recognise triggers or spot patterns in their changing mind-set.

The support of family and friends is paramount as they have a very important role to play in supporting and helping those with bipolar. It is often parents, siblings, offspring or partners, who know their loved one well, that can spot an approaching episode of either depression or mania. Please remember there is no substitution for a loved one's intuition and care. Seeing someone's behaviour change or knowing that they are perhaps stressed or anxious, which could potentially trigger a bipolar episode, can present the opportunity to gently raise this with them.

The thing that those with bipolar need, above all, is love and understanding. While their extreme moods, which could include delusional behaviour, can be hard to fully comprehend, understanding that it is very real to them can be of huge comfort. Being open about the illness is vital, so that they do not feel ashamed or that it is something to hide. It is also important to help them maintain a lifestyle that is conducive to good mental health, encouraging healthy eating, exercise, a clear routine and good sleep pattern.

Dean, who suffers from bipolar disorder, says of his experience:

> When I was in the depths of my illness, I wasn't really able to do anything properly; I wasn't taking my medication regularly, I was barely sleeping and struggled just to get on with life. My sister took it upon herself to try and get me back on track. She made sure I started taking my medication regularly (which I do think was the main component in helping me get better – it made my sleep routine better – not perfect but better) and she helped me get into doing a little bit of regular exercise.

Cyclothymia disorder

People with cylcothymia can in turn experience depressive episodes and happy, energetic phases. The mood swings are similar to those felt by people with bipolar, but they do not last as long and are less extreme – the lows are not as low, and the highs not as manic. As a result, the symptoms are not acute enough to be given a bipolar diagnosis. However, when someone's mood is as changeable and seemingly erratic as it is for those with cyclothymia, it can still have an impact on their quality of life, interfering with work, relationships and home life and also having a negative effect on self-esteem.

The good news with cyclothymia is that it can be managed and people with this condition can go on to lead full and productive lives. As with all types of depression, it is important to seek help as early as possible – which is often easier said than done when it can be hard to pinpoint this lesser-known illness – as not only will this make it easier to treat, but it may also stop it developing into full-blown bipolar disorder, which can happen if left unchecked.

As with bipolar disorder, treatment may be medication to treat the different phases of the illness, or may take the form of counselling, cognitive behavioural therapy (CBT), or other psychological support. In addition, those with cyclothymia, along with their family and friends, can make a real difference by learning as much as possible about the condition and recording in detail the effects on the individual, helping to track triggers and recognise what support is helpful and what is not. Following a healthy lifestyle, maintaining a clear routine, and finding ways to reduce stress can also help relieve some of the potential triggers for an episode.

Premenstrual dysphoric disorder (PMDD)

Many women suffer from premenstrual syndrome (PMS), experiencing feelings of sadness and upset in the days leading up to the due date for their period. While those symptoms can be difficult to handle, premenstrual dysphoric disorder (PMDD) takes the low feelings of PMS to the extreme, often leaving sufferers feeling completely overwhelmed, floored by daily life, angry and irrational, marooned from society, and sometimes plagued by thoughts of taking their own life. In addition, the physical symptoms of PMS can be magnified, including stomach cramps, breast pain, bloating and bowel problems.

Many of those with PMDD are first misdiagnosed with a more general depressive disorder and it may only be when they really start to monitor the timings of their episodes that they can begin to see a pattern linked to their menstrual cycle. They may find that they spend one or two weeks of their cycle, generally before their period, battling against an onslaught of destructive symptoms. They then spend the remaining two weeks frantically piecing their life back together before the next phase of their PMDD takes over their world once again.

Unsurprisingly, those with PMDD are highly sensitive to the hormonal changes that occur during the menstrual cycle. It is officially defined as an endocrine – or hormone – disorder but is also listed as a mental health disorder due to the way that many of the symptoms present themselves. Thus, successful treatments may be a combination of antidepressant medication, talking therapy and hormone treatment. As with all treatments, how they are used together can vary from person to person, and the effect that each has can very much depend on the individual and how their body responds to them.

For those with PMDD, it can be an uphill struggle to get their symptoms to be taken seriously. Many people may dismiss the signs as PMS, giving little understanding to the extreme nature of the symptoms that sufferers experience. This is where caring friends and family can have a crucial part to play. Taking the concerns of those experiencing PMDD symptoms seriously and supporting them to seek appropriate help will inevitably lighten their load and relieve some of the shame or fear they may be experiencing. Helping them maintain a healthy routine and supporting them to plan their lives around the phases of their cycle will help them feel more in control of their own lives. It can also be helpful for both them and you as supporter to understand the reasons behind some of the hurtful things that they may do or say at the height of their symptoms.

Annie shares her experience:

> The best way for me to describe it is that – once a month – I feel like my whole world is falling apart around me. It is like I have pressed a self-destruct button. It then takes me a good week to put my life back together. Each month I say to myself that I won't do it again, but I just don't seem to be able to stop it.

Persistent depressive disorder

Sometimes known as 'dysthymia', someone with persistent depressive disorder may feel very low the majority of the time, over years rather than weeks or months. Although their actual symptoms may not be as disruptive to their day-to-day life as more severe forms of depression, the length of time for which this illness persists can be debilitating in itself. In addition to feeling depressed, people with persistent depressive disorder will experience at least two of the following along with feelings of hopelessness:

- poor appetite or overeating
- sleeping too much or too little
- low energy
- low self-esteem
- poor concentration and/or
- difficulty making decisions.

The two main treatments for persistent depressive disorder are medication and/or talking therapy. The treatment approaches a doctor recommends can depend on a range of factors, such as how severe the sufferer's symptoms are and what treatments, if any, they have used in the past. The doctor should look at their individual circumstances to decide the best way forward.

Tara shares her experience of suffering from persistent depressive disorder:

> It actually took a long time for me to realise there was something mentally wrong. I started feeling a little low when I was in my late teens, but it took over me very slowly. I don't exactly struggle to get through the day like other people, but I know my outlook on life is quite negative and I am affected by situations very easily. It is a bit like living on the edge, and something very small will just push me over.

Psychotic depression

A small number of people with severe depression may also experience delusions and hallucinations, also known psychotic episodes. These people may imagine a catastrophic situation that is completely false. They may believe that they are going to die or that they have played a personal role in a disastrous situation that may be a real or imagined event. Psychosis may affect someone once or it may come and go a few times. For some, it will be a persistent part of their life.

Psychosis can leave people feeling anxious, scared and confused. It can be particularly hard to deal with as others may see someone who suffers in this way as being dangerous or out of control. In fact, very few people with psychosis hurt anyone else and this misconception can make sufferers feel even more ashamed about their illness and further isolated from society.

People with psychosis may not be aware of this aspect to their illness or realise that they are acting strangely. Due to this lack of insight, loved ones need to be particularly vigilant and help them to get the support that they need. A GP may be a first port of call during an initial episode but if the delusions or hallucinations are putting the person or others at risk, loved ones should take them to hospital emergency services immediately.

Atypical depression

Atypical depression – also called depression with atypical features – sounds as if it is a very rare sort of depression, but in fact that is not the case. What it actually means is that in some respects a person's symptoms do not completely conform with those typically seen in 'traditional' depression; in fact, it may be the case that some of the characteristics of typical depression are reversed.

With the atypical type of this mental illness, sufferers may

43

experience the most recognisable features of depression, including persistent feelings of sadness and hopelessness, low energy, and have little interest in activities they once enjoyed. They may also experience 'atypical' feelings such as significant weight gain and sleeping for long periods. People with atypical symptoms may also react extremely negatively to anything they consider to be a slight or criticism.

It is thought that this type of depression may start earlier than other types, with the teenage years often a time when it can begin.

Most significantly, people with atypical depression may find their depressed mood brightens in response to positive events. So, for example, they may be able to go out for the day to a family or friends' occasion and apparently enjoy themselves, only then to head home by themselves with the feelings of despair and worthlessness settling back over them once again.

This ability to react positively to happy events means that family and friends may not be able to spot the signs of the depression as clearly as they might in other forms of the illness. As a result, this type of mental illness is thought often to remain under-diagnosed; consequently, those with the illness may not be getting the help they need, which could make a real and lasting difference to their lives.

Molly speaks of her up-and-down experiences with atypical depression:

My depression started when I was around 15 years old. I have always enjoyed being around other people and am part of quite a big family. When I do not have any plans and my thoughts have time to run away with me, I can get myself into a very dark place. It took a long time for my diagnosis though, I think because, as soon as I am around family or close friends, I am able to really enjoy myself and the company. As soon as I am back on my own or not keeping busy I am back to square one and the dark thoughts return, almost at the click of a finger.

To conclude

Let me end this chapter with the thought that recovery is always possible. Most people suffering from depression will have people around them who can, and most likely will, support them. What is crucial, however, above all else, is that sufferers themselves really want to recover; recovery *has* to be driven by them, remembering always that recovery is both achievable and sustainable.

Chapter 3

Recognising depression and seeking treatment

Having an understanding of how the mind of someone suffering from depression works and being knowledgeable on the subject are probably the two most powerful tools you, as the carer, can have when approaching a loved one or a friend who you think may be suffering from depression. Even though it is a relatively common illness, depression is still woefully misunderstood and sadly, at times, not taken seriously.

The bridge between being ill and seeking and receiving treatment for sufferers of depression is a precarious one to cross, not only for sufferers themselves, but for the people around them. Leading up to and after diagnosis, many parents, partners and/or carers of depression sufferers make themselves ill by worrying, blaming themselves, raking over the past with a fine-toothed comb and frantically trying to pin-point where they went wrong. Sleepless nights, high levels of stress and even depression in themselves can ensue. This is totally counterproductive, because the feelings of guilt can run two ways – sufferers of depression tend to have a hugely over-developed sense of guilt, which can be magnified when they see the effect their illness is having on their loved ones and friends. Their solution to these feelings of shame, is usually, to bury themselves further in their illness, and so the situation can become a vicious circle.

Angela shares her feelings of guilt:

> The most difficult aspect was remaining calm when he refused
> LOVE, or even a touch on the arm. It felt like rejection. He could
> not even look you in the eye and as a parent you have thoughts
> of being guilty that you are not doing enough.

It is also important for parents, partners and carers, to be well enough to support the process of recovery. It is essential for all concerned that carers try to maintain their own physical and emotional well-being during this incredibly difficult time. Whether the sufferer is young and still living at home, or older and living independently, the people around them will be of the utmost importance in supporting and guiding them towards health and recovery.

Recognising depression

Unfortunately, there is no quick and easy laboratory test that can give an immediate diagnosis. Focusing on the physical symptoms only, may lead to missing the emotional signs. Knowing this is the parent's/carer's biggest ally, as depression can often be extremely difficult to recognise in the early stages.

Angela shares her experience with her son:

> All you can do is LISTEN to your loved one. They don't want
> you to solve the problem, because YOU can't. I recognised
> that something was terribly wrong with my son as he gave up
> rugby and his music; he was apathetic about his studies, life
> and friends. If you notice a change in your loved one, mention
> it calmly but not as a NAGGING question. Despite their denials,
> offer support.

Let's go back to that first step: realising that something could potentially be wrong. While the clues can often be physical as well as emotional, they are usually just that – clues. Piecing together what at first may seem unconnected pieces of a puzzle is often the first step to recognising a mental illness such as depression.

There are certain patterns and tendencies that may help you to determine that something could potentially be amiss. In my personal and professional experience, a dramatic change in personality and behaviour can be one of the biggest warning signs. Whether your loved one is usually eccentric and quirky or insular and private, you may know them well enough to be able to recognise the differences over and above their usual mannerisms.

Pete, who suffers from major depressive disorder, says of how his mother was the first person to recognise that something wasn't quite right with him:

> My earliest recollection of symptoms is what I subsequently learned was anxiety. It started to happen in my first few weeks at uni. I couldn't sit still in lectures and used to feel my heart racing for no reason at all. I also started to dread going to lectures and social occasions. My depression emerged in a way that I recognise one summer vacation when I just seemed to grind to a halt. I couldn't seem to do anything but lie on my bed or the sofa. I normally had loads of energy but had become very lethargic. My mum noticed this before I did really. I knew something wasn't right and went to the doctor. I was given some sleeping tablets but it took another seven or eight years to reach a proper diagnosis, by which time I was having regular suicidal thoughts and was very anxious and depressed.

To give you more of an idea, below are some of the emotional and behavioural changes that may be present in someone with depression. The person may:

- feel worthless and helpless
- seem anxious or worried a large proportion of the time
- seem to be getting little enjoyment out of life or things they used to like doing
- appear to have very low self-esteem, to be overly self-critical and to feel weighed down by guilt and self-doubt

- become very distant, preoccupied and uncommunicative
- seem irritable and intolerant of others
- stop wanting to go out, even to places they used to enjoy visiting
- have suicidal thoughts or appear to be harming themselves, whether through a method such as physical self-harm or substance abuse.

Once your attention is drawn to some of the initial personality changes, you may gradually notice other behaviours starting to emerge, which are out of character for that person. As depression is an illness of the mind and cannot always be seen, the person's disordered thoughts may be more difficult to detect initially. So once again, the person's behaviour and overall demeanour can play a crucial part in recognising something is not quite right, thereby potentially leading to early intervention.

Some physical signs and behaviours you may start to notice include the person:

- having trouble sleeping, such as waking intermittently
- eating less or more, and their weight possibly showing quite a marked change
- seeming to lack energy
- having a dip in their sex drive
- having unexplained aches and pains
- seeming to do things more slowly or even speak more slowly
- in some cases, displaying irrational and even delusional thoughts, seeing or hearing things that other people cannot
- breaking down in tears for seemingly no reason or in unexpected situations
- seeming to find day-to-day life difficult, perhaps not eating or washing properly.

It is important to say here that just because someone is

showing some, or all of these symptoms, it does not necessarily mean that they have depression. As a loved one or care giver, I would advise you to use your own intuition to guide you in identifying whether these symptoms are typical of the person you know or are somewhat out of character for them.

Lou shares her first signs of her depression:

> The first sign I noticed with my own depression was no longer being able to enjoy the things I used to. I stopped reading books and watching TV, which in the past had been a way to escape and relax. I could no longer concentrate enough to watch or read anything.
>
> I had always been obsessively clean and tidy, but my home started to become very untidy and I started hoarding. There were times when I couldn't get into my front door and periods when I couldn't get into my bed as it had become a dumping ground for my clothes!
>
> I spent much less time on my appearance; some days I didn't brush my teeth or shower. I wouldn't leave my flat unless it was absolutely essential. I became withdrawn and didn't want to speak with anyone.

Rita says of the behaviour changes she noticed in her sister:

> Paula had always been impeccably dressed and very conscious of her appearance and how others perceived her. I slowly noticed a dip in her appearance and moods. She had never used to go a day without lipstick, but then I noticed she stopped having her nails done and her hair coloured, let alone wearing lipstick. If I'm honest, her appearance, and her lack of interest in it, was the first sign I realised something was wrong.

While in some people the symptoms may be quite noticeable as a distinct change from their normal behaviour and/or way of doing things, others may try to hide or mask the signs of their depression and how they are feeling; and some can successfully do so for a considerable length of time. They may feel misplaced shame or embarrassment about how they are feeling, or they may worry that revealing their symptoms could disadvantage them, perhaps socially, educationally and/or in the workplace. As a result, they may do all they can to disguise how they are feeling.

Nikki can now spot the signs if her husband is slipping back into depression:

> With Craig, I didn't see the signs when he was depressed. He kept it hidden very well. But now I can recognise when he's dipping. He becomes snappy, doesn't want to get out of bed, showers less and drinks a lot more alcohol.

Recognising depression in yourself

Sometimes it can be easier for family members, friends and colleagues to pick up on the signs and symptoms of depression than it is for the person suffering to do so. Recognising the illness within yourself is vital as it is the first step towards seeking help and getting the right support or treatment needed to get better.

So how then do you know if you have depression? The short answer is that you may not know until you actually go to a doctor and describe exactly how you are thinking and feeling. However, if you have been feeling persistently low, hopeless and lacking in drive and interest in things you once enjoyed for a period of time, it is important to take those feelings seriously and consider in more depth the other ways you may be affected.

As I mentioned earlier in this chapter, it is important to be aware of the physical symptoms, such as, poor sleep patterns, loss of appetite (or over-eating), lack of motivation for anything, and lack of sex drive, which could also be indications of depression.

Rachel shares the first signs that tell her she needs to slow down:

> For me, the first bat squeaks that something is wrong is when I can't get to sleep. In addition, waking bolt upright at around 03:00 is a sign I need to step back, reduce my commitments and take stock of my mental health.

Remember that the symptoms can range from mild to severe, so you could be suffering from a mental illness – and could benefit from professional advice and possibly some form of treatment – at any point along this spectrum.

The way in which depression differs from 'feeling down' is that it generally persists and does not lift when something that could be considered positive or happy happens. People who have experienced low mood for a few weeks should be alert to other signs of depression and seek the opinion of their GP to find out what steps they should take. Delaying too long could cause the depression to worsen and prolong the time it then takes to recover.

Please remember that depression cuts across ages, genders and social divides. Some groups are more susceptible than others; traumatic experiences can also play a part in some cases; and for some people there could be a genetic link involved. However, no one should consider themselves immune from depression – you can develop this mental illness even when there is no apparent or obvious reason or root cause.

Dr Ian Drever, MB ChB, MRCPsych, psychiatrist and founder of the Academy of Mental Fitness, shares his thoughts on being able to recognise the early warning signs:

Depression and anxiety ... they're the scourge of modern society, and it doesn't look like they'll be going away any time soon. A relentless and rising tide of demands on all of us, and our 'always-on, always-connected' culture sees to that.

It's no wonder, then, that our bodies and minds become completely exhausted with the grinding, non-stop nature of it all. And yet, if we step back and start to engage with what our bodies are trying to tell us, there are some vital early warning signs we can become aware of and if we take appropriate action, can actually help to prevent an illness episode, or at least help lessen its severity.

I refer to this as the body's 'dashboard' – a finely tuned, highly sensitive range of warning lights which the body uses to flash up its distress to us when we're facing too many demands. So, what are the warning lights on the dashboard? Here are four, for starters...

> **Sleep** – *Disturbed sleep is a classic early warning feature that something's not right. If you're taking longer than normal to get off to sleep at night, with your mind churning like a washing machine, or else you're waking up at 3:00 or 4:00 am and can't get back to sleep, this is likely to be your body telling you that you've got a lot on your plate.*

> **Cognitive abilities** – *Memory and concentration can be badly impaired, so that even minor daily tasks can feel daunting, or fall to one side, lost in a jumble of preoccupations and worried ruminations. Meetings and other commitments can be forgotten and lists might be needed to stay on top of even the most mundane activities.*

> **Social engagement** – *Whereas socialising may once have been a pleasure and done with ease, it now becomes a chore, something to be avoided or even dreaded. The thought of having to put on a 'mask', be strong and play the part can all feel too much.*

> **Bodily aches and pains** – *Even minor levels of depression and anxiety can 'turn the volume up' on pain. The pain is absolutely real and it certainly isn't something that's imagined, but it's felt more intensely, more acutely, more naggingly, when your mind is also overloaded.*

The really unfortunate thing about these warning lights is that although we're all able to recognise that they're happening, we generally don't understand what they mean or how to respond appropriately. For instance, a common reaction to experiencing these warnings is to berate ourselves and to 'try harder'. We may do things like stay even later at work to make up for our lack of output, trying to find some way to force ourselves back to normal.

This turns out to be the worst possible thing to do; it's like seeing an accident on the road in front of you and actively accelerating into it. As soon as we see any of these warning lights, we should be recognising them as a first step and then taking appropriate action.

Most likely that'll involve pulling back from commitments, taking stock of everything that's going on and off-loading as much as possible. It may also include drawing boundaries, learning to say 'no', managing the expectations of others and building in some personal down-time for a deep recharge. If all doesn't settle soon, then perhaps finding some professional help from a trained therapist or doctor could be the next step.

As with most things in life, a problem nipped in the bud can be turned around more quickly than one that's allowed to build. So, keep an eye on your body's dashboard, stay on top of what it's telling you and you'll definitely have the well-being edge.

Stay alert

Sometimes with depression, symptoms can deteriorate very swiftly. In these circumstances, the depression needs to be treated particularly quickly. Waiting for sufferers themselves to see that they need help may not always be an option and instead, as carer/friend/family, you may have to insist they visit their GP promptly. If they are resistant to this, call NHS 111 (if you are in the UK) for advice or turn to the specialist knowledge of a charity such as SANE or MIND.

Sadly, suicide is a real risk for those with depression. If you have reason to believe that your loved one may be feeling as if they want to take their own life, it is crucial to take their thoughts and behaviour seriously and to get them to seek help immediately. Talk to them about how they are feeling and try to help them think of other ways forward. In the immediate short term, seek help from their GP, NHS 111 (if in the UK) or local Accident and Emergency department. Even if that particular crisis seems to pass, ensure that care and treatment are followed up and that things are 'joined up' between the GP and local mental health teams.

The importance of early intervention

The first and most important step towards recovery from depression is that the sufferer must want to get better themselves. As soul-destroying as it is, attempts to rehabilitate sufferers who are not yet ready to acknowledge and deal with the issue are likely to prove fruitless. (However, with the assistance of the right kind of therapy and a positive environment, a sufferer can be stabilised, so that their condition does not worsen. Getting actively better is what requires the sufferer to engage totally with treatment and the recovery process as a whole.)

The way in which you, as a loved one or carer, act at this point is very important. It is of course tempting to adopt a wait-and-see approach, but the vice-like grip that depression can have on a sufferer's mind-set can develop or worsen with astonishing speed. Waiting for more obvious physical signs may mean that you could underestimate the rapid psychological rampage of depression. We know that it is possible to make a full recovery from depression – there is always hope – but we also know that the earlier sufferers are able to access treatment and receive the right help and support, the better chance they have of making a full recovery.

Angela tells us of the quick action they took after her son opened up to her:

> The moment my son opened up to me and told me exactly how he had been feeling, we immediately made an appointment with a private therapist. After trying two different therapists, this did not seem the right avenue for him as he felt uncomfortable

speaking with a stranger and preferred to speak with me. We then took him to the GP where he was prescribed medication as he was now over 18 years old. The medication helped him to cope with life and his exam stresses and seemed to calm him down. He stayed on this for 18 months and is now living a happy life. He always says he takes each day as it comes and tries to not worry too much about the future.

There are few things more frustrating than watching someone we care about suffer and being unable to intervene. So, what can be done in the meantime? Again, in this instance, knowledge is power. There is a variety of treatments available, and it is important to understand what they entail and how they work. In this way, when the sufferer expresses a desire to get better, their family and friends can leap into action and find the most appropriate source of help as quickly as possible.

To help with this, there is an unbiased guide to some of the treatments available in the next chapter. The speed with which you, as a parent, carer or loved one, might act at this point in time is also of paramount importance. Often the sufferer might yearn for recovery in peaks and troughs, so it is important to place them in a positive and suitable environment while they are in the correct frame of mind and before any seeds of self-doubt are sown by their depression which could begin to fester and grow. Remember, they have to really want to embrace this thought process if they are to totally engage with any form of treatment.

At the same time, it is important for carers to show that they are willing and able to help at any time. However frustrating and upsetting it is to see your loved one suffer, it is crucial to keep the lines of communication open, so they know deep down that you are always there for them. Creating opportunities to talk can be vital. A simple way to do this is to keep pursuing the activities you love doing together. Whether that could be taking the dog for a walk, watching your favourite television programme or going for a trip to the shops together, by continuing to maintain those opportunities for emotional closeness, you will not only be giving them the green light to turn to you for help, but you will also be maintaining some much needed normality in what may be an increasingly disordered life.

Jonathan describes how important it has been to keep up the things he and his mum, who suffers from depression, have always shared together:

> Ever since I was young, before my mum started struggling mentally and physically, we always watched some of the soaps on TV together. We still try and keep up this tradition as it takes our minds to a happy place and we get to spend quality time together too.

Starting the conversation

There is no specific time for a worried parent, carer or loved one to wait before they intervene, but if you are unsure about the mental state of your child, family member, partner or someone close to you, and you have a hunch that something is not quite right, then it should be investigated further. The most effective way to intervene at this point is through communication. It is important to pick the right moment and location: it should be at a time when it is just you and them, otherwise the person may feel 'ganged up on'. It should also be a place where they feel safe; phones, tablets and laptops should all be switched off, so there is nothing to distract you or them. Sometimes people worry that by telling someone, it could make things worse. You therefore need to be very clear from the start that you are there to support and help them and that you will not do anything without discussing it with them first.

Communication should take place in a straightforward manner. Do not assume that you know what the problem is; you might be mistaken and could run the risk of talking for ages about something that they cannot relate to. Let them tell you about their feelings and fears first.

Angela says of how important it is to approach the subject carefully:

Since the summer, I had known something was not quite right with my son. It got to September and I just said to him, 'I think you are depressed'; he replied with 'It's personal. I'm dealing with it.' I realise now, that I had to let him come to me and my job was to make sure he knew he could. Two months later, I could see he was still really struggling; one day I said to him, 'I am always here; if you are out and you feel sad, call me.' I reminded my son every week that I was always there, too. Soon after this I got a call; he had reached out to me, which was the first step in opening our communication and towards his recovery.

The most important thing, whatever they may say to you, is not to judge them; this may cause them to clam up. Show them that you respect their emotions and also their view point, even if you do disagree with certain things that they may be telling you.

Watching for reactions is important. You can tell when you have hit on a sore point or are getting close to an uncomfortable subject by their eye contact and body language and how quick they are to defend themselves.

Remain calm. Although you are unlikely to feel calm inside, you must try to stay strong in the situation, because, if you are not, the person could start to panic. If you do not act as though there is a solution to their problem, and everything will be okay, they may start to despair. They are looking to you as someone to hopefully take some of their pain away.

Examples of how to start a much-needed conversation with them can include:

- 'I have noticed that you are not quite your usual self at the moment... Is something wrong?'
- 'You have not seemed yourself recently. Is there anything wrong?'

- 'You have been very quiet lately... Is something troubling you?'
- 'Is there anything I can do to make life a bit easier for you?'
- 'Can you describe to me how you are feeling?'
- 'Would you rather write down how you are feeling on a piece of paper for me?'

Acknowledge that the conversation is likely to be difficult for them. Tell them that you are proud of the strength they are demonstrating in telling you about their issues. They might also be reassured if you tell them that there is nothing they could say that will make you stop caring about them or loving them. Tell them it is okay to be frightened and they do not have to put on a brave face, because you will always work it out together.

My Charlotte shares her thoughts:

> Having been around mental illness for 15 or so years and from now working with Mum, I have seen how mental illness impacts the lives of everyone around it: not just the sufferer, but also family and friends. One of the most important things I have learnt is to talk. If you think something is wrong with a family member, friend or loved one, always talk with someone you trust; try not to brush things under the carpet, and be as open and honest as you can be.

The general practitioner (GP)

After having recognised that there is a problem, whether it be the sufferer themselves reaching out for help or a loved one encouraging them, the first port of call should be the family doctor or general practitioner (GP). At this stage, please remember that no-one's time is ever wasted even if the diagnosis is not depression. Remember, the earlier the condition is identified, the earlier intervention can take place, with the hope of a quicker and more effective recovery for the sufferer and their loved ones.

Actively seeking help can be a vital first step forward towards recovery. However, it is important to remember, that GPs are not miracle workers or mind readers, nor are they mental health specialists, and whilst some may have substantial knowledge and a special interest in depression and other mental health issues, some may not. Sadly, in the UK the very limited time slot they are allocated for each patient can sometimes be insufficient to assess all of their patients objectively. In a sector dictated by guidelines and under constant scrutiny, time is one thing most GPs are sadly unable to offer.

Ahead of the GP's appointment, it may be helpful if the sufferer makes a list highlighting their symptoms and how they feel they have changed with time, including details about how these feelings are affecting them on a day-to-day basis. The notes should also include information on any distressing and/or upsetting events that have happened, either in the past or more recently, as well as details of any other mental or physical conditions or symptoms they may have. In addition, compiling a list of questions to put to the GP could also be helpful. This can include queries about what treatment path they might prescribe and what lifestyle changes might also be helpful.

By preparing in this way, it may help the sufferer if they become anxious during their time at the surgery and forget some of the crucial facts. A diagnosis is only as reliable as the information the patient provides, so keeping the lines of communication as open as possible with the GP will assist greatly in their diagnosis and moving forward, not only during the initial appointment but in the long term. It might also be extremely helpful to arrange for someone to accompany the sufferer to their appointment. Having an advocate present is beneficial to both parties and can help the sufferer understand and remember the information given to them by the GP, whilst feeling reassured that they are being supported and listened to. With a typical NHS GP appointment lasting around just 10 minutes, it may be useful if possible to book a 'double appointment' to ensure there is enough time to cover everything the sufferer is concerned about, without feeling rushed or under unnecessary pressure.

Jonathan says of how he supports his mum at regular medical appointments:

> I always try to attend the appointments with my mum. As she struggles with depression and multiple physical illnesses too, sometimes her mind isn't in the right place to take things in. It helps as then I can reassure her and remind her of important points made during these appointments.

It is really important, at this stage, to encourage the sufferer to be as open and honest as they feel they can be with their GP/family doctor in the time frame they have, however frightening, uncomfortable and complicated it may be. Reassure them that they are not alone – according to a new survey by the mental health charity MIND published in June 2018, 40% of GP appointments in the UK are related to mental health.

Expectations of GPs can be unfairly high and unfortunately not all appointments will conclude the way the patient or carer would like. The sufferer may feel the GP has not taken their concerns seriously enough. If this is the case, it would be prudent to make another appointment straight away to see another doctor in the practice.

Jamie shares his family's experience:

> My parents had several GP appointments that, at the time, I was unaware of as they were so concerned. Through these appointments my parents were told it was 'just a phase' and my mum was being 'over-protective'; you can imagine their anger! They booked an appointment soon after with another GP for a second opinion only to be told if I carried on the way I was without hospital treatment I wouldn't survive the next few weeks!

While many people with depression will follow a treatment path directed by their GP (usually antidepressant medication [see page 71], talking treatment or a combination of both), in some cases the doctor will decide to refer them on for specialist help from a psychiatrist or local community health team. That is when further delays can occur. Unfortunately, the waiting lists for NHS mental health treatments can be very long. A 2018 study from the Royal College of Psychiatrists found that over half of mental health patients interviewed had had to wait at least four weeks to see an NHS mental health specialist, while 6% had to wait a year.[7]

There is no right or wrong way at this juncture; some people may look at seeking private help, to avoid these waiting times. Weighing up the advantages and disadvantages of joining an NHS waiting list as opposed to seeking private alternative help should be carefully thought through. Private treatment costs money and this may prove a stumbling block for many. My advice to parents, loved ones and caregivers would be to read, learn and research as much as you possibly can about the diagnosis. As I cannot say too often, knowledge is power and will help you make the right choices going forward with and for the sufferer.

Dealing with a diagnosis

Getting a diagnosis of depression can provoke a considerable range of feelings; the sufferer may question why this has happened to them and what the implications may be for them and their future. They may also have to deal with the fact that they may have another mental or physical illness, as depression often does not occur in isolation. As someone who cares for them, it is essential to remind them that they are not the sum of their diagnosis.

People's reactions to being officially diagnosed with depression can vary hugely from sufferer to sufferer. These are some of the most common ways they may feel, although it is by no means an exhaustive list:

Relieved – now they can understand why they have been feeling as they have.

Shocked – as they struggle to comprehend what this means for them.

Hopeful – that they can find a treatment that will help and make them feel better.

Angry – that out of all the people they know, this had to happen to them. (Statistically, it's actually very likely that they also have friends and acquaintances with a diagnosis of depression.)

Guilty – that perhaps they did something that caused the depression.

Ashamed – that there is something wrong with them and that they are somehow flawed.

Grief-stricken – for the life they believe they would or could have had without depression.

Powerless – as if their illness will control them, rather than them being able to take control of it.

All of these feelings are absolutely valid and understandable, as is anything else that a person feels when they have been given a diagnosis of depression. In time, as they come to terms with their own illness and the nuanced impact on their own lives, their feelings may shift and change. For some, they will be able to feel more optimistic, whilst for others, the outlook may seem bleaker. As they weather this downpour of feelings, it is important to give them the time and space to explore and accept them, in the hope they will then feel more comfortable to discuss them openly.

Hayley shares her thoughts on when she was first diagnosed:

> When I was taken to the GP by my partner, I was in a very bad way and could not understand why I was feeling the way I was. In a way, it was a relief when I was diagnosed; at least I wasn't an alien and there was some way out, even though I didn't know what that was yet. The diagnosis helped with my feelings of guilt and shame and actually gave me a little boost to try and fight it.

It can be quite normal to get stuck at the 'why me?' stage for some time. However, after that needs to come a plan of action to move forwards. In other words, receiving a diagnosis of depression is the starting point for a longer journey towards finding the right kind of help and support and to start making the changes needed (however small) to be able to embark on the road to recovery. As the sufferer themselves embarks on this journey, so too do their loved ones. Learning as much as possible about depression, and understanding that it does not detract from the person you care about, is crucial. As they seek help, perhaps from support groups or helplines, care givers and friends may also find it helpful to seek out others who are in a similar position.

People with depression may be advised to write down how they feel, recording their concerns and questions and noting any changes or patterns in how they are coping. The same can also apply to those who are caring for them. Expressing thoughts and feelings on paper (or electronically) can be really helpful in working through them. Further down the line, a record like this can also serve as a reminder of how far you have all come.

Janet, whose husband suffered from depression, shares her own experience:

I started keeping a diary of my husband's emotions when he got really bad. I wanted to see if there was a correlation between this and something else. I actually didn't find anything but now I look back at it, I realise how far he has come in his recovery.

Every sufferer's path to recovery is different, as are their individual experiences of the NHS (if in the UK), private health-care and any alternative medical professionals they encounter; each person is unique and responds differently. If one treatment proves ineffective, it absolutely does not mean that the patient is 'incurable'; it simply means that the treatment is not working for that person, so maybe it is time to start looking for another – do not be afraid to try different avenues.

Recognising potential relapse and possible triggers

The reality of depression is that for many people it can remain an unwelcome visitor in their lives for many years. There will be times – weeks, months or years – when life feels brighter and, in some cases, back to 'normal'; however, as with any mental illness, it can have a nasty habit of recurring – especially at times when people leave themselves more open and vulnerable. The good news, however, is that you can take action to reduce the chances of it happening. Should the depression start to return, there are ways in which you can identify and reduce the chances of it making a comeback.

Recognising a potential relapse of depression is vital in order to be able to act on it and do all you can to nip it in the bud. While in some cases sufferers themselves can be astute enough to see the signs, often it is the people around them who are best placed to observe changes that may be significant.

Nikki says of how she is aware of her first signs of potential relapse:

When I first became ill, I had no idea. It was only when the
suicidal thoughts were crowding my brain and I wanted
to act on them, that I realised something was very wrong.
Now, I'm very aware of the first signs that my mental health
is deteriorating. I become snappy, my head gets full of lists,
negative thoughts start entering my brain and I cry more easily.

The symptoms of depression vary between individuals
which makes it essential for every sufferer to understand their
own illness and what behaviour or changes may be symptomatic
of the kind of depression they suffer. That is also true for those
around them: knowing the difference between what is 'normal'
for their loved one or friend and signs that need to be acted on
can really make a difference.

In general terms, these are the kind of symptoms or changes
that may indicate an approaching bout of mental ill health. Being
able to recognise them early enough will help prompt action to
prevent them from escalating into something more serious.

- Struggling to sleep or sleeping too much
- Feeling constantly stressed out and in a rush
- Worrying more than usual or feeling on edge
- Having negative thought patterns and noticing the inner
  critic gaining a voice
- Suffering from headaches or stomach upsets – this may
  indicate stress or anxiety taking hold
- Turning to alcohol or drugs to help cope with difficult
  feelings
- Suffering or approaching a stressful life event.

Once you notice these triggers creeping in, please do not
ignore them. They could indicate that those prone to depression need to slow down and to give themselves some time and
space to breathe and re-evaluate. This is where it is important to
remember all the things that have helped and made a difference

in the past and start putting them back into practice once again. That could be healthy eating, exercise, talking to someone and/ or indulging in a therapeutic hobby such as art or walking. It is also helpful to recognise stressful or challenging situations that may be approaching and working out a strategy for how to deal with them, rather than having to deal with the consequences afterwards. Perhaps if necessary speak to a therapist or see the sufferer's GP to tackle the potential problem before it progresses further.

These measures are strategies that someone prone to depression should be, if possible, incorporating into their day-to-day life, creating a protective shield against depression. Doing so when the black cloud is approaching is essential, but also making it part of everyday life is likely to be even more effective.

For me, being mindful and able to recognise a possible relapse either within oneself or within a loved one is a big part of recovery. My original fight with depression began around the middle of 1999 and it was not until the summer of 2002 that it started to lift. Then in the spring of 2018, I began to feel the dark cloud looming over me and as much as I tried to blow it away, it seemed intent on staying. Looking back, I remember my mum saying to me that you have to have bad days to know what good days are …. This of course is very true. However, I soon began to realise that the bad days for me were far outweighing the good ones. I was under a lot of pressure with my work commitments and my writing deadlines, and coupled with some personal struggles, life was becoming more and more challenging. I could feel I was slowly beginning to slip back under the dark cloud again.

By the summer of 2018 I was not sleeping properly and day-to-day functioning was becoming a struggle. Supported by my wonderful family and close friends I went to see my GP, who was brilliant and said I was mentally exhausted. I knew then I had to do something about it before I was dragged even further under the dark cloud. I began to exercise again on a regular basis and completely changed my diet – which over time helped me to sleep better. With a clearer head I took myself back to my wonderful life coach, Jeff Brazier, who supported me as he always does to work through my chaotic work life and find a balance which, looking back, I did not have and definitely needed. This in turn eased the unnecessary pressure I had put myself under. With time, and allowing myself to have the space to work on 'me', I have emerged a better, stronger and happier person for it. I am enjoying life again with a real smile on my face as opposed to a fake one.

Thankfully I am blessed with some good people around me, including my best friend, Kate:

> I can usually tell when something is not quite right with Lynn as she tends to retreat into herself and not get in touch with me. Lynn usually has an upbeat and bubbly personality so it was obvious that something was wrong when she seemed to lose her zest for life and motivation to do things. I think the most important thing that I did for Lynn during this difficult time was to listen to her and not judge. I also tried to make sure that we could meet up regularly even if it was just for a quick chat over a cup of coffee.

To conclude

If possible, however difficult things get, try not to allow the sufferer to fall at the first hurdle; it is important to try and all move forward together, making a joint effort to find the right path that works for everyone. There will be ups and downs along the way and it is very much a 'two steps forward, one step back' scenario for a while. It can be a long road but acceptance, understanding and perseverance are key. The sufferer needs all the encouragement you can give them to keep going until they get the right help they need and deserve, so patience and open-mindedness are of the utmost importance. Propping the sufferer up for a little while is okay too, but they have to be able to walk alone at some point and take ownership of their road to recovery. For the process to flourish and be a success, they really need to want it 100% for themselves.

Being afraid of the unknown is a perfectly normal feeling and reaction when faced with the challenge of tackling a loved one and their mental illness. Please try not to feel daunted by the prospect of what lies ahead; have courage, be strong and stand side by side with the sufferer, standing up to the testing times that are to come by communicating and uniting to confront it head on.

Jenni Philipps, deputy safe-guarding lead at Oak Academy in Bournemouth, ends this chapter with:

Mental health should no longer remain a taboo subject. The voices of young people and adults coping and struggling to manage their mental health need to be heard in order to empower those struggling to come forward and seek help. It is nothing to be ashamed of and it certainly is not something that only a minority experience.

Always remember, recovery is possible.

Chapter 4

A guide to therapies

As discussed earlier in this book, each and every form of depression will manifest itself in a different and unique way, because each sufferer is different and unique. In the same way there is no 'ultimate' treatment. One sufferer may respond very well to a certain treatment, while it may have little or no effect on someone else who has also been diagnosed with depression. For some, a combination of therapies can be the answer. Whatever decision is made, it is essential that the sufferer and their carers choose a course of therapy which fuels and strengthens the desire to recover, as opposed to drowning and eventually killing it.

In order to be proactive during this frustrating time, one step which parents, carers and friends of sufferers can take is to arm themselves with a thorough knowledge of the various treatment options available. Below is an unbiased guide to many of the different talking therapies available, both within the NHS (if you are in the UK) and outside it. I have asked specialists within each field, all of whom I know personally, to explain a bit more about their therapy, with the aim of helping you to understand how their individual discipline can assist in combating depression. (You may notice some approaches overlap with others or combine elements from one with another – this is all part of the wide variation in what works for different individuals.) These talking therapies are:

Cognitive behavioural therapy (CBT) – this comes first as this is the most likely talking therapy to be prescribed within the NHS (if you are in the UK) (page 78)

Dialectical behavioural therapy (DBT) (page 80)

Interpersonal therapy (IPT) (page 81)

Psychodynamic psychotherapy (page 81)

Counselling (page 82)

Coaching (page 85)

Neurolinguistic programming (NLP) (page 89)

Havening (page 93)

Hypnotherapy (page 97)

Eye movement desensitisation and reprocessing (EMDR) (page 99)

Thought field therapy (TFT) (page 100)

Psychosensory techniques and principles (Psy-TaP) (page 103)

After describing these I include the usefulness of self-help groups (page 107) and mental health apps (page 109) and finally, as it continues to be offered in very severe depression, electroconvulsive therapy (ECT) (page 109). But I start by talking about medication because for many people it does have a place and can be particularly helpful in conjunction with a talking therapy. Many people wish to avoid medication and fear potential side-effects and addiction, so I talk about these concerns below also.

Medication

Medication for depression, generally known as 'antidepressants', can be used alone or alongside most other forms of therapy.

Antidepressants act on two key chemical messengers in the brain ('neurotransmitters'), serotonin and noradrenaline, which carry signals between nerve cells and can have a positive effect on your mood and emotional state; they are known to boost concentration and outlook so that you feel more able to face up to day-to-day life and take more pleasure in the things you once enjoyed doing. Effectively using medication can get someone with depression into a place where they might then be more receptive to drug-free therapies and lifestyle changes.

That does not mean that doctors will automatically turn to a prescription of antidepressants for patients diagnosed with depression. This kind of medication is generally not recommended for mild to moderate depression, and even in those with a more severe form of the illness, doctors will generally start with the lowest possible dose they think will help to improve symptoms to minimise the risk of side-effects. It can then be gradually increased if deemed necessary.

It can take a week, and often longer, to feel any effect from the antidepressants and a course lasting at least six months is generally recommended for a sustained recovery and to help prevent symptoms from returning. Some people may have to stay on the medication longer, while others may have to continue to take antidepressants on an ongoing basis.

Pete, who suffers from major depressive disorder, tells us of his experience:

I have taken citalopram for a number of years on and off. I think it does help me and helped in getting me to a place where I could take some active steps towards recovery.

It is important to remember that everyone is an individual, and although some medications can be very effective, one person may respond better than another. However, as a variety of medications are available on the market, often there can be a 'trial and error' phase, to decide the most effective drug for that person.

As Charliee, who suffers from bipolar, says of her own experience:

> Medication helps me to a certain extent. I currently take lithium and quetiapine, which helps with sleep and to stabilise mood. There are so many different psychotropic medications that it can take a while to find the right cocktail!

The most common form of medication prescribed for depression is a group called selective serotonin reuptake inhibitors (SSRIs); these work to boost levels of the neuro-transmitter serotonin. They have names such as fluoxetine, paroxetine, sertraline or citalopram, but they are often known by brand names, such as Prozac – a brand of fluoxetine. SSRIs tend to be prescribed by doctors as an initial form of medica-tion as they tend to have fewer side-effects than some other older-style antidepressants.

However, the doctor may prescribe other antidepressants and psychiatric medications, depending on the age of the sufferer and the diagnosis and what they feel may work better for the individual sufferer.

Younger people (under 18) are treated with particular caution when it comes to prescribing antidepressants. There is some evidence that medication can lead to an increase in suicidal thoughts in young people, so antidepressants are prescribed far less often for them and only after psychological therapy has been tried. They should be prescribed with great caution under the direction of a psychiatrist and the young person taking the drug should be monitored very closely.

No matter what age someone is, a GP should always be at the centre of decisions about medication, and the risks and benefits should be explained. Do not be afraid to ask any questions about anything that you are unsure of with regard to the drugs being suggested or prescribed to your loved one. Should you notice any drastic changes in the sufferer's behaviour or any severe side effects, you should recommend that they consult their doctor immediately.

Side-effects

As with most medications, each one can have its varied side-effects, so it is always advisable, before starting, to read the information leaflet provided. This will help the sufferer and their carers understand the possible changes that may be experienced, as the drug begins to get into their system, and hopefully starts to work.

Common side-effects of SSRIs include:

- Feeling agitated, shaky or anxious
- Nausea
- Indigestion, diarrhoea or constipation
- Dizziness or headaches
- Disturbed sleep patterns
- Low sex drive and other sexual problems.

The side-effects should improve within a few weeks, although some can occasionally persist.

If you are a carer, loved one or the person taking the anti-depressant, it is extremely important to keep in mind that there are cases in which a serious side-effect can include suicidal or self-harming thoughts; please contact your GP or medical professional straight away if there is any hint of this arising.

Those who have been prescribed antidepressants should also be very careful about drinking alcohol, as it can counteract the benefits of the medication.

Serotonin syndrome

'Serotonin syndrome' is a rare set of side-effects linked to

SSRIs and another class of antidepressants called serotonin-norepinephrine reuptake inhibitors (SNRIs) that can nevertheless be potentially serious. It occurs when the level of serotonin in the brain becomes too high and can also happen when the medication is being taken in combination with another medicine or substance that also raises serotonin levels, such as the natural remedy St John's wort.

Symptoms include agitation, shivering, sweating, diarrhoea and muscle twitching and in the most serious cases can lead to seizures, an irregular heartbeat and loss of consciousness.

To avoid this, patients should never take two different types of antidepressant at the same time without their doctor's clear guidance. Patients should also make their doctor fully aware of any natural remedies or treatments they are intending to try in case they are counterproductive to the medication and treatment plan they have already been prescribed.

Coming off antidepressants

Sometimes, believing they are well, people 'just stop' taking their antidepressants. Not only can this undermine their effectiveness, but it can also lead to them experiencing some difficult side-effects. Instead, they should reduce the amount they take under the guidance of their psychiatrist or GP. Stopping suddenly can lead to withdrawal symptoms, such as stomach upsets, anxiety, dizziness and/or even seizures. Even if a recently prescribed medication does not appear to be working, it is important to keep on taking it until the GP suggests otherwise. If there are severe side-effects, seek guidance straight away.

Antidepressants are not, as some people worry, addictive, in that you do not get cravings for them or need to keep increasing the dose to get the same effect. However, if someone has been taking them for a while, their body will have adjusted to the change in chemistry they have brought about. This is why it is always best to reduce the dose slowly under the guidance of a medical professional.

St John's wort

St John's wort (*Hypericum perforatum*) is a herbal remedy that can help lessen some of the symptoms of mild and moderate depression in some people. It has a history of being used for centuries to help treat mental illness. As with all other types of natural remedy, and prescribed medication, you should always consult your GP or other medical professional prior to taking it.

The first question to ask is: 'Does it really work?' While there is evidence that it can help some people deal with the symptoms of mild depression, like many herbal remedies it has not been through the same rigorous scientific trials as traditional medicines and thus large-scale proof of its efficacy is hard to come by.

Instead, researchers have pulled together many smaller trials to try and gain a better picture of how it works. A 2016 review of 35 studies concluded that St John's wort reduced symptoms of mild to moderate depression more than a placebo and to a similar degree to prescription antidepressants.[8] Another analysis a year later, looking at 27 studies, found that St John's wort had similar effects on mild to moderate depression as antidepressants. Those researchers also noted that fewer people stopped taking St John's wort, compared with antidepressants.[9]

Nevertheless, the use of St John's wort is not currently recommended by the National Institute for Health and Care Excellence (NICE) so doctors in England and Wales do not normally write prescriptions for it. As a result, most people buy it over the counter, where it is freely available. This can make it an easily accessible remedy, but with St John's wort coming in many different forms, from tablets to teas, and from a wide range of different companies, finding the right product for each individual can be confusing and sometimes overwhelming.

It is important not to turn to St John's wort instead of seeking help from a GP. While the doctor may not prescribe it, they will be able to give advice on whether it is safe for someone to take or whether there is something else in their lifestyle or health profile that could deter them from doing so. This is particularly important to bear in mind given that St John's wort can also have side-effects and can interact negatively with many other medicines.

When taking St John's wort, it is important to be aware of some of these potential side-effects. Some people can use it without experiencing any negative effects; others may report symptoms, including feeling nauseous, being sick or having diarrhoea, headaches, tiredness, confusion and/or dizziness. A rare side-effect also reported is increased sensitivity to sunlight.

With such a plethora of St John's wort products to choose from, it is also important to select one that is best suited to your needs. St John's wort products are licensed by the Medicines and Healthcare Products Regulatory Agency (MHRA) under the Traditional Herbal Medicines Registration scheme. Under this scheme, registration is based on the long-standing use of a plant as a traditional herbal medicine, and is not based on clinical trials. Those thinking of taking St John's wort should look out for the 'THR' mark on the packaging to get a licensed product.

Different brands will contain different amounts of hypericin or hypericum extract – the active ingredient. To find out how strong each product is, read the box or information leaflet to see how much each contains and also how often each needs to be taken. This can help the sufferer and their carers monitor how much they are taking and what level helps them.

As such, taking St John's wort puts the onus on the sufferer and their family and friends to find the right product at the right dose. For someone experiencing depression, monitoring the dosage and watching for side-effects can feel like another hurdle to jump. Supportive family and friends can be of invaluable help with this.

Tina, who has taken St John's wort on and off for a number of years, says of how it helps her:

> When I can feel a dark patch coming, I start taking St John's wort. I find it lifts my mood and works well for me. It takes the edge off, which allows me to take back control.

Cognitive behavioural therapy (CBT)

CBT is one of the most well-known forms of therapy for depression. It uses a discussion-based approach to change or reduce unhelpful thoughts, which in turn will reduce damaging and harmful behaviours that are part of depression. CBT also helps people to set achievable, realistic treatment goals and to reinforce all the behaviours that are useful in meeting those goals.

Dr Ian Drever, psychiatrist and founder of the Academy of Mental Fitness, explains how CBT works:

We tend to think of CBT as something new, trendy and cutting edge, but like many good things in health, its roots go back millennia.

Some of the earliest writings on what could now be considered the forerunner of CBT were from ancient Rome. There, the famous physician Galen, attending gladiators before their fights, noticed that some of them were quivering wrecks, while others were steely calm.

Galen reasoned that the difference between the two presentations must have been due to their individual mind-sets – after all, they were all facing the same impending challenge, but those who held positive, empowered and confident beliefs remained calm, whereas those who doubted themselves were the most nervous.

And so, the link between our thoughts and our moods was made. This is the essence of CBT – it teaches us the skills and winning mind-sets of those who tend to navigate life most effectively.

We can see evidence for this all around us in our daily life. For instance, take the experience of going through a difficult life experience, like a divorce. Some people will bounce back with focus, vigour and a sense of a new chapter opening up in their lives, while others worry, wilt and become consumed by their predicament.

One of the key tactics of CBT is to identify 'thought distortions' – these are entrenched, unhelpful ways of thinking which we are often completely unaware of, but which can powerfully influence our outlook on the world and how we feel in our mood.

One of the most common thought distortions is something called 'catastrophisation', which is a grand name for nothing more than making a mountain out of a molehill. It's all about taking a negative situation and going into all kinds of 'what ifs' and worst-case scenarios, even if they're never actually remotely likely to happen.

Another biggie is 'selective abstraction'. You can generally spot this one in action when you hear someone using words like 'always' or 'never': 'I always make a mess of job interviews' or 'I never get lucky in relationships'. Here, we're making sweeping negative generalisations about ourselves and likely outcomes, based on some selected negative past experiences – and what then happens is that our negative beliefs end up becoming a self-fulfilling prophecy. If we think we're going to do poorly in a job interview, then we go in with a mind-set of failure. No wonder we end up feeling miserable.

What's so powerful about CBT is that when we realise what we're thinking, we then have the power to change this and to prevent our mood becoming so low or anxious. It's also hugely freeing to realise that no-one can 'make us' feel anything – that's a phrase we hear a lot, but in fact, no-one has this power over us. Our emotions are internally generated.

The father of using CBT in modern practice is an American psychiatrist called Aaron Beck. Typically, CBT sessions will be held once or twice a week, with 'homework' often prescribed, particularly keeping a thought diary to help make the link between thoughts and feelings more explicit. An average course of treatment might be around six to 12 sessions, although sometimes more may be needed.

It's worth remembering that whilst an exceedingly useful skill-set, CBT isn't a magic bullet. Some criticisms of it are that it can feel a bit 'mechanical' and that it doesn't focus on past events; sometimes, exploring past events like trauma can be really important.

Many people choose to go through a course of CBT and then take away whichever tools feel most relevant to them. These can then be built into a personal collection of strategies for staying well, and for batting off life's inevitable curved balls.

Dialectical behavioural therapy (DBT)

DBT is an adapted form of CBT, developed by Dr Marsha Linehan. It focuses on accepting uncomfortable and unhealthy behaviours and feelings instead of struggling against them. It was developed originally for those diagnosed with borderline personality disorder; however, it has also been found to be an effective treatment for other mental illnesses, such as depression. It is a structured form of therapy with the aim of achieving self-acceptance and change by helping the person to regulate their emotions and decrease negative behaviours.

Eve, who has experienced both CBT and DBT for depression and an eating disorder, tells us more about how the treatments benefit her:

I had CBT for an eating disorder related to my depression. This helped me to challenge and change the unhelpful behaviours that I was showing, such as restricting what I was eating and purging when I did eat. This helped to improve my emotional regulation, and I was able to look at developing personal coping strategies such as grounding and self-care (e.g. taking a bath to make myself feel 'pretty') and then I was able to look at solving whatever current problems I had rather than punishing myself for them.

Then the DBT I had was about four years after the CBT. This was more around treating my BPD [borderline personality disorder] (major depressive disorder is a huge part of this). It built on the skills I had from CBT (grounding, self-care) and helped me to also see that emotional dysregulation wasn't 'wrong' - it was a product of an emotionally abusive upbringing.

Interpersonal therapy

Interpersonal therapy is one type of talking therapy that it is thought may help people with depression, particularly when the illness may be linked to difficulties in how the sufferer relates and reacts to others. IPT can help them to understand these relationships and how they may be having an impact on their mood and well-being. It can also help them interact more effectively, which in turn may have a positive effect on their mood and how they feel.

It can be particularly helpful where a significant relationship in their life is a source of tension or distress, or when a relationship shifts significantly as a result of a new challenge or life change. IPT can also be beneficial in dealing with the longer-term effects of grief or loss that have escalated to the point of having an impact on a person's day-to-day life. It can also be effective in helping people recognise and tackle a long-term patterns of difficulty in their relationships with others.

Psychodynamic psychotherapy

Psychodynamic psychotherapy is another form of talking therapy that has been found to have a positive effect on those dealing with depression. It involves a therapist helping someone talk about how their past experiences have affected how they think, feel and act, and how to move forward from those past ties that can sometimes weigh them down.

Delving into the past, looking at the effect it has on their subconscious, is not an easy process for many people, nor possibly for those around them who care about them. It may be harrowing and upsetting; however, it can also help unravel deep-rooted feelings and anxieties that can play a part in depression or other mental illness.

Counselling

The word 'counselling' covers a multitude of different disciplines. Often counsellors will use an element of psychotherapy, CBT and NLP within their method. Most broadly, however, counselling offers an opportunity for patients to talk. Within an anonymous and safe environment, they are afforded the opportunity to speak about anything, while being gently guided with questions by their therapist, which allows them to come to important realisations about the origin and nature of their illness.

Counselling has a number of benefits for those suffering from depression. Firstly, it allows them to feel valued. People suffering from depression and other mental health issues often feel isolated and misunderstood. Counselling provides a forum for them to explore their feelings. Secondly, counselling is, by its very nature, tailored to the individual. There is no set format for counsellors, which means that they must, to some extent, treat everyone's case individually. As such, it is crucial in counselling – perhaps more so than with any other type of therapy – to find the right 'fit' in terms of a practitioner. A good counsellor should make their patient feel safe, secure and valued at all times. They should establish a bond of trust with their clients and make it easy for them to discuss potentially painful or difficult issues.

As a mental health counsellor myself, I ensure I have met with a sufferer's parents or carers before I commence working with them, if they are under 18. Many people are surprised that I insist on this; I have always been of the opinion, however, that rehabilitating someone with depression, or any other mental health problem, is a group effort and one which will involve constant channels of communication between clients and the people who are most influential in their lives. If a client is over 18 and they have approached me independently, I will usually bring carers into the process a little further into therapy. Under the Data Protection Act, I of course have to obtain the client's permission to share information with carers. Once I have explained the paramount importance of trust and communication, this permission is usually granted. I like the families of my clients to understand my methods and the work I will undertake with their loved ones so they can be as helpful and supportive as possible throughout the recovery process. Recovery can sometimes be a long process, with the sufferer's mindset changing at each stage, sometimes on a day-by-day basis.

It is important that carers are aware of the changes to help them to gain a real insight into how their loved one is thinking and feeling at each juncture. This is why I prefer to keep them in the loop. Before a client sees me for the first time, I research their interests, whether it is films, music, clothes and/or particular hobbies; this enables me to establish a rapport with them during their initial sessions. It is important for sufferers to feel understood and accepted. It is also crucial they perceive themselves as a three-dimensional person, rather than as simply 'A Mental Health Issue'. Depression can envelope the identity of the sufferer. By talking to my clients about their interests, hobbies and passions, I am demonstrating to them that they are individuals, who are not defined by their illness. This sets in motion the journey towards my client envisaging life without their issue – a huge leap in terms of the recovery process. Encouraging clients to acknowledge their struggles and open up about the factors which might have influenced them is not always easy – it requires time, patience and perseverance.

I tend to work very intensively with my clients initially, seeing them two or three times a week. The challenge to negative emotions and feelings should be worked through as swiftly as possible. This also helps to quickly establish a bond of trust and friendship during this time. Eventually this can be maintained with less frequent sessions.

Caroline and James talk of their experience of my working with their daughter:

We were introduced to Lynn by a friend when our happy, confident 13-year-old daughter's mental health deteriorated and she plummeted into a very dark place. We couldn't quite get to the bottom of it. We knew she'd had some friendship issues previously and was feeling low because of some low-level bullying that had gone on for a few months beforehand, but our lovely girl gradually became withdrawn from our family unit. She was writing down some very worrying things and her behaviour changed while we were left on the outside desperate to help but struggling to reach her.

She started meeting with Lynn twice a week and because of Lynn's gentle, kind approach, she quickly developed a strong bond with her. Lynn gained her trust and did some incredible work with her and told us she felt she was suffering from mild depression and anxiety. Sometimes they would just talk and other times they would chat while doing crafts, which made it less intense. Sometimes Lynn did mind maps and other activities with her and other times she simply listened. Slowly, Lynn started to help her unravel everything that was going on in her head, and there was a lot! Her progress was quick once we had the right support in place for her. Lynn was on hand to support us too which was invaluable. It was very upsetting to see our daughter in such a desperate place. Home life was difficult as we were treading on eggshells, making sure we didn't say or do the wrong thing. Knowing Lynn was there alongside us, reassuring us and supporting us on this journey, made it much more bearable and gave us the strength we needed to help our daughter. Lynn also accompanied us to school meetings, which was a huge help.

After a couple of months we were able to reduce our daughter's sessions to once a week and more recently she has started going only when necessary. We know that Lynn will increase their sessions straight away if she sees any sign that our daughter is deteriorating again. Lynn has a very clever approach in the way she works and our daughter now comes away from her sessions with a smile on her face. She is gaining strength all the time. Without Lynn's help and expertise we dread to think what might have happened and we will always be grateful to Lynn for helping our daughter through this difficult time in her life. We have no doubt that there will be times ahead when she will need to turn to Lynn again for help and it's lovely to know that Lynn will always be there to support her when she does.

Coaching

Life coaching can help and support people to align their life, taking them on a journey to become who and what they want to be at a personal and a professional level. Life coaching encourages people to discover their own answers to challenges and obstacles under the guidance and help of their coach.

Judith Cocking, a resilience and performance coach, tells us about how coaching can benefit those suffering from depression:

With the increased stresses and pressures associated with modern-day living, it is no surprise that increasing numbers of people are suffering from depression.

The first key question is, 'Can a coach help somebody suffering from depression?'

Coaching is not a substitute for the appropriate medical help and counselling, but the answer is, 'Yes, it can help, not least in supporting a person to follow through with their therapeutic goals.'

My experience gained from clients, friends and close family members suffering from depression is that coaching can play an important part in recovery, offering encouragement and support to those struggling to engage with day-to-day activities and ultimately helping individuals move forward with passion, purpose and joy.

So, in more detail, what can coaching do?

A coach will act as a guide, supporter and motivator to help clients move forward, and define and achieve their goals. Coaching is a bespoke process tailored to the individual being coached. A coach will not dictate or provide answers, rather they will ask questions, listen and guide to help clients find the answers for themselves.

I believe my role when working with clients is to support them to be their best selves and to live the life that they really want to live, both personally and professionally.

People suffering from depression can find it hard to focus on the future.

This is equally true of highly stressed individuals. Difficulty in decision-making is a common symptom and can make meaningful discussion about goals difficult. Therefore, helping an individual to get themselves to a position where they can start to determine how they want their future to look becomes a goal in its own right. This is often the starting point with a new coaching relationship.

These are a few quick and easy tools and techniques I use with my clients to 'still' the mind and allow space to move forward.

Heart-focused breathing

Heart-focused breathing is a very simple exercise, developed by HeartMath(r), which helps to calm the mind and rebalance the autonomic nervous system, leading to greater resilience. This is what you do:

Place your hand on your chest in the area of your heart. Imagine that you are breathing through this area.

Breathe in for a count of 5 and then out for a count of 5. Continue for five to 10 minutes.

You will find that focusing on your breathing makes it difficult to think of *anything else and helps to promote calm. It also has the added benefit of decreasing the stress hormone cortisol (levels are often elevated in patients suffering from depression). This is important for a number of reasons:*

1. *Elevated cortisol levels can affect the production of serotonin, the 'feel-good' hormone that appears to influence mood, appetite and sleep;*

2. *Elevated cortisol levels can make depression therapies less effective. The more you practise heart-focused breathing, the better you will get at it.*

Focus on the positives

All human beings have a tendency to focus on the negatives. The brain is actually wired to do this, but for people suffering from depression this can be even more extreme. In order to retrain our brains to a more positive way of thinking we need to take some positive action. I recommend keeping a note book and writing down all the positive things that happen to us during the day, however small. This provides us with an excellent reference point to revisit and reflect on the good things in our life. Over time this will help to improve the ratio of positive to negative thoughts, improving overall well-being and happiness.

Do something you love

Taking some time to do something you love, just for you, can help you to reconnect with who you really are. Listen to your favourite music, take a walk in the country, enjoy your favourite meal. It doesn't matter what it is just as long as you love it. Enjoyment encourages dopamine production.

Dopamine is a neurotransmitter produced in the brain which helps our focus, motivation and productivity.

Setting goals

Depression can make setting goals particularly challenging, but goal-

setting is an important part of wellness. A coach can help clients to identify the areas which may be lacking in their life and support them to develop goals to address these areas. Together they can work on the 'new you', removing negative and unhelpful ways of thinking and making way for more positive and productive thoughts and behaviour.

I have found the Wheel of Life to be an excellent tool to help individuals to decide on their priorities. All you need is a piece of paper and a pen. Draw a circle on the piece of paper and divide it into eight sections, like a pizza. Think about the eight things that are most important to you in your life and label each section accordingly. These eight things will vary dramatically from person to person and there is no wrong or right answer; just make sure they are meaningful to you. Then score each section out of 10 and draw a line in the relevant section to indicate your score (see figure 4.1 below). The 0-10 scale represents each person's 'satisfaction score' with each element, '0' being at the centre of the circle and representing 'very dissatisfied' and 10 being at the outer edge and representing 'fully satisfied'.

Figure 4.1: The Wheel of Life, showing eight priority areas each marked out of 10 for satisfaction

The Wheel can be used to help clients prioritise the areas they want to work on first.

88

Chapter 4

They set themselves manageable targets, such as to take action to move 'Friends' from a 3 to a 5, rather than trying to achieve a 10 in everything. I have yet to meet a person with a perfect life!

There are many benefits to setting goals, including greater focus, peace of mind and more freedom of thought. The key is to start small and build on these as the client's recovery progresses. A coach can support a person in recovery through the process.

This is some feedback from one of Judith's clients:

> The relationship has been very beneficial in helping me understand more about myself and how my deep-set feelings and fears can affect the way in which I operate. There has definitely been a positive change in me which can be attributed to the coaching experience with Judith.

Neuro-linguistic programming

NLP was created by Richard Bandler and John Grinder in California, USA, in the 1970s. It relates to the way we communicate with ourselves. 'Neuro' means 'of the mind', and 'linguistic' is the study of language. Therefore, NLP purely means that you can re-program the language of your own mind – that is, the way that you think and the words you choose to think with.

Michele Paradise, a Harley Street personal development practitioner, NLP trainer, Havening Techniques practitioner and clinical hypnotherapist, tells us of how NLP works:

Neuro Linguistic Programming (NLP) is quite a mouthful but is a very powerful set of techniques to enable change.

I had the privilege to be trained by Dr Richard Bandler, the co-creator of NLP, and Paul McKenna, and to assist them on their courses for 10 years so I saw a lot of change right before my eyes and I know how powerful it is in shifting behaviours, especially around depression and old, unhelpful emotions.

As Dr Bandler has said for many years, NLP is not a thing. It is the study of modelling excellence in others, using the newly learned strategies and teaching the client how to think on purpose; not just react to their circumstances.

In 1972 in Santa Cruz California, Dr Richard Bandler and John Grinder set out to study very successful therapists of the time, such as family therapist, Virginia Satir, the world-famous hypnotherapist, Milton Erickson, and the innovative psychotherapist, Fritz Perls, to identify the strategies they used to get great results and teach others how to do it.

What they learned was that we use our five senses to explore the world and map it. In other words, the world is so vast and rich that we have to simplify it to give it meaning and we 'chunk it down' by looking for familiarity and patterns with things and situations through what we see, hear, feel, taste and smell. For example, every time you see a door in front of you, you have a pretty good idea how it works. You will see a door knob or handle and turn it in a direction that you've turned it many times before to open it. You don't need a set of instructions every time you see a door, they're all pretty much the same and there is a familiar, similar pattern to opening them.

Our brain loves familiarity. It enables us to feel that we know about the situation, even if it's the first time we've encountered it. This is especially true with people. We are more likely to like people who are more like us, not less. You've probably met someone who reminds you of someone in your past and you think to yourself, 'They look like or remind me of Uncle John.' If you like Uncle John, you are more likely to like them and feel more comfortable around them. If you don't like Uncle John, they will be at a disadvantage with you and it may take longer for you to get to know them.

We do this in all aspects of our life; especially behavioural patterns. We develop patterns when we need them. Some behaviours are referred to as coping strategies and we run them every time we are in a situation where we need to cope with something that may be stressful. After a while, we have learned them so well that they are now stored in our unconscious and we don't even have to think of them anymore; they just get 'fired off' when we need them. A bit like being able to open a door without really thinking about it.

Depression is a great example of 'firing off' feelings based on things that we frequently can't control and it's always about living in the past or the future, but not in the present. It's about running old behaviours that do not fit the current situation or catastrophising about the future and living in pain before we even get there. We all unconsciously run films of situations, whether we realise it or not, and wouldn't it be better to run a Hollywood romcom instead of a Hollywood disaster movie?

Depression is always based on a belief – a belief that we're not loveable, not good enough, a failure, not desirable enough... and so on and so on. However, it is just a thought based on something someone might have said to us years ago and we still carry around to this day. We've built a whole world of belief around it and have 'made' it true for us. We then 'run a behaviour' to help us cope with this belief and sometimes the easiest thing to do is to remove ourselves from interaction with others and literally hide under the duvet.

In order to keep these beliefs alive, we need to run patterns and behaviours that sustain them and this is where NLP is magnificent. Through a process called meta-modelling, we can easily find out what beliefs and values the client has, how they run the patterns and behaviours around them so that we can teach them a new way to think and behave and change their beliefs forever.

Think back to a time when you firmly believed something to be true, like Father Christmas, the tooth fairy, or a haircut that you thought made you look amazing. Now you may not believe any of these to be true anymore and the change in belief probably happened in less than a minute. Maybe someone said something to you or you caught your mother putting money under your pillow and discovered the truth. Whatever it was, the belief changed instantly and you never believed it again.

The really good news is that we're not born with that behaviour; we learned it. And if we can learn something, we can unlearn something; thanks to the concept of neuroplasticity, which means that the brain has the ability to form and reorganise synaptic connections, especially in response to learning. So in a nutshell, we have the ability to relearn something and rewire our brain with the right training.

The metaphor I use to describe this is that we're on a very unhealthy 'hamster wheel' in our lives that seemed to serve a purpose at one time but we have hung onto these behaviours too long and they have passed their sell-by date; however, we're stuck on that wheel and don't know how to get off, which is where I come in. I metaphorically stick my finger in one of the spokes so that you fall off, wake up and find a new and better way to deal with an old issue.

Through fast and effective NLP techniques and hypnotherapy, I can enable a client to change the way they think, shift their behaviour and live a life with freedom and choice.

A session with an NLP practitioner like myself starts with what I call an 'archeological dig' to find out what the client's beliefs, values and strategies are. A client rarely presents with the real issue. By the time they get to me, they are manifesting a set of symptoms and it is my job to find out how the issue began. The history of the issue can be content-free if the client can't remember how it began or the memory is too painful. I then use many and varied NLP techniques until we get the client's desired outcome and finish the session with hypnotherapy so that the unconscious comes on board and allows the client to shift and change.

Phil, who has suffered from mild depression for a long period of his life, says of how he benefited from NLP:

I went for multiple weekly sessions of NLP after reading quite a lot about it and being recommended by a friend. The lady I saw really helped me to change my negative thinking into positive thoughts and actions. I felt like this was the push I needed to get out of my negative thinking patterns.

Havening

As mentioned earlier, Michele Paradise is a Havening Techniques practitioner as well as a trainer in NLP and a clinical hypnotherapist. She tells us how the Havening Techniques work:

Havening Techniques, a psychosensory therapy, was developed by Dr Ronald Ruden, a neuropharmacologist in the USA. 'Psychosensory' simply means that it is a therapy that connects the mind and body when treating the client.

Havening is a process designed to eliminate the consequences of traumatic memories; post-Havening, the response to an emotional trigger is delinked and/or eliminated. It is extremely effective in removing phobias, stress, anxiety, grief, somatic pain, pathological emotions and many other conditions, including depression.

We are electrochemical beings and when stimuli enter the body that are distressing to us, they travel up the spinal cord and quickly pass through the part of our brain known as the 'reptilian brain' or 'primal brain', also known as the hub of the autonomic nervous system, which is the life support system of the body. When it is overstimulated, such as by a traumatic event or memory, our heart beats faster, we become short of breath and our hands begin to sweat, to name a few symptoms.

Havening uses touch, distraction and imagination to create electrochemical changes in the brain to change the emotions around the memory. The client can leave the session with the memory but with the memory no longer triggering the negative thoughts and emotions.

The stimulus then travels quickly to the area of the 'mammalian brain' known as the 'limbic system' where the structure called the amygdala lives. Think of the amygdala as the third eye. It is an almond-shaped area of grey matter positioned roughly between the eyes and is where trauma is stored, gets 'stuck' and sets off the all too familiar responses, such as fight, flight and freeze.

When the amygdala is 'lit up' or activated, it can cause the pre-frontal cortex of the brain to go offline and 'flip its lid'; we then manifest behaviours that are out of character and harmful, or revisit old habits, such as drinking, taking drugs, over- or under-eating, even if we haven't done these for years. Until the trauma is delinked and decoded, the amygdala will get activated whenever a similar trigger or memory appears.

Havening is comprised of a series of techniques:

- Firstly, activate the traumatic event and measure it on a SUDS (subjective unit of distress) scale of 0 to 10, 0 being no emotional link to the memory and 10 being a very high emotional link.
- Secondly, apply the Havening touch, with the client's permission, on the face, shoulders to elbows and hands, which releases delta waves – the brain waves that occur in our deep sleep and healing state. (Havening is the transitive verb from the noun 'haven', which means a safe place; so we put the client in a safe place so they can delink the negative memory from their amygdala.)
- The client then counts their footsteps as they walk in a place of safety, such as a beach or park. They then move their eyes laterally to the right and left and finally hum out loud two verses of a nursery rhyme.

These three distraction techniques enable the client to interfere with the memory whilst being in a healing state. We do as many rounds of this until we have the number down to 0 or 1. Often, the delinking of the traumatic memory from the amygdala can be done in one or two sessions, but every case is different.

There are four components to the perfect storm of trauma, which is referred to as EMLI:

Event – An event that has caused trauma. It can be first, second or third person so we may have experienced it, watched it, read about it or seen it on the news.

Meaning – The meaning that the event has to us; it is sometimes difficult for other people to understand why it encodes traumatically.

Landscape – What is the condition of the landscape of the brain? Is it *resilient or vulnerable? This will be determined by the person's emotional health and can be affected by their socioeconomic situation, their child- hood, their current relationship situation and their health.*

Inescapability *– This is the feeling that you can't leave. You get stuck in the trauma and feel that there is no way out.*

The best way to demonstrate this perfect storm is to use a client story as an example. Joe (not his real name), a 28-year-old professional, came to see me for depression. He wasn't able to get out of bed in the morning and had lost his job as a result. Through a comprehensive intake ques- tionnaire and session questions, I quickly found out that his mother had committed suicide when he was 10 years old and he had gone to live with his grandmother and uncle, who both died when he was 16 in a house fire. His trauma was very profound and he had bounced from one relative to another until he got married at 25. When I met him he had layers of trauma that caused him to live in the past and keep replaying the events. This had led to depression, a bad back and obesity.

The Event was the trauma of his mother's suicide and his grandmother's and uncle's untimely deaths.

The Meaning was that he was now alone and felt abandoned, scared and lost.

The Landscape of his brain during these traumatic events was definitely vulnerable. His parents had divorced before his mother's suicide and his father had started a new family with another partner.

The Inescapability, the trauma he could not escape, was profound. He couldn't go back home, his mother would never come back and he was only 10 so couldn't live on his own.

When I met Joe, I knew exactly what to do to help:
- *Firstly, I did an 'archeological dig' to find out what the encoding trau- mas were. (As I have said, this can also be content-free if the client finds it too painful to talk about.)*
- *I then, with his permission, Havened him to delink and down-regulate the traumas from his amygdala.*

- *Finally, I worked with him over several weeks with the three pillars of Havening, which are healing, empowerment and growth.*

I'm delighted to say that he made a very good recovery and went back to university to finish his degree so that he could get a better job, which he did.

I then taught him how to self-Haven with affirmations to support the healing process. You need no equipment, no complicated algorithms... just your hands. Figure 4.2 shows what facilitated Havening looks like in session:

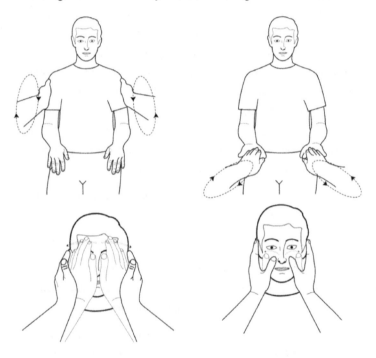

Images © Michele Paradise

Figure 4.2: The Havening touches to the arms, hands and face to induce delta brain waves

When you know how to self-Haven you can 'interfere' and down-regulate any future negative or traumatic events and create a resilient brain landscape. So in the future, when Joe may feel vulnerable and ungrounded, he can self-Haven by saying positive affrmations whilst Havening. Follow the

diagrams above and give it a go yourself to self-Haven whilst saying something positive like 'I choose to feel safe'. You will quickly notice the feeling of being more grounded and safe.

Hypnotherapy

Largely owing to the way hypnosis is described and presented by the media, there is a great deal of myth and misconception surrounding it. For a large majority, the word 'hypnosis' conjures up visions of magician-type performers persuading unwitting volunteers that they are a chicken, can fly, have an otter in their trousers. We are led to believe that hypnosis involves the total surrender of the will to another person, who is then free to manipulate their hypnotised subject in any way they please. In reality, hypnosis is simply a deep (and very pleasant) state of relaxation. It can be compared to when we awake on a Saturday or Sunday morning and have nothing to leap out of bed for; we tend simply to lie still and enjoy the sensation of being somewhere between sleep and total alertness. We would still be able to jump to attention in the event of an emergency and we are aware of the thoughts that drift in and out of our minds. It is this state which hypnosis exactly replicates.

Kate Guest, registered nurse, coach, speaker and hypnotherapist, explains, what hypnotherapy is and how it can help with depression:

Hypnosis has longevity. It has origins dating back before the 10th century in one form or another. Its story is varied and fascinating, involving many famous and some less well-known contributors. It has also been surrounded by mysticism, cynicism and debate.

Fast forward to today and we now have plenty of research and science to support the effectiveness of hypnosis.[10] Whether you're a fan of stage hypnosis, therapeutic hypnosis or both (as I am, everything has its place), hypnosis is very powerful.

Think of it as a tool for change. Can hypnosis be part of the therapeutic toolbox for things like depression? Indeed it can.

Here is a most recent comment from a client who came to see me with a history of anxiety and depression:

> All the work I've been doing with you has been without any of the antidepressants that I had been on for over 40 years. I just wish your work was more recognised by the NHS because you are better than any of the pills that just knock you out. Having hypnosis sessions with you means I haven't turned to tablets, which to me is a miracle!

When working with clients with a diagnosis of depression, we don't focus on the depression. We work on the understanding that 'what you focus on, you get more of'. We focus on what you want to have happen, how you want life to be and how you can create change to make that happen. It's about pattern change.

So who am I to tell you about change with depression? Depression can be exogenous (something happens outside ourselves; we react to something external) or endogenous (biological or genetic causes).

My experience was endogenous (a daily melancholia) exacerbated by external events. The side-effects of medication made me turn to hypnosis and NLP and through this, I was able to move forward.

I visited a hypnotherapist myself, found the process fascinating and wanted to learn more. My journey through depression using hypnosis and NLP gave me first-hand experience to help others and I still use self-hypnosis and NLP techniques daily now.

One of Kate's clients shares their experience of working with her:

> Kate took time to listen to me and understand the difficulties I have been having. She helped me realise that I can deal with

my problems in small, simple stages which felt so much more manageable and achievable. The hypnotherapy was very relaxing and gave me the opportunity to really let her positive statements sink in. Kate has taught me some very valuable skills that I will continue to use as I overcome the challenges in my life. Thank you.

Mary, who has suffered from situational depression, tells us of how hypnosis has benefited her:

I had a course of hypnotherapy when I was in my early twenties, which was great, very relaxing, and I still think back to what I learned at the time.

Eye-movement desensitisation and reprocessing (EMDR)

EMDR is recognised by the National Institute for Health and Clinical Excellence (NICE) and the World Health Organization as a treatment for post-traumatic stress disorder; it can also be used to treat types of depression.

Kate Guest, registered nurse, coach, speaker and hypnotherapist, explains what EMDR is and how It can help with depression:

Eye movement desensitisation and reprocessing is a more recent addition to my toolkit. Reportedly created by Francine Shapiro, a psychologist, in the 1980s and argued to have actually come from John Grinder, the co-founder of NLP for whom Shapiro worked, EMDR can be extremely effective. Mainly known for its use in PTSD, it is also now used for depression and other disorders.

Interestingly, this is one of the few accepted treatments in the NHS and is even referred to in the nationally recognised Mental Health First Aid two-day course.

Using either light therapy (not to be confused with light therapy for SAD), clicking sounds, following an object or fingers moving across the visual field and physical tapping (again, not to be confused with TFT or EFT tapping), EMDR can reduce or deplete the emotional reaction to a memory or event and thus have a positive effect on the associated depression.

I use a combination of any or all of the above along with the other thera-peutic tools I have, depending on the client I have in front of me. No one treatment suits all. Every client needs to have a bespoke experience.

One of Kate's clients says of her experience:

> I had four sessions of EMDR. Things began to shift steadily and by the end of the fourth session, I was able to leave the therapy room with a new outlook on life. My depression was no longer mine; I had let go of the label; I chose to have something new – hope. This hope and having a different emotional reaction to things that have happened to me are priceless. I am no longer held back by my emotions.

Thought field therapy (TFT)

TFT was developed by Roger Callahan in the USA. It is the practice of tapping in a set sequence (algorithm) on acupuncture pressure points to realign 'meridian energies' within the body to promote internal healing.

Dionne Curtis, a hypnotherapist and NLP, TFT and Psy-TaP practitioner, explains the technique of TFT and how it can help with depression:

TFT is a drug-free therapy that has been used to solve many psychological and emotional problems without producing any known side-effects – a totally natural way of healing.

How does it work? We all have set programs in our own minds that cover every emotion which are totally unique to each of us and consequently our actions upon those emotions are also particular to each individual. For example, when we get angry some of us will throw things and perhaps shout loudly, whilst others will take the anger inside and silently fume.

TFT interrupts the program between experiencing the emotion and responding to the emotion; this is necessary only when the response to that emotion is inappropriate or disproportionate – crying when angry can be a release and healthy; however, sobbing uncontrollably to a point where it is affecting life is a disproportionate response.

During Roger Callahan's research[11] he discovered that one of the primary indicators of why some people live longer than others is heart rate variability (HRV) – which is 'a measure of functioning of the autonomic nervous system, the body's complicated network of nerve endings and electrical impulses that control involuntary functions such as heartbeat, digestion, perspiration, breathing and so on'.

Once armed with this knowledge, the use of TFT was tested to see what effect, if any, it had on HRV and it was proven that tapping did indeed improve the HRV. Virtually within minutes of one TFT treatment HRV improved by as much as 156%, which in turn suggests that TFT is accomplishing something powerful, deep and biologically restorative.

What is the relevance of this to depression?

It is believed that severe depression causes physiological damage to the sufferer. Because of these changes it becomes almost impossible to improve HRV. Dr Robert Carney and researchers at the Washington University School of Medicine said, 'It is possible that heart rate and HRV never return to normal once there has been an episode of major depression.'

However, when Dr Callaghan did his own research[11] he found that not only did TFT rapidly get rid of the depression, but it improved the HRV in one session. So these improvements left the patient feeling not just mentally stronger but physically stronger as well. Dr Callaghan found that people suffering from severe depression whose HRV was taken prior to using TFT improved more than 150% – which is extraordinary, almost unheard of. In all cases, TFT totally eradicated depression, taking only minutes rather than the months other forms of therapy need.

Admittedly, this was not a detailed scientific study, but the results do challenge the thought that permanent *biological damage is done during bouts of deep depression. Dr Callaghan showed that, when treated with TFT, depression can be rapidly eliminated and that TFT can improve overall health.*

What makes TFT different from other treatments/therapies is that clients are shown how to treat themselves. Once the algorithm they need is identified they are shown how to use it to lift their depression. This allows sufferers to take control of their own treatment which makes them realise that they are playing a fundamental part in their own recovery. This is particularly helpful when the client faces difficult situations in the future – they have a procedure to follow and the expertise to carry out their own treatment whenever they need it, which is hugely empowering.

Whilst TFT is an extremely quick form of treatment, clients still need to invest time and be committed to allow themselves to follow the practice; there is no quick-fix solution. With depression, medication may be prescribed and required; in these cases TFT can be used alongside the medication without any side-effects.

Simon talks of his experience with TFT:

I had suffered from depression on and off for some time and I had already tried several complementary therapies when I found TFT. What I liked most about this form of treatment was that there were no side-effects and, although I went into the session feeling a bit apprehensive, I was surprised and amazed that it worked for me. The tapping was easy to follow and I was given a leaflet of exercises that I needed to do. I would highly recommend this treatment for anyone who wants a natural treatment; it changed my life and gave me the tools I needed to keep my symptoms at bay.

Psychosensory techniques and principles (Psy-TaP)

Kevin Laye, a Harley Street-based therapy practitioner and founder of Psy-TaP, whose current work is endorsed and supported by Paul McKenna, explains what Psy-TaP is and how it can treat depression successfully:

I believe the solution to depression may be in the word itself; when someone says, 'I am depressed...' maybe they mean they need a 'deep-rest' Depression is hard work and requires a lot of energy; that is why most depressed people appear to be exhausted.

My name is Kevin Laye, and I am the Founder of a system called Psy-TaP, which stands for 'psychosensory techniques and principles'. The system is based primarily around speed and simplicity. In Psy-TaP we have what we refer to as KEVS law: Keep Everything Very Simple. The system is based on a combination of known therapeutic practice combined with principles of physics, neuroscience and engineering knowledge. We have done studies to prove its efficacy and even a replication study as a verification process. We look at the epistemology of a symptom – the 'How do you do that?' or 'What do you need to do, to do that?' Once we have worked that out we then reverse-engineer the pattern using the body's naturally occurring system and put in a pattern break. We keep doing this until we have repeatability of efficacy in the technique. We find often the simplest techniques we develop are the most effective.

So let us review depression...

A few things spring to mind here. Depression is a symptom, often of a trauma. If you refer to the 'trauma tree' illustration (Figure 4.3), we posit there is a 'root' cause event to most things. The problem with most conventional therapies and medications is they are dealing with the branches, and may eventually get to the trunk. I refer to this as 'psycho-topiary'. My approach is finding the root and pulling it out so that the tree will die. Simple thinking I know, but both logical and effective.

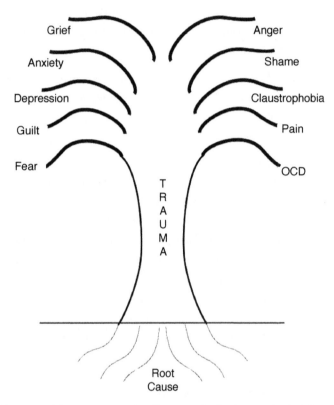

The Trauma Tree

Psy-TaP

Grief

Anger

Anxiety

Shame

Depression

Claustrophobia

Guilt

Pain

Fear

OCD

T
R
A
U
M
A

Root
Cause

Figure 4.3: The trauma tree that illustrates the fundamental principles of
Psy-TaP

*So how do we apply this thinking to depression? The first thing you have to
do is to look at the epistemology (the 'how do they do that?'). In NLP, they
have what are known as predicate Drivers, which are: Visual-Auditory-
Kinesthetic-Olfactory, and Gustatory – the shorthand is VAKOG. So using
this to look at the process, in which some, or maybe most people are able
to 'do' the behaviour we refer to as 'depression', I think this is the strategy.
You wake in the morning and Visualise upon opening your eyes the 'world'.*

You then say to yourself Auditorily (with internal dialogue usually): 'Here we go, another miserable day.' You then, in turn, feel Kinesthetically 'bad-sad or depressed'. So we have a V-A-K strategy. This can be extended, by confirming auditorily: 'See, I knew it was going to be a bad day,' upon which you can feel worse, making it a V-A-K-A-K. You can then run this program loop over and over and over again. This I believe is what those with depression do.

So, just as a contrast, let's look at the strategy of a naturally positive and upbeat person, using this same process. The positive person wakes, opens their eyes to visualise the world, and says to themself, 'Wow, another great day to be had,' at which point they feel positive and upbeat. They can then repeat to themself more positive things and feel even better and they can run this program over and over and over again. The strategy they employ is V-A-K-A-K...

So we have the same strategy in both cases, the only difference being the direction of focus. So change the focus and the easiest thing to change is the change right at the front end, and that is the visualisation. You change that and everything downstream of that must change too. This exercise may just enable you to do this.

Positive imagery exercise

Raise your right hand up and to the right of you so you are looking up at it.... Look into your palm and create a compelling image of what you want to be like assuming that nothing can fail.

Then double the intensity of the picture and brighten it. Then double it again and again... When it looks amazing, and only then, take a deep breath in and as you exhale pull the image into your chest and absorb it through your heart. Then, as you breathe in, intensify the image and as you exhale drive the feeling through your body into every cell, muscle fibre and tissue until you are saturated with the good feeling.

Then repeat with another good image.

Do this as often as you like... after all, who can ever have enough good feelings?

Another thing we do in Psy-TaP, which works well for depression, is the following technique. We ask sufferers to explain their depression to us and after 30 seconds or so, we ask them to stop. We then ask them to start again and repeat what they just told us, but this time when they tell us, they must do it with their eyebrows raised. The amazing thing is they cannot and they look confused or even giggle; on a rare occasion, someone may get angry or feel that we are mocking them, but when you explain what is happening, most people get it.

I discovered this technique when looking at the work of Paul Eckman and in particular, whilst reading his book, Unmasking the Face. *Paul states that the face is truly a representation of what is happening in our brain, and gives away many of our thoughts and feelings, unconsciously. So I thought, what does a depressed face look like and what would happen if you opposed that, by making the face look surprised as opposed to disappointed. I tested it on some people and 'eureka', it worked every time I tested it. I loved the simplicity. The Universe conspired to help a little, because a few weeks after I had begun to play with this technique, someone sent me a link to a study done by Professor Cheng at the University of Warwick in the UK. He had found that neurologically if you make someone make a surprised or raised-eyebrows face, they cannot maintain depression. Apparently, the scans and science have shown that the lateral and medial orbito-frontal cortices go into opposition and into conflict, and disable the ability to 'do' depression.* [12]

There was also a study done where Botox was injected into the 'frown' muscle and thus froze it and disabled the ability to frown. This also helped alleviate or stop depression. There is an old trick in psychology too, where you get someone to put a pencil in his or her mouth and this simulates smiling. This again reduces the ability to be depressed. [13]

I suggest you also look at the work of Amy Cuddy, who did a remarkable TedTalk on this subject. By holding the 'Yes' pose (see Figure 4.4) for a few minutes several times a day, depressive symptoms were alleviated or reduced.

Figure 4.4: The 'Yes' pose.

You see, in Psy-TaP we believe, if you break the pattern enough times, and break it rapidly, it shocks the brain into finding another strategy and creating new neural circuits. The unused circuits succumb as we sleep to a process known as 'synaptic pruning'. Then in their place the new neural pathways of not being depressed fire off and, according to Hebbs law of 'What fires together, wires together', a change is made. This is an organic non-medicated approach with no known side-effects.

Try these techniques out. What do you have to lose?

Self-help groups

Meeting with others and realising that others are dealing with the symptoms of depression can be really helpful for some people. Listening to others' experiences can be very therapeutic, helping people realise they are not alone in their situation; whilst, at the same time, talking and sharing feelings and experiences in a safe, non-judgemental setting can also be a valuable release that may actually help ease the isolating effects of the illness.

Self-help groups are not just about talking about feelings. They can also be an opportunity to discuss helpful strategies and therapies, to share knowledge and beneficial experiences with each other. Furthermore, being able to offer help and support to others can be therapeutic in itself, strengthening feelings of self-worth which can, at times, be damaged through depression.

Like other therapies, finding the right self-help group, which makes the sufferer feel at ease enough to participate, may take time. Even in the right group, it may take weeks or months of listening and observing before the sufferer feels able to actively participate and speak up. All this is absolutely natural and the experience should not be rushed.

Families and loved ones of those with depression may feel upset that the person they care for would seemingly prefer to talk to strangers than those closest to them. Understandable as these feelings may be, it can also be very natural to find it easier to talk to someone outside the immediate circle. Instead of feeling threatened, try to support your friend or relative in finding whatever therapy is helpful for them. Continue to make it clear that you are always there for them whenever they want to talk, but also show that you support them in seeking help from others who have their own experience of depression.

Self- help groups can also benefit carers, giving them a safe place to discuss their thoughts and feelings with people in similar situations.

Katie shares her positive experience at an NHS CBT group:

It is an excellent tool for anxiety. The funding in the NHS is limited so it tends to be offered through the doctors as group therapy, which can be daunting and off-putting for some but I know through my own experience some individuals brought a family member or friend along for moral support. There is no public speaking and you don't get picked on, you can just sit at the back and quietly take notes! CBT is a tool I use all the time, excellent for rationalising thoughts and behaviours. Really effective for those who are ready to challenge the way they confront situations.

Mental health apps

It may seem contradictory to suggest that someone with depression – often an isolating condition in itself – could seek help from an app, but there are a surprising number of different ways that these could help people with mental illness move forward. From mood trackers to support apps, all kinds of different help can be found on your phone or laptop. There are apps available to help track exercise – a proven mood booster – and others, such as the NHS app WellMind, to help you understand the symptoms of depression and how to tackle them.

Podcasts can also be helpful. Both those with depression and those who care about them can benefit from listening to the experiences of others and finding out what helped them. The Mental Health Foundation, Man Talk founded by Jamie Day, and MentallyYours founded by Ellen Scott and Yvette Caster at MetroUK are equally good starting points for finding podcasts to help with specific areas of difficulty and concern.

Using a mental health app should not replace going to a GP and seeking medical help. However, for some people, mental health apps can complement other therapies and help to provide the motivation that can often be so hard to muster when someone is suffering from depression.

Electroconvulsive therapy (ECT)

Lastly, it is important to include ECT. ECT, popularly known as 'shock therapy', is a form of brain stimulation which may be used to treat the most severe depression that has not responded to other treatments. It is usually only offered if the other treatments have proved unsuccessful or when the situation is thought to be life-threatening.

There are many fears about ECT, not least due to (often out-dated) depictions in films or on television; the reality of modern day ECT contrasts acutely with that portrayal. Nevertheless, ECT should not be undertaken lightly and, if possible, families and carers should help gather all the information they can about the therapy and why it is being offered to their loved one before it goes ahead.

During ECT, a carefully calculated electric current is passed to the brain through electrodes placed on the head. The current stimulates the brain and triggers a seizure, which may help to relieve the symptoms of depression. It is always carried out in a hospital by a specialist doctor under a general anaesthetic and patients are given a muscle relaxant to stop body spasms.

Like any therapy, it does not work for everyone and there can be side-effects which should be taken into consideration by the sufferer and their carers prior to treatment. These can include short-term memory loss, headaches, confusion and muscle aches.

Do not be afraid to ask your doctor questions. This is where having a family member or trusted friend present is invaluable. The doctor should clearly explain how ECT works and what they hope to achieve from using it. It is also crucial to have all the information to hand about the benefits, risks and possible side-effects to be able to make an informed decision to give consent to go ahead with ECT.

To conclude

There is no 'correct' or 'right' path to recovery. You may find either a single treatment or a combination works best. The important thing to remember is that there is, without doubt, a form of treatment available that can help your loved one overcome their depression. If one treatment is not working, do not be afraid to change tack and try another. It is quite common for sufferers to try various therapies before they find the right one for them as an individual.

Your loved one showing a willingness to get better is a huge step forward, and sometimes it can be frustrating and challenging for carers and sufferers when there is a delay in finding an effective treatment. I hope this chapter has assisted you in making sense of some of the terms, buzz-words and theories and will help you in making an informed decision about what to try next, always remembering that recovery is possible. At the back of this book you will find a list of resources (page 314) and practitioners (page 329), all of whom I have personally worked with, researched and/or spoken to at great length about the treatments and methods they offer. I do urge you to get going as soon as possible before the depression becomes completely habitual; if you can afford to, start a treatment that seems right in your case rather than waiting for state-funded help as this can, sometimes, take a long time to be available.

Chapter 5

Depression and well-being

We live in an age where what was once considered alternative treatment is now becoming much more mainstream and widely accepted. I would encourage you, the reader, to be open-minded towards all the potential avenues of therapy, both conventional and so-called 'alternative' that are available to you. The methods listed below are not mutually exclusive to conventional treatment but can work successfully hand in hand with it, aiding healing for the sufferer and, in some cases, the carer as well. It goes without saying that the basic self-care is of paramount importance, including the right amount of sleep, exercise and good nutrition. This has been borne out by my own experience both personally and professionally. It is also advisable to talk to your GP before undertaking any kind of therapy.

I have asked specialists within each field included, all of whom I know personally, to help give you an understanding of how their individual discipline can help mental well-being for both sufferers and carers alike. Approaches described are:

Exercise (page 113)

Sleep (page 120)

Nutrition (page 124)

Mindfulness (page 127)

Yoga (page 130)

Exercise

Exercise is good for the mind, body and spirit.

People who exercise regularly tend to do so because it gives them a greater sense of well-being. They tend to have more energy throughout the day, sleep better at night and have sharper memories, and most tend to feel more relaxed and positive about themselves and their lives.

Activity and exercise are especially important for people living with mental illness, not least because people in this situation can often have a higher risk of physical illness. Similarly, people with physical illnesses can be at a higher risk of developing a mental illness, such as depression, anxiety, disordered eating and/or OCD. The body and mind exist in balance, directly impacting one another.

Tan, an experienced personal trainer, adds:

There is such a strong link between physical activity and mental well-being that it simply cannot be ignored. Taking part in regular exercise reduces anxiety and depression whilst improving self-esteem, confidence and overall quality of life. Whether it's going to the gym or being outdoors, with friends and family or a personal trainer, exercise can play a vital role in maintaining health in both body and mind.

Scientists and research studies[14] have discovered that exercise causes the brain to release chemicals (including the neurotransmitter serotonin) which can make you feel good; these are the same components which are enhanced by antidepressants, but without the side-effects! Regular exercise can promote all kinds of changes in the brain, including neural growth, reduced inflammation, and new activity patterns that aid feelings of calm and well-being. It can also release endorphins, which are powerful chemicals that leave the person feeling energised and positive. Exercise can also serve as a distraction, allowing the person to find some 'time out' to enable them to break out of the cycle of their negative and distracting thoughts that feed their mental illness.

Pete, who suffers from major depressive disorder, tells us of the change he saw and felt within himself after adding exercise to his life:

> The biggest change has been through exercise, and running in particular. This has proved to be the best treatment I've ever experienced and I can honestly say it has changed my life. Since getting a place in the 2017 London Marathon for Mind I've run three marathons and seven half marathons as well as taking part in virtual races where I have tried to run every day for a month and reach a total over the month of 130-140 miles. Running has made me fitter, helped me to lose weight and, by getting me actively involved in sport again, restored my self-respect and self-confidence. I now believe I can achieve almost anything I put my mind to. I recognise now that I am resilient, tenacious and have a huge amount of determination. It has helped me to focus on always seeing the positives and to look to get out of my comfort zone and experience new things. If I have a bad day, a run or an hour in the gym can help me to reset my mind in a way I couldn't before.

Mental and emotional benefits of exercise

There are huge benefits to mental health from taking exercise, some obvious but many less so.

More energy

Increasing the heart rate several times a week will help you to have more energy.

Stronger resilience

When faced with mental or emotional challenges in life, exercise can help you cope in a healthy way, instead of turning to alcohol, drugs or other negative behaviours that will ultimately make you feel worse. Regular exercise can also help boost your immune system and reduce the impact of stress.

Better sleep

Even small amounts of exercise at regular intervals can help to regulate sleep patterns.

Improved self-esteem

Regular activity can improve the mind, body and soul. When it becomes part of everyday life, it can foster a sense of self-worth and make you feel strong and powerful. You will feel better about how you look and, by meeting personal goals, you will gain a sense of achievement.

Sharper memory and thinking

The same endorphins that make you feel positive can also help with concentration and improve the sharpness of your thinking when facing the tasks at hand. Exercise also stimulates the growth of new brain cells and helps prevent age-related decline. Jay Hurley, a highly experienced personal trainer, says:

When suffering from depression it can be very easy to be caught in the vicious circle of inactivity. Sometimes the thought of starting can be daunting, but it's important to go through the process slowly and comfortably because physical activity or an exercise programme can be hugely beneficial to the sufferer and can help ease the symptoms of depression. It's important also to note that there is a difference between physical activity and an exercise programme. Physical activity is anything you can do that would slightly increase your heart rate. This can be going for a walk, walking a dog, going for a slight jog or even doing some gardening. An exercise programme is more systematic and can be based in a commercial gym using a variety of cardiovascular machines, resistance machines or strength equipment. There are three main benefits to physical activity or exercise:

- Endorphin release
- Better self-confidence
- Social interaction.

When we do exercise or physical activity a number of chemical responses happen within our body and a range of 'feel good' endorphins are released; this is also known as the 'runner's high'. In bouts of depression, this can be a successful and quick way to boost your mood.

Exercise is a great way to improve self-confidence and can lead to an overall sense of achievement. Improving yourself, feeling healthier and stronger and boosting your energy levels through exercise together produce a side-effect of improved self-confidence.

It's important to find an activity that you enjoy as you are more likely to stick to it. This could be an exercise class, dance class, gym programme or a sport. Social interaction is a vital tool in the recovery process of depression; exercise or physical activity can be a great way to bring social interaction into your everyday life. Suggesting a walk with a friend is a good way to start, or even taking part in a group exercise class together. Gym-based exercise and group classes are also a great way to meet new people and develop a new support system, which in turn can also lead to improvements in emotional well-being.

Barriers to taking exercise

A person does not need to devote hours and hours of their day to exercise, or train at a gym, sweat buckets or run mile after mile to reap the benefits of it. They can obtain all the physical and mental health benefits of exercise with 30 minutes of moderate exercise five times a week, or even two 15-minute exercise sessions will work equally well.

Someone suffering from depression or any other mental health issues may find it difficult to take the first step into exercise. As Emma, who suffers from depression, says of her experience:

> Sometimes I feel too tired to walk but try and make myself do it in the knowledge that I will feel better about myself.

Here are some common barriers and some ways in which they can be overcome.

Feeling overwhelmed

When we feel stressed, anxious or low, the thoughts of adding another obligation can seem overwhelming or even impossible. It is important to remember that physical activity helps us to do and cope with things better. So, try to think of exercise as a priority and find ways to fit small amounts into everyday life.

Feeling exhausted

When we are tired and lethargic, it can feel like working out will make things worse and is all too much effort. However, it is worth remembering that physical activity is actually a powerful energiser. Studies have shown that regular exercise can dramatically reduce fatigue and increase energy levels.[15] The best place to start is at the beginning – for example, if you go for a five-minute walk around the block or up and down the road, with the idea of increasing the time by a minute or two each time. As you start to feel the benefit from it, it will hopefully not be a chore but something you enjoy.

Feeling hopeless

Even if you are starting at rock bottom, you can still work-out. Exercise helps us to get into shape. If you have no experience of exercising, start slowly with a low-impact movement for a few minutes each day, slowly building up from there.

Feeling bad about yourself

Most people are their own worst critic. No matter what your weight, age or fitness level, there are many others with the same goals of getting fit who feel the same. Being with people who are all in the same boat can help. Perhaps take a class with people who are at a variety of fitness levels. Accomplishing even the smallest of fitness goals will help you gain body confidence, which can only lead to your feeling better about yourself.

One of the many people I have had the privilege to meet is the wonderful man and former professional boxer, Frank Bruno. Over the years his own challenges with bipolar disorder have been well documented, in relation to which Frank has been very vocal about the importance of ongoing exercise as a contributory factor in the recovery process, and as part of everyday life.

> It was hard to exercise when on heavy medication. However, even a small amount every day, building up the time gradually, for example starting by walking then running or going to the gym, is helpful. You don't have to be a body builder. Look at it as part of your essential medication.
> Frank Bruno

Having used exercise as part of his own recovery, Frank has gone on to start the Frank Bruno Foundation, which provides structured, non-contact boxing sessions aimed at relieving the social, emotional and mental distress that adversely affects the mental health of children, young people and adults.

Joe, who is also in recovery from depression and alcohol

abuse, shares his positive experience of how belonging to a boxing club 'saved' him:

> My boxing 'family' was there for me in a dark time. I didn't have the most spectacular career but it helped straighten me out and gave me motivation. It gave me stuff I still use today – the work ethic, discipline, a regimented mind-set – but overall it made me feel part of something like a family and I will always love my old club for that... Boxing gives you so much more than skill and fitness; it literally saves people.

Exercise can be enjoyed in many ways: throwing a frisbee with a dog or a friend, walking around a shopping centre, cycling to work or simply going for a walk. Activities such as gardening or even doing small improvements in the house can be good ways to start moving around more. As well as helping to become more active, these activities can also leave you with a sense of purpose and accomplishment.

Exercise can also have a beneficial social component. Being part of a team or club can help you to feel you have a sense of identity and belong to a network of people, united by their passion for a particular activity. Working as a team through sport can help to build self-confidence and self-belief as well. All of which has to be a much healthier way to socialise than via the internet.

Billie, who is now in recovery from depression and substance abuse, says of the positive impact being part of a martial arts club had on him:

> My martial arts club have become my extended family. They taught me so much, from physical strength to mental strength, but in times of need they were always there too. I learnt discipline and self-control; this was a major step in my recovery from depression and it helped me to control my feelings in a more productive and positive way.

Sleep

Sleep plays a vital part in good health and well-being throughout life. Getting enough quality sleep at the right times can help to protect our mental and physical health, quality of life and overall safety. According to the National Sleep Foundation, for overall health and well-being, school-age children (6-13 years) need approximately nine to 11 hours sleep per night, teens (14-17 years) need approximately eight to 10, and adults (18-64 years) need approximately seven to nine hours.

Linda, who has now recovered from major depression, explains how important sleep is to her:

> I get at least seven hours of sleep per day. Just resting after a day's work gives me energy to spur on. I try to honour my sleeping time; I've become very self-aware and so when it is time to sleep, I go to sleep!

There is a close relationship between mental health and sleep. Many people who experience mental health issues also experience disturbed sleep patterns or insomnia. Over a long period of time, disturbed sleep can actually lead to a mental health condition or make an existing mental illness worse. With lack of sleep, we may:

- experience lowered self-esteem through inability to cope
- experience feelings of loneliness, social isolation and an inability to carry out usual social activities
- struggle to deal with everyday life
- experience low mood
- experience low energy levels
- develop depression and/or anxiety.

Most importantly, being constantly tired can affect our ability to rationalise anxieties and banish irrational thoughts. It can feed into negative thinking patterns which are often associated with depression and other mental health issues. This can also work the other way around, with the anxiety and over-thinking that are typical of depression leading to restlessness at night that can make sleep so much harder to achieve.

The night-time hours can be especially daunting for those with depression. There can be a vulnerability associated with sleeping: a dread of the terrors that sleep may leave them more open to, as well as the fear that slumber will undermine the resolve and single-minded focus that they cultivate during their waking hours.

The sufferer may therefore fight against sleep, facing the next day exhausted and even more vulnerable to the dark and ir-rational thoughts that fuel the illness. So, the continuous cycle of physical exhaustion and mental distortion serves as a huge hurdle to sustained recovery.

Maty shares his experience of how important sleep is to him:

> Sleep helps me take time out from all the hard things that are getting me down, resting and reconfiguring the way to go about the day's tasks.

While some experts recommend that adults should have between seven and nine hours of sleep a night (see above), others say that the quality of sleep is far more important than the quantity. For example, if a person has six hours of high-quality, uninterrupted sleep they will receive more benefit than having eight hours of restless, interrupted sleep.

Sleep is not just time out from people's busy routines; everyone needs sleep to help both their mind and body recover from the stresses of everyday life. Sleep is a healing process, one I cannot champion enough for people suffering from depression and, indeed, any other mental illness.

Sleep has played a vital part in my daughter Samantha's recovery, as she says:

> Although sometimes I found it hard to get to sleep as my head was full up and I could not think straight, I would listen to relaxation music which would help me to drown out the thoughts, making it easier to get to sleep. I found that having slept I would wake up feeling more refreshed. Sometimes if I was able, I would have a nap during the day which I found really helped me to think more clearly too. Without sleep I did not have the energy and headspace to cope with and move past the thoughts. Sleep has been a major part in my recovery.

Samantha's experience makes so much logical sense, but sleep is often a forgotten ingredient in the recovery process from a mental illness. Like many people in the general population, those with depression easily fall into poor bedtime routines, checking social media late at night or watching TV as the hours tick by, forming habits that undermine good mental health and lead to physical and mental exhaustion in its place.

Getting a good night's sleep is crucial for both the sufferer and their carers alike. There are things that we can all do to help us achieve this:

- If possible, get into a routine of going to sleep and waking up at the same time, although this is not always realistic for everyone, I know.

- Develop a pre-bed routine, which may include having a bath, reading or listening to relaxation music, getting your mind into a relaxed state; this should help you to drift off more easily.

- Allow no iPads, smart phones, television or electronic games in the bedroom. Some people experience disturbed sleep due to the use of technology in the bedroom and blue light from many devices can enhance wakefulness. Going to bed and then spending time on these devices can stimulate the brain, making it more likely to wake up in the night and then have trouble getting back to sleep, due to feeling the need to check for messages, social media etc.

- Make sure the bedroom is dark and as quiet as possible, and the temperature is comfortably cool (but not cold).
- Alcohol and caffeine can also disturb sleep, as does rich food eaten late at night, so avoid these.

Katie tells us what works for her:

> Sleep aids rest; it's so important to try and maintain routine with the sleep pattern. I learnt about Feng Shui, sleep hygiene which had a positive impact. For example, no TV/phones before bed to allow the brain time to slow down and recognise it's time to sleep.

The benefits of adopting regular and positive sleep habits can be huge. For people with depression, having the energy to do things that they love, to connect with others and build a meaningful life away from the illness are the cornerstones of recovery. However, these foundations are so much harder to build if the sufferer is exhausted.

It is also important to be aware that as the sufferer's mind is so active and full, the sleep they get may not always be 'quality sleep'. As Sheila, who has suffered depression on and off for 30 years, says:

> I would love to be able to sit down, put my head back, relax and enjoy what is around me... Instead... when I sit down I can actually feel the depression overwhelm me when I doze off! I feel as if I have been awake all the time. I guess you could describe it as 'asleep and awake at the same time'.

Having seen and experienced at first hand how regular, good-quality sleep has benefited both Samantha and myself, giving us the energy and strength we needed to be able to challenge and overcome the negative thoughts in our heads, I cannot reiterate enough the power and importance of sleep.

Nutrition

I am sure most of us have heard or been told at some point, 'You are what you eat', but we may ask ourselves, what exactly does that mean? Put simply, food is fuel; the types of foods and drinks you consume determine the types of nutrients in your system and can impact how well your mind and body are able to function.

Lyndy Stanway-Marsh, health and peak performance coach, explains this in more detail:

Mental health issues are a growing problem around the world and in the UK in 2018 recent estimates suggested that one in four of us have been diagnosed with a mental illness. One of these conditions, depression, will affect one in five of us at some point in our life.

But as we well know, there is no blood test to diagnose depression. It is a name which we give to a collection of symptoms of how we feel, but no one person feels the same or experiences their depression in exactly the same way. I believe from personal experience and from working with clients that the food we eat can really impact the way we feel and support us in moving forward through our depression.

When you are suffering from depression, learning how to balance your sugar levels is a very powerful support in helping you to feel better. Often many symptoms of depression can get significantly better by eating foods that keep your blood sugar stable, such as high-quality proteins like eggs, and healthy fats like avocados, olive oil and nuts. Rather than focus on calories I'd like you to focus on colour.

What foods hinder our recovery? A diet full of beige foods! I would like you to imagine the following...

You start your day with a cup of coffee and cornflakes. Then you have a cup of tea and a biscuit mid-morning. Lunch is a sandwich and a packet of crisps and a drink. Mid afternoon, another cup of tea and a biscuit, and then dinner is maybe fish and chips and a drink with chocolate or some treat after. Not an unusual day for many people.

Now I'd like you to imagine having all this food and drink on a table in front of you. Think about how it looks and how it feels. Does it feel heavy or light? Dull or bright?

On the other hand, what foods support our recovery? Eating a rainbow most of the time! I would like you to imagine again....

You start your day with a cup of water. Then you have eggs and avocado, with some tomatoes. Mid-morning you have a handful of mixed nuts and some water. At lunchtime you have a yummy vibrant rainbow salad with salmon and sweet potato with lots of mixed seeds. Then mid-afternoon you have a few oatcakes with nut butter and a banana. In the evening you have a big chicken stir-fry with lots of colourful veg and rice noodles.

Now I would like you to imagine having all of this food and drink on a table in front of you. Think about how it looks and feels. Does it feel heavy or light? Dull or bright?

My guess is the second picture made you feel a lot brighter and lighter. As we are on the inside, so we are on the outside. So, if we are filling our bodies predominantly with a diet of beige (dead) food we aren't going to feel very energetic or bright ourselves. I know that when you are feeling depressed, often you have no energy to make healthy food for yourself, but there are now lots of healthy readymade options in the shops which is better than no rainbow at all.

To keep it simple, **always try to create a rainbow on your plate with every meal** *. For example, if you are eating a sandwich, can you add in some cucumber or cherry tomatoes?*

These are my top tips for foods that can improve depression:

1. *Eat foods in the form that your great grandmother recognised as food. These are foods that grow in the ground or that you can recognise came from their natural form.*

2. *Eliminate processed foods and highly refined carbohydrates – processed foods are anything in a packet that has loads of complicated ingredients that you realise could only have been made in a factory*

and not grown in the ground. Highly refined carbs are things like processed breakfast cereals, biscuits and breads; these turn into sugar very quickly and can have a negative effect on your mood.

3. *Reduce refined sugar intake – Adding in sugar can have a negative rollercoaster effect on your mood, causing highs and then lows. You find refined sugars and hidden sugars in all sorts of foods. Look for foods with under 10 grams of sugar per 100 grams. One of the easiest ways to be a food detective and spot them is to look for words ending in 'ose' in ingredients. Also, where sugar is listed as an ingredient, see where it comes in the list;. if there are 15 ingredients and sugar is listed first, most of that product is made up of sugar as these lists have to reflect the relative proportions of the ingredients. Meanwhile, though fruit isn't a refined sugar, fruit juice can affect our sugar levels as, separated from the fruit's fibre which would slow down eating and make us feel full, we are likely to consume too much sugar in one go. (You wouldn't eat four bananas, four apples and four oranges at once!)*

4. *Increase healthy fats – You can stabilise your mood and blood sugar by adding lots of healthy fats to your diet. These include more avocados, olives, nuts, seeds and eggs. Even good quality red meat in smaller quantities can be beneficial.*

5. *Eat more oily fish – Fatty fish such as salmon, sardines, mackerel and anchovies are a brilliant source of good omega-3 fats which are essential for brain health and function. For vegans and vegetarians, chia or flax seeds and walnuts are a good source.*

6. *Eat more probiotic foods – There is more and more scientific research coming out on the gut being our second brain. That means that we can heal and treat many concerns, including depression, by healing our gut. There are trillions of bacteria that live in our gut; how healthy and balanced they are plays a critical role in determining our mood. They get upset by overuse of antibiotics, constant stress and various other food and lifestyle factors. The best way to increase the good balance of these is to eat more soluble fibre such as is found in leeks,*

onions, garlic, broccoli and cauliflower. Having a cup of bone broth a day is also immensely nourishing and healing for the gut. In addition, eating fermented foods such as sauerkraut, kimchi, kombucha, miso or kefir, can have a hugely beneficial effect on depression.

7. *Eat a low inflammatory diet* – This means swapping out things like excess tea, coffee, refined sugars, refined carbs, red meats and alcohol and adding in more of the rainbow foods that I have mentioned above. Also adding in more water, which helps focus and concentration, in turn has a positive effect on our mood.

We really have the power to improve the way we feel by controlling what we put on our plate and in our mouths. Food is such a powerful way to enhance your mood and support you when you are in such a heavy place.

Naomi, a former sufferer of depression, describes how eating the right foods really helped her in her recovery:

> When I was really struggling with depression my diet was so bad, I just would grab the closest, easiest and tastiest thing to eat. This would make me feel better for about five minutes. Usually the foods I would eat would be high in sugar, fat and everything bad for me. A friend of mine suggested I start eating a little more healthily and it might make me feel better. Even though I was aghast that she would say this to me, deep down I knew she was right. I slowly began to make healthier choices and, to be honest, it felt like healthy food was my medicine. The better I ate the better I felt.

Mindfulness

Life can at times be hectic; therefore, it can be easy to rush through each day without stopping to appreciate the here and now. Paying more attention to the present moment – to your own thoughts and feelings and to the world around you – can improve your mental well-being. Some may call this awareness 'mindfulness'.

Catherine Kell, mindfulness teacher and parenting coach, explains what mindfulness is:

Mindfulness is a way of training the mind to be present. It is a secular meditative practice, which involves being aware of your own moment-to-moment experience and doing so with an attitude of kindness, acceptance, compassion and non-judgement. When we learn to observe our thoughts and feelings, and not engage with them or try to change them, we can create space to respond rather than react. It is in this space that we can break the cycle of our habitual reactions and patterns of thinking and this has huge significance for maintaining our mental health.

When asked how mindfulness can benefit mental health, Catherine says:

Mindfulness can have a very positive effect on mental health and general well-being, and more and more studies are now being conducted to gain longer-term evidence of the mental health benefits of mindfulness. For example, for people suffering from recurrent depression, studies have shown that following their participation in a full mindfulness-based cognitive therapy (MBCT) programme, they are less likely to experience future depressive relapses. Details of studies and ongoing clinical, peer-reviewed research in various mindfulness-based interventions can be found easily online and specifically at the Oxford Mindfulness Centre at www.oxfordmindfulness.org.

I know from my own work that learning and practising mindfulness has been beneficial to many clients who are suffering from depression. Of course, I work in a supporting role alongside their medical practitioner. I always recommend that each new client sees their GP or other medical doctor first in order to ascertain their suitability for embarking on any complementary therapy if they have been diagnosed with depression. Most GPs and specialist doctors are well aware now that mindfulness is helpful in a wide range of areas and can provide someone suffering from depression with a hugely valuable tool to use independently.

A key area where mindfulness is helpful is learning how best to manage our relationship with thinking and to recognise that thoughts are just thoughts. Clients have described to me that over-thinking, ruminating, worrying and coping with a 'storytelling' mind are incredibly hard to bear and they come to enjoy a mindfulness session where they describe experiencing a sense of space around those feelings.

Mindfulness strengthens our awareness and helps us pay attention in a new way, which is very helpful in recognising a build-up of difficult emotions and learning to respond to those rather than simply react. Mindfulness also helps to build a more appreciative and grateful mind-set and, crucially, a lot of those appreciative feelings can be for the self.

Mindfulness aids our emotion-regulation and resilience too, and also alleviates stress, nerves, tension and anxiety – all of which can present alongside depression. Mindfulness can also benefit sleep, which is so essential for our nourishment and rejuvenation and is another area of our lives that depression can impact.

For some, mindfulness is completely transformative in terms of ending painful cycles of depression. Not only can mindfulness improve mental health but, importantly, learning mindfulness can also provide a person with tools and practices to enable them to maintain good mental health for themselves and to stay well. Learning to unlock the mind from over-thinking, as well as recognising the patterns of thinking that cause unhappiness, is so useful because depression, for many, can recur. Practising mindfulness, even through the easier times, is beneficial in aiming to prevent these recurrences.

Emily, who is in recovery from severe depression, tells us of how daily mindfulness helps her manage her condition:

> Mindfulness is also something I make sure I carry out every day. It helps me to find a distance and a sense of peace from what, at times, I would describe as the washing-machine-feeling inside my mind. It helps me to be present and aware of where I am and what I am doing and to reduce any overwhelming

feelings of whatever may be going on around me. Doing this on a daily basis helps me manage my depression and other mental health conditions much more effectively.

Yoga

Yoga is fast becoming a part of many people's everyday routine, with many feeling the benefits of it both mentally and physically. Speaking from experience, both the carer and the sufferer can potentially benefit greatly.

Yoga specialist, Debbie Pennington, tells us more about yoga and how it can benefit depression sufferers and general mental health and well-being:

There have been several studies over the years in relation to the possible benefits of yoga to people who suffer from depression and the results are very positive. Yoga is often used as an avenue towards dealing with depression; the practice of yoga has been shown to enhance self-esteem whilst also decreasing anxiety, depression and stress levels without any negative impact.

The practice of yoga is not just an exercise class; it's a lifestyle. Working on the whole body, we use postures (Asanas), breathing techniques (Pranayama) and meditation. This may even result in a different way of looking at life and the world around you. The aim is to lead a holistic life. As you may know, holistic means a balance of mind, body and spirit. These three components of each of us are inter-connected and when one is impaired it has an effect on the whole. Practising yoga helps us to re-align and to bring a sense of calm, balance and self-worth back to us, among many other benefits.

The process of meditation as practised in yoga helps us to focus on something, such as our breathing, to start to calm the busy and, quite often constant, chatter of our minds. It's perfectly normal to have a seemingly endless stream of thoughts in our heads, but it's a fact that a lot of this is worry and non-positive thought. With many people, their feelings of depression can worsen when in a state of anxiety; yoga meditation sets us on a journey to start looking at our thoughts from a different perspective and then to try to calm our mind, creating space and a sense of peace and contentment, even if just for a minute. These skills can then be taken through daily life by practising mindfulness in our daily activities. If suffering from mental health issues, such as depression, these skills can be invaluable.

There are different types of yoga out there and it can be difficult or even daunting to know which to choose. Vanda Scaravelli-inspired yoga highlights the importance of being kind to yourself; this seems to be the obvious way forward to many of us. To make changes, you need to listen to your body, going with it and not against it, taking the time to know yourself. It may be that no changes are to be made and we learn acceptance. It is not about pushing your body into that perfect textbook-shape but thinking about what needs to be released to move in a certain way and what needs to be engaged and – tadah! – you have found yourself there and found out something about the real you along the way.

The philosophy and theory of yoga were written down thousands of years ago and they have stood the test of time. GPs and medical organisations are recognising yoga's benefits more and more, which is excellent. Being yogic does not mean we are ignoring the pathological facts when we have problems like mental illness but that we are also recognising what cannot be seen and does not show on an X-ray. Alongside our human knowledge of anatomy, it all fits together and makes good sense. Let's try to address the root of a problem and not just treat the symptom or subdue it with pharmaceutical drugs.

Martine shares her experience of yoga and how it helped her depressive moods:

> Yoga helped me overcome my depressive moods; it allowed me to be present in the moment. I find that at the end of the class I have a sense of achievement from putting in hard work and focusing on my body rather than my mind so much. I try to do it regularly which has also improved my sleeping patterns – I really find this helps to achieve a more positive mind set.

Meditation

Meditation is the practice of deep thinking or of focusing one's mind over a period of time. While there are many forms of meditation, the ultimate goal remains the same – a feeling of relaxation and inner peace. It can help people to manage their thoughts and is becoming widely used in many different areas. In the UK it is recommended by NICE (the National Institute for Health and Care Excellence) as a preventative exercise for people who experience recurrent episodes of depression.

Christina McDermid, holistic well-being therapist, explains more about the benefits of meditation for mental well-being:

Meditation is an ancient practice that has become extremely popular, especially during the last 10 to 15 years. There is no coincidence that this has come about alongside the digital explosion in 21st-century living and the additional stresses addictive cyber contact and social media have created.

Meditation can be a remarkable support for good mental well-being; practised regularly it can really help control our incessantly thinking minds by teaching us to observe our thoughts rather than being affected or reacting to them. Our thoughts are made up of past, present and future ideas and some of these can cause us to be unsettled and anxious and generally lower our mood because they pull us back into past events or forward to future desires that we have no control over in this present moment. They can be negative or upsetting and if we're having to deal with a physical or mental illness these low feelings can disrupt and upset us and slow down our healing and recovery.

I've seen many people of all age groups with varying mental health concerns find a sense of peace in knowing that they have an internal 'toolkit' to help them through periods of anxious and negative thinking in their lives.

For someone new to meditation, sitting in silence can feel awkward or uncomfortable at first. How would you start to consciously create it? Would you be safe? Would you fall asleep? Like anything new, it's in regular practice that confidence will grow. It would probably help to join a group or practise with a family member or friend at home. Try creating a calm area where you won't be disturbed, turning off phones and anything that will disturb you. Close your eyes and focus on your breathing as you breathe in and out. Thoughts will always try to distract you, so when you're aware of this, re-focus on breathing in and out. You will have to do this many times to begin with; it is the nature of our minds.

Many of us will struggle in finding the time and place to meditate so here are a few suggestions:

Busy mums: while the children are sleeping during the day or at night; in the bath.

Commuters: on the train or bus; during lunch and tea breaks.

Busy households: find a quiet spot and ask not to be disturbed or ask if anyone wants to join you.

Try any of these suggestions and it could really help. Don't give up if you think it's not working. Meditation is like a muscle – it gets easier to do the more you practise, just like when you go to the gym or an exercise class.

Emily, who is in recovery from severe depression, tells us of how meditation helps her gain inner peace:

Every morning and evening I do a guided meditation to help me feel as calm as possible within my mind; this helps me to experience an inner peace within myself. It helps to improve my concentration for a period of time through working on my focus inwardly and to gain back some form of balance with my emotions. At night time, meditation helps me to guide my mind away from any intense thoughts and feelings and to get focused on releasing any tension, so my mind can become relaxed and my body can feel calmer and relieved, so that I am able to have that time of peace and calmness.

Acupuncture

Traditional acupuncture is based on ancient principles which go back nearly two thousand years. Over this time it has been found to have great benefits for mental and physical health and function. The focus is on the individual and not the illness, therefore two people with the same diagnosis could receive different acupuncture treatment. It is believed, by traditional acupuncturists, that illness and pain arise when the body's qi, or vital energy, is unable to flow freely – therefore, the overall objective of acupuncture treatment is to restore the body's balance.

Gill Bescoby, a registered and licensed acupuncturist, tells us more about acupuncture and how it can benefit a person suffering from depression:

Acupuncture is a key component of traditional Chinese medicine, dating back well over two thousand years. The process of acupuncture involves the insertion of needles into certain locations within the 'channels' and 'collaterals' to stimulate the body's healing energy and to balance the opposing forces of yin and yang. It is only recently that acupuncture has been recognised in Western cultures as a safe and reliable method to treat a variety of conditions, benefiting many patients worldwide.

Depression is a very common problem affecting many people from every background, gender and age. Most historical research regarding acupuncture and depression has been carried out in China using Western drugs as the comparitor, but since the early 1990s, studies around the globe have suggested that treating depression with acupuncture has a very positive effect on depressed patients, particularly when used in conjunction with psychotherapy.[16] Psychologist John Allen and acupuncturist Rosa Schnyer conducted a controlled study on treating depression symptoms with acupuncture. The study findings suggested that using acupuncture alone could be as effective as other types of treatment used for depression symptoms in Western medicine. There is still so much more research to be done regarding acupuncture and depression, but the findings so far show great promise.

From a Western perspective, acupuncture is believed to stimulate aspects of the nervous system, releasing various neurochemicals (endocannabinoids, dopamine, oxytocin, endorphins, serotonin and GABA [gamma amino-butyric acid] to name a few), altering the chemistry of the brain and resulting in better emotional and physical well-being. Acupuncture can be used as a stand-alone treatment for some patients suffering from mild to moderate depression or alongside antidepressants, thus reducing some of the major side-effects of these drugs.

According to traditional Chinese medicine, the health of an individual is dependent on creating complete balance and motivating the flow of energy smoothly and effectively through channels lying just beneath the skin. The flow of energy can be disturbed by many factors, including emotional states such as grief, anger, stress or even excessive joy, and physical issues such as poor nutrients, trauma, hereditary disease or infections. These imbalances therefore have to be addressed. An acupuncturist will insert tiny needles (approximately the size of a human hair) into chosen acupuncture points along the channels to stimulate healing and restore balance.

When assessing a person within the context of Chinese medicine, we look at how the person is experiencing his or her depression and what precipitating factors have led to their present condition. Emotion only becomes a cause of disease when it is excessive or prolonged. As human beings we cannot avoid becoming angry, sad, worried, anxious, stressed etc, but these emotions have to be kept in check. An acupuncturist will identify this and create a framework to understand the symptoms, developing an individual treatment approach for each patient, based on their symptom pattern. An acupuncturist will always look at a patient holistically, taking into account their emotional, physical and spiritual health. To formulate a treatment principle the pattern of disharmony will have to be identified, allowing a treatment protocol to emerge. The treatment will then include the insertion of sterile, disposable needles into specifically chosen points to correct this disharmony.

Acupuncture is a painless and most often an enjoyable experience. There will be subtle sensations as energy moves throughout the body. This is usually well tolerated. It is not unusual for a patient to fall asleep or experience deep feelings of relaxation during treatment. At times, emotional release may occur such as deep sighing or crying. One of the great advantages of acupuncture is the absence of major side-effects.

From a personal perspective within my own clinic, I have treated many patients suffering from depression, stress, anxiety etc over the 10+ years I have been in practice, with some amazing results. Whilst championing acupuncture, I do feel it is vital to keep the advancement in treating depression comprehensive, drawing together and encouraging flexibility in using both Western and Chinese medicine to formulate the best possible treatment for each individual case.

One of Gill's clients says of how acupuncture has helped her:

The effect of acupuncture, not only on my mind but also on my physical health has been unimaginably incredible! With regard to depression, I can honestly say that I cannot ever recall having a mind that did not race the whole time and overthinking that exhausted me constantly; when that stopped, I was both shocked and amazed. I had been in some very dark places over the years, without any light at the end of the tunnel. Acupuncture really has changed all that. The change was gradual; I found I was less tearful, more on an even keel rather than bobbing along with my head just above water and then deep drops. I was functioning better and more productively during the day and began feeling like I had a purpose in life. Hormones played a part too around the time of my period and acupuncture has helped all of this. I am no longer taking antidepressants and am able to cope with events life throws at me, without a massive decline in my mental or physical health - which have always been impacted greatly in the past.

Reiki healing

Reiki is a Japanese technique used for stress reduction and relaxation that also encourages physical and mental healing. It can also help to support mental clarity and spiritual well-being.

Christina McDermid, holistic well-being therapist, explains more about how Reiki works:

Reiki is a healing practice that originated in Japan and was rediscovered by Dr Mikao Ursui, a Buddhist monk who lived in Kyoto in the mid 19th century.

Reiki, like all energetic healing approaches, takes a holistic approach that looks beyond the physical body to accessing our subtle energy systems (meridians, auric fields, chakras, etc) where the cause of disease, anxiety and upset can be located and even blocked within our physical body.

Trauma, emotional and mental stress, false belief systems (low self-esteem, for example), physical distress and other blocks to our personal growth can be stored in the energy fields of our bodies, so impacting our ability to function at our full potential.

At times we can be our own worst enemy in believing negative things about ourselves which simply aren't true! 'Self-sabotage', for example, comes from these false beliefs suppressing our creativity and stopping us from moving forward in life.

Reiki healing can assist the healing process by clearing away layer upon layer of blocked energy which may have been causing illness or upset for some time, repairing and rebalancing the energy systems so that the body can move to its optimal level of balance (homeostasis) from where it is able to access its inherent ability to heal. Reiki can also help us to identify 'issues' before they manifest as physical or emotional pain in the mind or body. It opens our consciousness to the areas which we need to work through and heal in order to bring our lives into balance and maintain health, harmony and vitality.

Reiki has historically been practised as a form of self-care. Increasingly, it is also provided by healthcare professionals in a variety of clinical settings.

A Reiki session usually lasts an hour. The person sits or lies down, fully clothed. The therapist places their hands lightly on or just above the body using a series of 12-15 different hand positions which hold the space for the gentle healing energy to flow through to where it its needed. It is incredibly relaxing.

Mary, who has suffered from situational depression, tells us how Reiki helps her:

> I have had some Reiki sessions and I will continue to go monthly because I do find them very relaxing and the overall health benefits are good e.g. reduction in number of headaches and overall feeling more confident and better in myself.

Reflexology

Reflexology is a complementary therapy that is based on the theory that different areas on the feet correspond with different areas of the body. Working these areas can help increase relaxation and allow us to cope better with the stresses that life can bring.

Christina McDermid, the holistic well-being therapist who has described yoga and Reiki, explains how reflexology can benefit mental health and well-being:

Reflexology is a form of natural holistic therapy based on the discovery that there are points on the feet which correspond to the organs, systems and structures within the entire body. This corresponding relationship is called a reflex . A reflex is when a stimulation at one point brings about a response in another point or area in the body, which can induce a state of deep relaxation. Reflexology stimulates a free flow of blood, oxygen and lymph supply to cells and tissues; this circulatory effect is crucial to good health. By helping to eliminate waste and toxins from the body, the cleansing and nourishing effects of reflexology are a major part of its effectiveness. Also known to stimulate nerve supply and the flow of nerve energy in the body, it can enhance positive feelings and vitality which will create an impulse for self-healing.

It is now well documented that over 75% of illness is stress related and stress reduction can be a major contribution to the return to good physical and mental well-being.

Having witnessed many clients confronted with a debilitating physical or mental illness, and their realisation that they can be part of their own healing breakthrough, has been a wonderful experience and one I have had many times. Reflexology creates feelings of self-awareness and inner calm, which can be very self-motivating.

Illness and disease can create feelings of fear, worthlessness and low self-esteem which inhibit and delay our natural ability to heal ourselves; overcoming these is one of the most powerful things we can do for ourselves.

Regular reflexology treatments, along with conventional medical care, can bring about positive feelings as you gather more self-confidence on how you can take steps, however small, towards recovery. Deep relaxation during a treatment enables the mind to rest and the body to find its centre and natural balance.

Massage

Massage therapy is a common treatment for the relief of sports injuries, strains and physical rehabilitation. However, its benefits are more than just physical; it can also be an effective way to relieve anxiety, depression and other mental health issues as well as help to improve sleep quality. Although life stresses are unavoidable, negative feelings and insomnia can be helped with the positive benefits that massage therapy can offer.

Laura Whitcher, a massage specialist, explains this in more detail:

Massage is physical and emotional – it is touch, it is beauty, it is relaxation, it is stress relief and it eases the muscles and other soft tissues to relieve pain and promote suppleness and movement. It has been suggested that touch releases hormones in the body that create a sense of emotional connection. Massage helps calm the mind and improve the mood, as well as easing physical stiffness, aches and pains.

Physically, massage is predominantly used when the muscles and connective tissues become stiff and rigid, thus limiting movement and causing discomfort and pain. Massage therapy helps relieve this physical discomfort by increasing blood flow, warming the body, breaking down tension areas and removing toxins from the body. Massage can also help relieve the additional physical symptoms associated with depression, such as sluggishness, back pain, joint pain and muscle aches. It can also help with fatigue and sleeping problems.

Massage is so much more than just a physical response. Just entering the therapy room knowing you are going to have a massage creates a sense of calm within the mind, and the body starts to relax. Most clients will find that massage offers immediate gratification and the ability to breathe better. It also allows for emotional opening and well-being:

Me time = quiet time = relax and recharge

Taking time for a massage is as important for people dealing with depression as it is for people dealing with physical pain and stiffness issues. Science has shown how massage can help depression by lowering cortisol levels. Cortisol is our body's primary stress hormone, an essential part of the flight or fight response. Consistently high levels of cortisol have been known to contribute to the onset of anxiety. Massage can counteract this cortisol influx by increasing levels of both dopamine and serotonin, our primary 'feel good' hormones. Low levels of dopamine have been linked to some of the more common symptoms of depression, such as lack of motivation and generally not being able to enjoy what life can offer.

Massage is also able to boost blood flow, thus helping with adrenal fatigue, anxiety and depression due to poor circulation.

As with massage and many other alternative therapies, a person needs to want to experience the treatment and realise that it will help. They need to relax and appreciate what is happening to them. At all times, the therapist needs to be understanding of the situation to make sure that the client is safe, not nervous and aware of what is happening within the area of the treatment.

Also, we need to understand that massage is not for everyone as some people do not like being touched as it is very personal. On its own, massage therapy will not cure depression as it does not focus on the emotional or chemical issues – but is does allow the body to relax and the mind to calm down.

Massage and a commitment to building a mind-body connection through self-care can help to maintain a positive mental state after treatment and beyond.

Well-being and emotional health workshops

Vivienne Barnes, well-being coach at Woolston Well Being, describes her work as interesting, affordable, short-term and enormously helpful for all who may be struggling with a current issue or having difficulty letting old, unresolved issues blight their life. It can also be helpful for those living with another whose issues are overwhelming them and, potentially, the relationship.

There is hope, there truly is. In my opinion, depression can be due to a physiological imbalance or a mind imbalance. I want to focus on the mind imbalance, possibly brought on by a loss of some description – health, money, partner, children, youth or self-esteem. I believe people know if their depression is a short- to medium-term or, indeed, long-term issue. In my opinion, if there is a 'just' cause and depression is due, say, to a loss, it is more likely to be a phase that the individual can work through.

We live in a world of quick fixes and think we can fix everything at the speed of light. In truth, our times of suffering are, or can be, our greatest times of learning. At my lowest point I recall thinking it was only when I touched the face of hell that I could fully propel myself back to my own normal. No one else's normal – mine! And this is where Well-Being Coaching Workshops can help. Please let me explain.

I qualified in the spring of 2013 as a therapeutic counsellor. Since then I have developed my portfolio of talks and workshops based upon the gems of wisdom I have learnt. Within the world of 'counselling' I consider my specialities to be well-being, emotional health and self-awareness. I believe that everyone can feel better about themselves, feel more resilient, understand what triggers particular responses, and handle their relationships with others better, with a little guidance.

The purpose in essence is to familiarise participants with the fundamentals of 'good mental health education', to enable their understanding of why we think as we do, and how this thinking affects every relationship, be it domestic, with friends and family or at our place of work/leisure. Also, to learn how these thoughts affect feelings, and feelings affect behaviour. In the workshops, we explore why we think as we do and consider why others may think as they do. Thinking affects our well-being and that is why this element of well-being is important on so many different levels, including if you are living closely with someone who is suffering from anxiety or depression and wish or need to understand them better.

Well-Being Coaching is offered in as informative, thought-provoking and interesting a manner as possible, bringing together new ways to look at yourself and your relationships with others, what makes you happy and how you can handle difficulties with your 'emotional toolkit'. The aim is that you should come away with greater self-awareness, ready to take on the challenges ahead that life has a habit of placing before us all.

The four-part workshops are held over four weeks and include:
- *One-hour workshops on emotional health and well-being*
- *A workshop workbook for personal use*
- *The opportunity to ask questions.*

And the final workshop provides:
- *A personal action plan*
- *A session on feeling and being happy*
- *A quiz on what has been covered earlier, with a small prize.*

Tim offers a testimonial for the benefits he gained from going to Vivienne's Well Being and Emotional Health Workshop:

> A huge thank you for today's workshop. It was most enjoyable and allowed the opportunity to pause and reflect on personal/ work situations backed up by sound theory and anecdotes. Also to reflect on self and others. I learnt some coping strategies to stop and think before acting/saying something – to avoid confrontation. Many thanks for a very interesting and thought-provoking experience.

You can find details of these workshops in the Resources section of this book (page 329).

Drama

I have seen at first hand how participating in drama has enhanced the sense of self and mental well-being of my own daughter. Samantha began doing drama workshops at our local theatre when she was well into the recovery process, but still felt there was 'something missing'. Being a naturally shy person, drama gave Samantha the safe place she needed to explore emotions. It has completely transformed the way she sees herself and her communication skills and has given her the confidence she so desperately needed. In some ways, I would say that it is drama and finally finding herself through it that has helped strengthen her recovery from mental illness.

Samantha says of how drama has helped her:

> Drama has given a home to my imagination and a place for my mind to run free; it's where I have always belonged but had never found; this is a feeling for which it is worth overcoming any mental illness to me.

In drama, we learn how to inhabit another character. If people can channel this skill and use it to create a confident version of themselves, they can practise walking, talking and behaving in positive ways until these become second nature. Those who suffer from low self-esteem can often go on to develop a mental illness. If people do not understand what motivates other people to behave the way that they do, they can end up believing that everything that happens around them is a reflection of them. People with low self-esteem and mental health issues can often feel guilty for no reason at all. Drama helps them to think about why characters might act the way that they do and understand that human beings are complex and not everything centres around them.

Ciaran McConville, director of learning and participation at Rose Theatre, Kingston, says:

Acting classes are an investigation into impulse, action and response. Actors are taught to employ the 'magic if' to explore how they might behave within imaginary circumstances. This in turn leads to a dialogue about impulse; how we 'listen' to impulse and then either pursue it or inhibit it, depending on what our character needs to achieve. A committed student develops an imaginative vocabulary around internal conflict and obstacle, using techniques such as Chekhov's 'Imaginary Centres' and 'Laban's Efforts'. Emotional memory might also be enriched as the student explores real-life relationships and experiences to find the reality of imaginary circumstances. All of this can be transformative, if approached safely and sensitively. What's particularly interesting is that acting offers a reason beyond self-therapy. Actors are storytellers. They investigate their own experience to tell a story to others. The deeper that investigation, the more truthful the storytelling and the more powerful the shared experience can be. I think that purposeful approach can often lead to personal dividends, because it doesn't feel like the spotlight is on our intimate self. Rather it's on our 'character'.

For shy people, drama is one of the few times in their lives where they can step out of the label of being a shy person. They are given permission to scream, and shout, and laugh, without fear of judgement. Drama pushes people's boundaries, helping them to realise that they do not have to conform to the label they have been given. It can help them to realise what they are capable of and what they can be. Most of the plays and television shows that are written are about consequences too. Looking at a human story from the outside, people can identify the ways that the characters might have made different decisions to bring about a more positive outcome. They can then apply this to their own lives, realising that they do have the power to influence what happens around them and, more importantly, to themselves.

Music and art

Some people find it really difficult to express how they are feeling. They might even feel that what they are going through cannot ever be expressed adequately by talking alone. For these people, a creative outlet might help them to explore and exercise negative feelings and embrace new and positive ones.

My Samantha tells us why she enjoys writing her poems (some of which are in this book):

> I write poems mainly as a creative outlet for all my thoughts, but also I feel I have an important message to share with the world that could possibly help others understand and overcome mental illness. The thoughts often come to me in the night; perhaps it is my subconscious pulling out the scars it has wanted to get rid of for so long in a way that can possibly prevent others having the same pain.

Rachel Kelly, British author and mental health advocate, tells us of her journey with depression and how poetry helped in her recovery:

> Just over 20 years ago, I was lying in bed in so much physical pain that I begged to be allowed to kill myself. That I didn't

was in large part thanks to my love of poetry and my mother. She would sit by my bedside and recite poetry aloud, healing lines and verses. Her head was richly stocked with beautiful examples to which she introduced me. I also had plenty of my own favourites from long ago. Then as I recovered, I started to be able to recite the poems myself, again and again, the words strong enough to bear the repetition.

They temporarily laid my anxiety to rest by fixing me in the present. It was as if the words had become embodied, almost physical in their power, something to hold on to and rub, like prayer beads for the mind. Favourites include the last lines of Arthur Hugh Clough's *Say Not the Struggle Naught Availeth*, also famously quoted by Winston Churchill in his wartime speeches.

'In front the sun climbs slow; how slowly,
But westward, look, the land is bright.'

Of course, the healing power of words has a long history, dating back to primitive societies who made use of chants. By the first century AD, the Greek theologian Longinus wrote about how he believed in the power of language to transform reality, to affect readers in deep and permanent ways and to help them cope with the vagaries of their existence. Spool forward to the 20th century, and by 1969 the Association of Poetry Therapy was established in the USA.

For me, poetry helps by recharging the spent batteries of my own language. Now I am calm and well, poetry helps me in a second way. Inspired by others, I now sometimes write poetry myself.

Studies have linked good psychological health with creativity. Research suggests that GPs who prescribed arts activities to some of their patients saw a drop in hospital admissions.[17]

In the same way that an artist spills their feelings onto the page, writing a poem can pin down good times, as well as make sense of adversity and anaesthetise trauma. My head may be full of chaotic pain, but I find the chaos lessens when I get my thoughts onto the page. At least I have created something concrete and tangible when before there was just a swirling and shapeless darkness in my mind. It feels like building a well when previously all I could see was desert.

Art and music therapy has long been shown to increase the effectiveness of traditional therapy methods like counselling and CBT when used alongside them. These activities often have a cathartic quality in themselves, without needing to be analysed.

In just the same way as drama, art and music are reflections of the human condition. They allow us to explore how we feel and behave, and why, in a safe and healthy way. They can also evoke emotions. Some people are often frightened of expressing feelings like sadness and so keep them cooped up. Music and art can connect them to their inner voice. They can be a way of unravelling complex or frightening situations and emotions.

Neil Long, radio presenter and voice and confidence coach, says:

Music can evoke strong feelings and memories. This process can, with the latest psychological techniques, be nurtured and created deliberately. This process could be used to create strong associations between self-esteem and a well-loved music track.

If a person is particularly 'into' an artist or band, this also helps them form a sense of identity and connect with others who think in similar ways, decreasing any sense of isolation.

Aiden Hatfield, founder of 'In Music We Trust', a music-inspired clothing brand which donates 50% of its profits to the mental health charity MIND, says:

I have been creating music since the age of 13. From the first moment I picked up a guitar, I fell in love with music; it instantly made me feel uplifted and changed my mood. Music became a way of expressing how I was feeling; still now, if I am having a down day, I will just put on a song I can sing to and it helps me deal with the depression a lot better. In other words, music is my medicine, being able to focus on music and working towards being a musician are my therapy and always have been.

My positive connection and journey with music inspired me to start up In Music We Trust to help support others in a similar situation. Since I opened up about my struggles with depression, I have found that it has encouraged others to be open too and realise that there is nothing to be ashamed about. In Music We Trust helps me enjoy each day; I do not have to wake up and dread the day ahead. I know I can wake up and love what I do, and in turn support others too.

Performance coaching for carers

Supporting others can be mentally and physically exhausting. As a parent or carer, you probably spend a lot of your time focusing on everybody else, always putting everyone else's needs before your own. However, looking after your own well-being is just as important for you, your loved one and the whole family, as they can only be as strong as you are.

Leanne Poyner, life and performance coach, echoes my thoughts:

As a carer for someone with any mental illness, there is a huge amount of physical and emotional pressure on you and you will most likely be living your life through the person you are caring for. By this I mean your thoughts will be consumed by them, how they are feeling, what their day is about and, physically, this may involve you carrying out many additional tasks in your day to minimise the burden on the individual you are caring for and make their day that bit easier to cope with.

Therefore, it is essential to ensure that you, the carer, are equally looking after your own mental and physical well-being to enable you to be that tower of strength for the individual. To enable this to happen, you need to take time for you and continue to have dreams, making short- and long-term plans to enable these dreams to become a reality. Performance coaching is key to this process.

A good analogy of how your life may feel at the moment is like a tumble dryer. All your thoughts and feelings are whirling around, with no structure, pattern or control. Performance coaching helps you to stop the tumble dryer, unpack the clothes, and fold them into nice organised piles. Working together with your coach, you can then start to identify things that are important to you, what motivates you and what you want to achieve. It could be big or small – the main aim is that it gives you a sense of achievement and it is something that you have control of. The key focus of coaching is that you are setting goals that are dependent on you, not reliant on other people, and that you are in control of. For example, it could be making time to go to the gym three times a week, setting up a small business, seeing your parents more often, or taking time to read for 20 minutes before bed each night.

A performance coach will not tell you what to do, will not judge, will not give you the solutions or tell you what your dreams should be. By asking the right questions of you, the coach will enable you to recognise what you really want, in line with your values, and help you to create your own plan of action, that you will work towards in a realistic timeframe set by yourself. The priority of performance coaching is you, and you need to be living your life as fully as you can, to enable you to have the inner strength and drive to help support others.

To conclude

The willingness of a sufferer to engage with alternative therapies shows that they are seeking positivity and a way to combat and conquer their illness. This is one of the most crucial and valuable steps towards recovery.

For carers, alternative treatments can provide respite in the form of 'time-out' to help renew their strength, emotionally and physically, and to enable them to face the challenges that they deal with in their role as a carer for someone suffering from depression.

I cannot reiterate enough that everyone is different, and if one therapy does not work for you or the sufferer, be open-minded and do not be afraid to try another. This chapter has provided only a brief description of each therapy. Full details of the therapists mentioned above are provided in the Resource section at the back of the book (page 329).

Dave Davies, manager of Frank Bruno and whose own mother and mother-in-law have had, and still have, depression, finishes this chapter with:

> I have seen at first hand how powerful simple day-to-day life changes can be to someone suffering from depression. Exercise, whether it be a short walk or a gym visit, eating a good diet, trying to regulate their sleep pattern and recognising their limits are all positive steps to moving forward and can start to make a real difference to the sufferer.

Chapter 6

Depression and other illnesses

Depression, for some, can occur in isolation, but for others it can equally co-exist alongside another psychological or physical illness, which can add another layer of complexity, often making it harder to unravel and fully understand for both the sufferer and their carers.

It is not uncommon for someone suffering from one mental illness to experience an overlap with another at any given time. Where depression can differ from other mental illnesses is that it commonly exists alongside or can be part of a physical illness. It may be a symptom or by-product of that physical illness, as may for instance be the case with Parkinson's disease or thyroid disorders. It can also play a part in triggering another health problem, such as chronic pain.

In this chapter, I will explore some of the different illnesses – both psychological and physical – that have been found to have a strong link with depression, looking at how the potential connection works and what can be done to support those dealing with its effects. In the first part of this chapter, I will be looking at the link between the most common psychological illnesses and depression:

Self-harm (page 155)

Anxiety (page 160)

Eating disorders (page 163)

Obsessive compulsive disorder (OCD) (page 170)

Post-traumatic stress disorder (PTSD) (page 174)

Body dysmorphic disorder (BDD) (page 177)

Borderline personality disorder (BPD) (page 178)

Schizophrenia (page 181)

Alcohol misuse (page 182)

Drugs misuse (page 185)

In the second part of the chapter I consider the interplay between depression and certain physical illnesses.

Depression and psychological illnesses

Astonishingly, and sadly, around one in four people in Britain will experience some form of psychological illness in their lifetime, ranging from the more common and well-known issues such as depression, self-harm, anxiety, eating disorders and OCD, to lesser known conditions. It is important to remember that this figure is only based on the registered sufferers actively seeking medical help. I am sure there must be countless others who are suffering in silence, adding to these ever-increasing numbers.

My personal and professional findings, more recently confirmed by a survey I prepared in which numerous people kindly participated via my social media channels, support the suggestion that depression may also be interconnected with other mental illnesses, such as anxiety, eating disorders, self-harm and/or OCD. A staggering 80% of sufferers who responded had at least one other mental health issue in addition to depression. The results of this survey highlighted how depression can frequently co-exist with other mental illnesses.

Chapter 6

In an ideal world, someone suffering from multiple mental illnesses would be treated as an individual, so allowing the multiple problems to be treated together; this would be a different and possibly more effective approach than treating each mental illness separately. However, sadly, due to an over-stretched and under-funded health system, this is not always possible.

Cheryl shares her frustration regarding her daughter's experience:

> My daughter has been having therapy for around 12 months. It can become very frustrating, but I try my best to support the programme she is on. She has been self-harming since she was around 13 years old, but also suffers from depression. As her mother I feel the depression is the cause of her self-harming; however, she seems to be being treated for the physical self-harming and not for the deep depression in her head.

To help you understand the possible links and connections, I will endeavour to explain the more common mental health issues in greater detail in this chapter together with the indicators when interlinked with depression.

Like depression, all mental health issues can affect anyone irrespective of their age, gender, sexuality, ethnicity or social background. The effect on each individual can vary, as can the length of time a person suffers from it. Individuals who have milder symptoms of mental illness may not appear visibly ill in a physical sense to the outside world, but the distress, and difficulty in mental functionality on the inside, can cause great fear and anxiety. These vivid thoughts and internal feelings can become stronger and much worse if left undetected and untreated, and the sufferer will most likely be ill equipped to tackle this alone. If the symptoms are more severe, there may be more obvious external signs. Either way, mental illness is just as serious as any other physical condition and deserves the same level of attention, respect and intervention; sadly, it is often misunderstood and dismissed because of the lack of visible evidence.

It is important to remember that it is the most natural thing in the world to feel happy and uplifted when something positive happens in our lives, as it is to feel sad, anxious, fearful or angry when something negative or worrying occurs. As I mentioned in an earlier chapter, my mum once pointed out to me that bad days are necessary in life if we are to recognise and appreciate the good days. Part of ensuring good mental health and well-being is having the ability to recognise the difference between 'natural' emotions and prolonged 'unnatural' ones, possibly indicating an issue that needs to be dealt with.

As with depression, other mental illnesses can be kept a secret by the sufferer, who may feel embarrassed, ashamed and/ or lonely at times. However, because of the elusive nature of these illnesses, it is difficult to measure the actual extent of their impact. Personally, I would be inclined to measure the severity by looking at the impact on the life of the person experiencing the illness and those of the people around them.

Questions you could ask yourself are:

- Can the person sleep at night?
- Can they concentrate in school? At work?
- Can they hold down a job?
- Can they socialise?
- Can they maintain friendships or romantic relationships?
- Are they looking after their body and physical health?
- Is their unusual behaviour causing disruption within their family or home environment?

All of these factors can be negatively affected by mental illness on quite a significant scale. Rita says of the changes she saw in her sister:

> My sister used to be quite a happy-go-lucky person, quite open to life, and nothing really fazed her. Then she started to find it

difficult to speak to other people, which was something she used to love; she also found it hard to concentrate on anything – work, conversation, programmes on TV. I knew something was wrong.

Before I begin to describe the signs and symptoms of some of the other psychological illnesses, I would like to reiterate that this is only a general and fairly basic guide. Everyone experiences mental illness in different and diverse ways, making it impossible to encompass each and every sufferer's experience. Parents, friends, partners and carers who regularly spend time with loved ones affected by mental illness will know them better than anyone else, but hopefully the information below will help to determine when the line is crossed between the angst that naturally affects us all and something deeper and potentially more sinister. At risk of repeating myself too much, there is no substitute for intuition, so if you feel that something is amiss then there is probably good reason for further exploration.

In my experience, there are five main types of common psychological illness, depression being one of them, so I have described the remaining four – self-harm, anxiety, eating disorders and OCD – and how they may present themselves, below. I have also given brief descriptions of post-traumatic stress disorder (PTSD), body dysmorphic disorder (BDD), borderline personality disorder (BPD), schizophrenia, alcohol misuse and substance abuse which can also cross over with depression. Although each has its own and very varied characteristic symptoms they are often intertwined and tend to mimic symptoms from one another.

Self-harm

Self-harm is one of the most prevalent and critical factors in mental illness. As a behaviour, rather than as a clinical diagnosis, self-harm is a key indicator across multiple psychological disorders, including depression. People who are self-harming are almost always suffering from mental illness, sometimes severely so, even if a precise and clinical diagnosis has not yet been achieved. For people who are regularly self-harming or know someone who is, it is imperative that professional advice and support are sought as soon as possible. Whilst suicide is a comparatively rare event, self-harm is a key diagnostic tool in suicide prevention, and it is therefore essential that it is taken extremely seriously. It should never be ignored.

Self-harm occurs when a person chooses to inflict physical damage to their body. It varies from person to person, but it is usually a way of indirectly dealing with difficult or complicated issues in a sufferer's life and is often inflicted by means of cutting, burning or damaging the skin. It can also involve a sufferer putting their safety in jeopardy by voluntarily being in hazardous situations or exercising to the point of pain. The mental health charity MIND defines self-harm as 'a way of expressing very deep distress'. Often people do not know why they self-harm. Though many sufferers can go to great lengths to hide what they are doing, it can be a means of communicating what cannot be put into words, or even into thoughts, and has been described by some as an inner scream.

Eating disorders can also be described as a form of self-harm due to the physical damage inflicted on the body in order to block out what is happening in the mind. As with other mental illnesses, such as OCD, self-harm is inflicted to bring relief to the sufferer, albeit only temporarily, so the cycle repeats and repeats with the behaviours becoming both physically and mentally addictive and, in some cases, more severe.

According to the Mental Health Foundation, the UK has the highest rate of any European country for self-harm, with it affecting 400 in every 100,000 (that is 1 in 250) of the population – males and females equally. These figures are more likely to be an underestimate though, as many people who self-harm do so in secret and seldom tell anyone. Although anybody can be affected, the majority of people who self-harm are between the ages of 11 and 25 years old.[18] Higher rates of self-harm are evident in people already suffering from borderline personality disorders (page 178), depression and eating disorders.

Self-harming can include scratching, pinching, hitting or cutting different parts of the body, hair-pulling, burning, or anything which is done deliberately to cause pain, including less obvious forms such as risk-taking, drug overdose or simply not taking care of physical or emotional needs.

In children, harming animals, pets or younger siblings can also be a sign of internal anxiety which, if left undiagnosed, could then lead to other mental health issues, such as depression, eating disorders and/or OCD.

Many young people who self-harm say that it enables them to feel something, rather than the numbness which can be associated with depression or other mental illnesses. Whilst teenage girls often use self-harm as a physical expression of familiar yet painful emotions, teenage boys are likely to self-harm because they do not have the emotional vocabulary to express how they feel.

The symptoms of self-harm can be very hard to spot in young people, because they will very often conceal them from their parents, teachers and friends. On the other hand, self-harm has recently been noted to be 'contagious' in schools, whereby students will emulate each other's inflictions, so it is a good idea to ensure that all friends connected to the person self-harming know that intervention is taking place, giving a strong and clear message that it is a very serious issue and not to be mimicked.

While generally done in secret, self-harm can be a way of attention seeking, physicalising an internal pain for an outside world to see in a way that demands interaction. It can also be an indicator of suicidal thoughts, allowing the person self-harming to test the water without actually attempting the real thing. It is often described as a pressure cooker of emotions that build up on the inside with self-harming as a way of releasing that pressure. It can be linked to feelings of self-loathing, unworthiness and low self-esteem.

Those who self-harm, young and old, will usually cut parts of their bodies – arms or upper legs most commonly which can be hidden under clothing. However, you know your loved one and you will recognise any change in their behaviour which could indicate self-harm: this could include unexplained bruises, hair loss or bald patches, scars, wearing long sleeves or long trousers even in hot weather, and generally spending a lot of time alone. Some of the signs of self-harm are explained as 'accidental', with the person self-harming making excuses for bruises or scars, so the most important factor to consider here is the frequency with which they appear and the persistence of the injury. Recognising the difference between a one-off and a recurring pattern is vital.

Some of the physical signs to look out for are as follows. The person may:
- have bruises on parts of their body
- have cigarette burns on parts of their body
- have cuts on parts of their body
- have excessive hair loss/unexplained hairless patches on the scalp
- exercise obsessively (more than daily recommended time per day) and to the extent of sustaining injuries
- keep covered with layers of clothing, especially long sleeves, particularly in hotter weather
- manifest low mood/tearfulness/lack of motivation or interest
- show changes in eating habits or become secretive about eating – including rapid weight loss or gain
- misuse alcohol or drugs.

Self-harming has reached a very dangerous era by way of the internet, where sufferers, once perceived to be secretive and ashamed of their self-inflictions, covering up to hide their scars or abrasions, are now joining online communities and sharing with others their scars like 'badges of honour', giving their painful and misplaced pledge of allegiance to a very disturbing worldwide club.

Depression and self-harm

Self-harming can be a visible indicator of a much deeper and very dangerous emotional issue that requires intervention, and it could be linked to another illness. In a 2014 study looking at all the different illnesses – mental and physical – that may be linked to self-harm, depression came out top.[19]

There can be something of a 'chicken and egg' relationship between self-harm and depression. While someone's depressive symptoms may lead them to employ self-harming behaviour as a way of coping with, expressing or blocking out their difficult feelings, the situation may also be reversed. In that scenario, the shame, guilt and/or upset they feel about injuring themselves may trigger depressive symptoms, including persistent low mood.

When it comes to treating the two, the psychological foundations of their illness must be uncovered and tackled. It is unlikely to be enough to cease treatment once someone stops their self-harming behaviour. Rather, it should continue until the root causes of emotional torment have been successfully addressed. Only by tackling the core of someone's psychological make-up can you minimise the chances of another mental illness, such as substance abuse or an eating disorder, from developing as a way to replace the self-harming.

Jo tells us of how her first signs of depression were masked by self-harming:

> I was 13 when I first realised something wasn't right. I was struggling socially at school. I started self-harming to cope. I was withdrawn. I didn't realise it was depression until I was at

sixth form college aged 17. Then I was in a psychology lesson about mental illnesses; depression was mentioned and it fitted.

Anxiety

Anxiety can be a stand-alone condition in the form known as 'generalised anxiety disorder' (GAD) and can be the starting point of many other mental illnesses. It is the most common form of mental illness in the western world and can be the glue that holds them all together, perpetuating the cycle where other conditions are involved: it is both the cause *and* the effect.

Anxiety is a general term for a variety of disorders that cause nervousness, fear, apprehension, paranoia and/or worry. Life can be full of stressful situations and most of us live with a heightened sense of unease accompanied by a moderate level of anxiety, due to the unsettling world we live in today; it is our nervous system's normal response to a perceived threat or danger. However, when this feeling gathers momentum and the sufferer finds it impossible to control, it can become a mental illness and can for many be physically and emotionally debilitating.

Mental and physical symptoms of anxiety vary widely, but the person may experience:

• feelings of unease, panic, fear, paranoia and/or insanity
• repeated thoughts or flashbacks of traumatic experiences
• disrupted sleep, nightmares and/or an inability to get to sleep altogether
• cold, sweaty, numbness or tingling in the hands and/or feet
• shortness of breath, rapid or irregular breathing and/or palpitations
• bouts of dizziness, nausea and possibly a dry mouth
• feelings of needing to avoid certain places or items.

Anxiety can be specifically an issue for the younger generation as they are not always able to verbalise or convey how they are feeling, let alone understand it .Children are growing up faster than ever before, and as parents or carers it can be hard for us to appreciate just how difficult they may be finding it, coping with the pressure of school and friendships as well as their feelings and ever-changing hormone levels as they mature. Their interaction with social media and the internet is often an attempt to understand the world and can cause its own problems. Listening to my clients of all ages, I often hear that their anxiety is heightened after spending time on social media sites or reading magazines, watching internet channels or reality TV shows, to the point that some even have to remove themselves to avoid the constant barrage of mixed messages and confusion. All of these can give a false perception of how they think their life should be and media influences such as these can make the sufferer, young or old, feel inadequate, insignificant, excluded or even invisible.

According to the Mental Health Foundation, in 2013 alone, there were 8.2 million cases of anxiety in the UK. These figures do not come as a surprise, bearing in mind the ever-increasing pace of life, combined with the pressures of everyday living.

A highly anxious person may develop some form of coping mechanism to help combat the overpowering anxiety, which then leads into another form of mental illness, stealthily linking them together, with anxiety being the common denominator (cause/effect) in nearly all mental illnesses.

Depression and anxiety

A significant proportion of people with depression also have generalised anxiety disorder (GAD) or another form of anxiety problem; these two conditions – anxiety and depression – are often interlinked because they can feed off and fuel each other. In some people, one will be the more dominant condition, although it is also possible for them to have a broadly equal impact on someone's state of mind. To further complicate matters, depression can often be tainted by a negative stigma, which in turn can exacerbate the anxiety.

Anxiety and depression overlap so much that sometimes the diagnosis can be cloudy and therefore they are not always seen as distinct illnesses. They share some symptoms and character-istics, such as feelings of nervousness, being on edge and having issues with sleep and concentration. However, they do have distinct symptoms that differentiate them as separate, albeit related, illnesses; being able to recognise them as such can be helpful in accessing the correct treatment.

The overlap between the two makes it difficult to say accu-rately how many people suffer from both, but according to a huge study in America, the National Comorbidity Survey, more than half of all patients diagnosed with major depressive disorder also have had an anxiety-related disorder. The latter may precede the depression, it may follow it, or – to complicate things – it is not unusual for someone to experience both at the same time. When the conditions do co-exist it can sometimes deepen their severity and/or how long they last.

In terms of treatment, similar approaches may be effective for both illnesses, with a talking therapy, such as cognitive be-havioural therapy (CBT), and medication being prescribed for both depression and anxiety. However, each person should be looked at individually and a GP should consider someone's whole lifestyle before deciding on a course of action. If the person turns frequently to alcohol or drugs, for example, as a misguided method of coping with anxiety – thereby potentially introducing a third illness: alcohol or substance abuse – then this may also need to be addressed and tackled as part of a treatment plan.

Natalie shares her experience with anxiety whilst also suffering from depression:

> I worry about everything and almost anything all the time. You obsessively worry. It's very difficult also. It's hard for others to understand that you CAN'T just stop. It's not a light switch. I wish it was.

Katie also shares her experience:

> I was aware of my anxiety a long time before the depression. I always focused on the anxiety where as I know other people would say they saw the depression a long time before I noticed it myself. I would often say, 'I'm on antidepressants but it's for my anxiety as I don't get depression with it.'
>
> I wasn't aware of the depression until I fully came out the other side of recovery, which was years later. I always put my problems down to anxiety. Looking back now I understand my depression was crippling.

Eating disorders

Generally, eating disorders are defined as a distorted pattern of thinking about food and everything associated with it. They involve the sufferer abusing food, exercise and their bodies to dangerous levels, however the issues originated, and are characterised by disordered thinking and mental distress. Like self-harming, they are an indication that something is happening in the brain with the effects on the body being the visual symptoms. Eating disorders can be measured not by a set of weighing scales, but by an assessment of feelings, thoughts and behaviours.

Interestingly, eating disorders often co-exist with other mental illnesses. They have been linked to alcoholism and drug addiction and have strong links with OCD, anxiety, self-harm and, of course, depression.

There are many types of eating disorder and within these types there are literally hundreds of variations and symptoms unique to the sufferer, but the condition usually begins with simply eating too little or too much and the obsession with eating, exercise and body image follows, leading to strict, tailored changes of certain foods in both the behaviour and lifestyle of the sufferer.

With so many variations on dietary preferences in today's society, such as veganism, vegetarianism, pescatarianism and food intolerances, it is becoming more difficult to define 'normal' eating. For the majority of people, however, food and calorie intake/expenditure do not preoccupy their thinking and their lives. An eating disorder is an illness that permeates all aspects of the sufferer's life from the minute they wake up to the minute they go to bed, though some sufferers even dream about food when they sleep, which therefore effectively dominates their lives 24/7. Any eating disorder is a serious health condition that can be both physically and emotionally destructive.

The three most well-known forms of eating disorders are: anorexia nervosa, bulimia nervosa and over-eating, which are all described in brief below, yet the most common actual diagnosis is OSFED (other specified feeding or eating disorder) which means that the sufferer does not completely fit within the official criteria for any one eating disorder in particular.

Anorexia nervosa

The official definition of anorexia nervosa is 'self-imposed starvation'. However, it is not really about how little a person eats, it is about their desire to control what they eat. The sufferer will normally know exactly how much they will eat in a day; at what times and how many calories they are consuming. They will often weigh and measure their food and are likely to become fearful in situations where they have to deviate from the food plan they have set for themselves.

The sufferer will go to great lengths to eat according to the rules their illness tells them are necessary. They will often hide their behaviour, lie to their loved ones and engage in morally questionable behaviours which prioritise their condition above anything and anyone else in their lives.

I have listed signs of anorexia nervosa below which will help distinguish it from a diet or fad-eating phase. It is important to note that usually there is more than one sign, although that is not always the case. The person may:

- avoid food and meal times
- make excuses to avoid eating, such as having 'eaten earlier'
- carefully weigh and portion food
- use continual self-effacing language, such as repeatedly claiming to be 'fat'
- check calories and fat content of food
- keep lists of food consumed
- deny hunger
- continually look for approval and validation
- hide food so that others believe it has been eaten
- pick out a few specific foods and eat these in very small quantities
- start doing intense and/or compulsive exercise.

The physical signs of anorexia nervosa include:
- rapid weight loss
- hair loss on the scalp
- dizzy spells/feeling faint
- constipation and stomach pain
- 'lanugo' – soft, downy hair on the face and body
- in girls, periods stopping or not starting in the first place
- poor circulation and feeling cold (particularly in the hands, nose and feet)
- dry, rough or discoloured skin
- dehydration.

The physical symptoms above usually clear up once the

sufferer enters into recovery. However, it is important to note that they are at risk of long-term health consequences, such as osteoporosis and infertility.

Jamie says of how his depression and anorexia nervosa co-exist:

> For me my depression and anorexia are very much linked. The depression I find myself in not only leads to increased thoughts of being worthless, not good enough, a failure etc but also leads to the thoughts of not deserving nice things, including food. I also used the lack of food as a way of communicating my depression and low self-worth as I felt unable to put my feelings into words or open up to anyone about it. To this day, the food I manage to allow myself will be the very basic – the cheapest options I can find – so I still struggle to convince myself that I deserve any better, if any at all.

Bulimia nervosa

Bulimia nervosa is just as serious as anorexia nervosa, yet it can be more difficult to detect from the outside, since sufferers are quite often a 'normal' weight, or even slightly overweight.

People who have bulimia nervosa continually 'binge eat' large quantities of food in a short period of time and then 'purge', finding ways to rid their body of the food consumed, most commonly by vomiting. Sufferers of anorexia nervosa may also 'purge', but it is the consumption of large quantities of food and the desire to rid the body of the calories consumed before any weight is gained that are the defining factors that distinguish bulimia nervosa.

Some signs of bulimia nervosa include:

- the urge to eat large amounts of food
- mood swings
- anxiety and/or depression
- constantly putting themselves down
- expressing feelings of shame and/or guilt

- vomiting after eating
- using laxatives
- compulsive exercising
- acting secretively and being reluctant to socialise.

Effects of bulimia nervosa on the body may include:
- a sore throat and/or bad breath
- dry or patchy skin
- irregular periods (in girls)
- tiredness
- redness around the knuckles
- puffiness of the face and fingers.

Charliee says of how her struggles with bulimia and depressive episodes were linked:

> My bulimia always seemed to be part of a vicious circle. My mood would drop and I'd absolutely loathe anything and everything about myself – my appearance, personality, 'qualities' etc. Then that would start a binge and purge cycle followed by self-harm, then the depressive phases would start again. I'd hate catching a glimpse of myself in mirrors or shop windows, I'd cover mirrors in the bathroom so I wouldn't have to look at myself and turn mirrors around in my bedroom, making sure I used the smallest mirror I could find to apply my make-up to prevent looking at my reflection! I'd work hard in therapy sessions each week but would always avoid the reason that supported the foundations of my ED [eating disorder]. Every time I purged, I'd go back to hating myself because I had relapsed again and the self-harm had given each vomit, a physical reminder.

Over-eating

Over-eating has only been recognised as an official eating disorder fairly recently, which is an important step forward; when people over-eat we do not tend to have as much sympathy for them as those who under-eat or purge themselves, even though the effects on the body and mind can be just as harmful and the underlying emotions just as distressing.

People who suffer from 'compulsive over-eating disorder' experience episodes of uncontrolled eating or bingeing, followed by guilt and most likely depression, although they do not then purge. In addition to eating large quantities of food, sufferers will also usually have a 'frenzied' feeling as though they are unable to control their actions. They may continue to eat long after they have become full.

Some signs of binge/compulsive eating include:

- a fear of not being able to control eating and/or not being able to stop eating
- a fear of eating around others
- fatigue
- sporadic use of popular diet plans
- hiding food in secret places to eat later
- secretive eating patterns.

Effects of binge/compulsive eating on the sufferer may include:

- weight gain
- believing that life would be better if they were able to lose weight
- self-denigration, especially after eating
- getting out of breath after light activity
- excessive sweating
- blaming personal failures in social and professional life on being over-weight
- depression/mood swings
- high blood pressure and/or cholesterol
- leg and joint pain
- decreased mobility owing to weight gain
- loss of sexual desire

- insomnia
- poor sleeping habits.

It is important to note here that it is possible to binge eat or eat compulsively and not to be over-weight. However, this is still a problem, both physically and mentally. Our health is dictated not by how much we weigh, but by how much fat is around our internal organs. It is possible to be a small size and yet have unseen 'visceral' fat around the main organs. Using food as a kind of drug is also not healthy emotionally. There is a difference between this and simply having a 'high metabolism' or 'large appetite'.

Max, who suffers from depression and over-eating, says:

> For me, it is a vicious circle: I feel the need to over-eat, if anything in my day has not gone to plan. The food makes me feel comforted in the moment, but as soon as I have finished, I then feel overwhelming shame and guilt. I feel so low and hate myself for it. This then leads on to the depression taking over. Once I am in the cycle it is so hard to get out of it.

Other eating disorders

Other recognised eating disorders are orthorexia (sufferers become obsessed with healthy eating to the extent that it totally dominates their lives), compulsive exercising and bigorexia (gym culture, especially among boys). Orthorexia and bigorexia are relatively new and becoming more widely recognised via the media and charities, raising awareness of mental health issues as the figures for these conditions sadly continue to rise.

Depression and eating disorders

Statistically, those with eating disorders have a higher incidence of depression,[20] and vice versa. Diagnosis and separation of the two conditions often remains blurred due to their striking similarities. Consequently, sometimes it can be difficult to see which – if either – illness came first.

Studies indicate that depression can be a factor in both the onset and continuation of an eating disorder, with a high proportion of people with eating disorders also having a history of depression, with persistent low mood contributing to the development of an eating disorder.[21]

The connection can also be reversed. If your body and brain are starved of nutrients, this can have an impact on your mood and outlook on life, locking you into a negative spiral. The constraints, obsessive behaviour and personal punishment that accompany the cycle of an eating disorder can also contribute to the onset of depression.

Treating these two separate, yet interlinked, conditions can present an extra challenge, not least because someone who has major issues about what they ingest may also reject any drug-based intervention for depression. What is clear is that purely focusing on the physical effects of an eating disorder is unlikely to tackle the accompanying psychological dimension that depression can be a part of. A carer who recognises the complex interplay between the eating disorder and the depression and who maintains their support through all the very toughest times can help someone in the grip of these two illnesses to see a way forward.

Obsessive compulsive disorder (OCD)

As the name suggests, this disorder is formed of two distinct parts – obsession and compulsion. Intrusive thoughts form the mental aspect of the condition and these thoughts often give way to compulsive (or repetitive) behaviours.

Most of us have worries, doubts and superstitious beliefs of some kind. It is only when your thoughts and actions make no sense to others, become excessive or begin to affect your ability to live a normal life and to impact people around you that it is officially recognised as a condition. Many people have described themselves as 'a little bit OCD' when what they really mean is that they like to keep their house clean and tidy or have a very organised filing system, for example. Neither of these behaviours is characteristic of the illness if they manifest in a manageable form. It is important to recognise the distinction between 'OCD' as a generalised slang term and the medical condition, which can be totally debilitating.

Some people experience intrusive thoughts, but do not have the desire to carry out compulsive actions. However, much of the time the two components will go hand in hand.

Obsessions are involuntary, seemingly uncontrollable thoughts, images or impulses which occur over and over in the mind. A person experiencing intrusive thoughts will not invite these thoughts or enjoy having them, but cannot seem to stop them from invading their mind. Some people describe such thoughts as being 'like a stuck record' and just as irritating, yet actively trying to stop them can, perversely, make them worse.

Compulsions are behaviours or rituals that must be acted out again and again. Usually, compulsions are performed in an attempt to make the obsession go away. For example, if you are afraid of germs and cannot seem to think about anything else, you might develop elaborate cleaning rituals. However, the relief is short lived. In fact, the obsessive thoughts will usually come back stronger.

In its simplest form, OCD occurs in a four-step pattern:
1. Obsession – The mind is overwhelmed by a constant obsessive fear or concern, such as one's house being burgled.
2. Anxiety – The obsession provokes a feeling of intense anxiety and distress, often causing the 'worst case scenario' to be envisaged or imagined, sometimes repeatedly.

3. Compulsions – A pattern of compulsive behaviour is adopted in an attempt to reduce the anxiety and distress, such as checking all the windows and doors are locked three times before leaving the house or going to bed.

4. Temporary relief – Compulsive behaviour brings transitory relief from anxiety.

Obsession or anxiety will almost always return after the above cycle has been completed, causing it to start all over again. Compulsive behaviours in themselves can often result in anxiety, as they become more time-consuming and start to demand more and more attention. Anxiety can manifest itself in obsessive thoughts and so the condition spirals.

It is difficult to give a definitive list of signs and symptoms of OCD, since there are infinite things that can trigger an obsession and the related behaviour. Some of the most common obsessions are:

- Fear of being contaminated by germs or dirt, or of contaminating others.
- Fear of causing harm to the self or others.
- Intrusive sexual, explicit or violent thoughts or recurrent images.
- Obsessive focus on religious or moral ideas.
- Fear of losing or not having things that may be needed.
- Order and symmetry – the idea that all physical objects must line up 'just so'.
- Special attention to something considered lucky or unlucky ('superstitions').

The most common forms of compulsive behaviour are:
- Counting, tapping, repeating certain words or doing other seemingly senseless things in an attempt to reduce anxiety.
- Spending a lot of time washing or cleaning, either the body or the surrounding environment.

- Repeatedly checking in on loved-ones to ensure that they are safe.
- Excessively double-checking locks, appliances and switches.
- Ordering or arranging objects into specific orders.
- Praying or engaging in rituals triggered by religious fear to an excessive extent.
- Accumulating junk such as old newspapers or empty food containers.

Without adequate coping mechanisms, OCD can eat into so much of a person's life that they find themselves unable to do anything else. This can result in extensive difficulties at home, school and work.

Depression and OCD

The link between OCD and depression is clear, with research suggesting that up to two-thirds of those living with OCD will experience at least one major depressive episode during the course of their illness.[22] While it is possible to develop obsessive compulsive behaviours when suffering from depression, the link between the two appears to work more strongly in reverse with the stress of living with OCD taking such a toll on the sufferer that depressive symptoms take root and develop.

It is not hard to see how this happens. By its very nature, OCD can be isolating and self-absorbing. It can take sufferers away from activities they once enjoyed and may leave them locked in a world that seems hopeless and inescapable. It is not a huge leap to see how these frustrations and fears can tip over into the wider symptoms of depression.

It can be easy to dismiss the depressive symptoms as simply a 'part' of the OCD. However, for the very best outcome, being able to recognise the two as separate (yet linked) is more likely to lead to a successful, long-term recovery. The sooner this can be done – as opposed to adopting a 'wait and see' approach – the more treatment plans can be tailor-made to meet particular needs.

While for some people the depression will lift once the OCD is successfully treated, in others further treatment for the depressive symptoms may be needed to ensure that all the 'roots' of mental illness are treated to minimise the opportunity for them to grow again.

The treatments for depression are very similar to those for OCD, with one of the most effective being cognitive behavioural therapy (see page 78). Some sufferers may also need antidepressant medications to help them recover (see page 71). Carers are crucial to this process. While their loved one's depression may mean they take less interest in caring for themselves, including taking medication or attending therapy appointments, the support of a caring relative or friend can make a real difference in achieving a positive outcome.

Johnny describes how he struggles with both OCD and depression:

> I struggle with deep intrusive thoughts which cause me immense distress pretty much all day most days. Sometimes I have the strength to fight them and some days I just don't. On the days I really cannot cope, I find myself in the depths of depression too; I just sometimes cannot see my life being any different. I think my OCD and depression feed off one another. It's a daily battle. But one day I will win.

Post-traumatic stress disorder (PTSD)

Post-traumatic stress disorder, often shortened to PTSD, is an anxiety disorder that is triggered by stressful, shocking or frightening events. When someone has PTSD, they often experience flashbacks and nightmares. They may have problems sleeping and find it a real challenge to concentrate on other areas of their life as they battle complex and disruptive feelings, including anger and guilt.

The disorder was first recognised in war veterans (you may have heard the term 'shell shock') but it is now said that it can be caused by a wide range of events and experiences, from witnessing a terrorist attack to suffering bereavement. Of course, it is normal to feel a range of emotions after a traumatic experience. However, for people with PTSD, these feelings persist, having a significant impact on their day-to-day life. PTSD is thought to occur in around a third of those who have been through a traumatic experience, although it is not clear why some people experience it and others do not.[23]

PTSD and depression

The link between PTSD and depression is well established, with between 30% and 50% of those with PTSD also having symptoms that meet the criteria for depression.[24] This is sometimes put down to the overlap in symptoms between the two – issues with sleeping, difficulties concentrating and markedly less interest in seeing people or getting involved with activities. However, the link is thought to run deeper than that.

Further research has suggested having a propensity to depression can make someone more at risk of developing PTSD after a traumatic incident or event. On the other side of the coin, there is also the theory that having PTSD is so distressing that it raises the chances of someone developing depression.[25] The relationship between the two is complex, but it is possible that the symptoms of post-traumatic stress are so distressing and hard to process that they can actually cause the depression to develop.

As with any mental illness, it is important to get support and help for PTSD as soon as possible rather than leaving the symptoms to escalate to the point where a second illness, such as depression, can take hold. Once the PTSD is successfully treated, studies suggest that any accompanying symptoms of secondary depression may be reduced.[26]

However, there can be many times when the depression should be acted on immediately, without any delay, particularly if it is causing any thoughts of self-harm or suicide. In cases where the symptoms of depression are so severe that they make treating the PTSD virtually impossible, the depression should be addressed straightaway.

Personally, I would rarely advocate a 'wait and see' approach for the symptoms of either PTSD or depression. As in most cases where more than one mental illness is present, in my experience I believe that treating both, or all, the conditions is likely to be the most fruitful way forward. While there may be occasions where one could be treated first, it is vital to make a health professional aware of the full picture and to work with them in seeking the best way forward. As with all mental illnesses, I would urge carers to be as involved and vigilant as possible. You know what symptoms and behaviours are out of character for your loved one and it is crucial that you are there as an extra pair of eyes and ears to help ensure that they get the correct treatment path for their individual needs and circumstances.

Craig says of how his PTSD and depression are very much linked:

In 2016 I had an accident at work. I'm a carpenter and one day while I was on site a scaffolder threw a 60 kg pallet off a rooftop above where I was walking. It landed on my head, causing me a head injury.

The weeks and months that followed were awful. I struggled with panic attacks, severe headaches and nightmares. I was diagnosed with PTSD but as the months went on my mood got worse. I felt I couldn't support or provide for my family, which made me feel like less of a man. I did a lot of things during that time that I'm not proud of. I tried to make myself feel like a man again. Depression made me feel vulnerable. Before the accident

I didn't feel that way. But as the depression got worse, I felt like a small child. I kept how I was feeling a secret from my wife. I felt like I wasn't a man for her financially or sexually. I felt weak.

Body dysmorphic disorder

Body dysmorphic disorder (BDD) is an anxiety disorder specifically linked to how people view their body. People with BDD see their physical appearance differently from how other people view them.

They may have obsessive worries for many hours a day about one or more flaws in their appearance – flaws that are invisible or nearly invisible to others. BDD sufferers may also develop compulsive behaviours around their physical appearance, such as obsessively looking in mirrors, using heavy make-up, or seeking cosmetic surgery.

These fixations will interfere with their day-to-day life, affecting their work, social life and / or relationships. These obsessions and routines can also trigger a range of emotions, including shame, guilt and loneliness, and may overlap with other mental illnesses, such as depression and OCD.

BDD and depression

While it is possible to have BDD without having depression and vice versa, it is also possible for the two to overlap and co-exist. The feelings and rituals that someone with BDD may have, which can include shame, guilt, loneliness and isolation, may contribute to the onset of depression, especially if the BDD is left untreated. Sadly, this can often be the case as many people with BDD delay seeking help because they are worried that others will judge them. They may therefore battle on alone for a long time before they get the support that they need, by which time their BDD may have escalated to the point where another mental illness, such as depression, has taken hold.

I would urge anyone who cares for someone with BDD to find out as much as possible about the illness and to offer opportunities to talk without judgement. Simply opening up may be the first step towards accepting that they need support, and this in turn can help them work through the thoughts and feelings bound up in the BDD, which may help to prevent depression from entering the already complex picture.

Once someone accepts treatment, stay with them on that journey, taking them to appointments if necessary or celebrating each and every tiny success with them. As they begin to move forward, their confidence and self-belief will grow; encourage them to step outside their illness and to rediscover the things they once enjoyed. Recovery from BDD and depression can be a slow process, but with time and support it can and will happen.

Sarah, who is in recovery from BDD and depression, says of how connected they are:

> I really do not know which one came first. I feel like they both came at the same time. I felt quite low about my appearance from the beginning of secondary school. I became quite picky about it and always thought I could look better. These feelings caused me to isolate myself into a pit of depression. Looking back I do feel though that I always had slight depression from the start. I don't know why I became like that. I really saw a different image in the mirror and it just wouldn't shift.

Borderline personality disorder (BPD)

Borderline personality disorder is a complex and serious mental illness, characterised by very unstable emotional and impulse regulation. People with BPD can have a contorted sense of self and may find themselves overly dependent on their relationships with others. Self-harming behaviour, such as hurting themselves, attempting suicide or abusing substances, can often be part of the illness. Given these manifestations of BPD, it is perhaps not surprising that a significantly higher incidence of depression has been found among those with BPD compared with the general population.

According to the *Diagnostic and Statistical Manual of Mental Disorders-IV (DSM-IV)* there are nine different criteria that can manifest within someone with BPD:

1. Frantic efforts to avoid real or imagined abandonment.
2. A pattern of unstable and intense interpersonal relationships characterised by the person alternating between extremes of putting the loved one 'on a pedestal' and devaluing them.
3. Identity disturbance – that is, strongly and persistently having an unstable self-image or sense of self.
4. Impulsivity in at least two areas that are potentially self-damaging (e.g. spending, sex, substance abuse, reckless driving, binge-eating).
5. Recurrent suicidal behaviour, gestures or threats or self-mutilating behaviour.
6. Emotional instability due to highly reactive mood (e.g. intense episodes of unease/dissatisfaction, irritability or anxiety, usually lasting a few hours and only rarely more than a few days).
7. Chronic feelings of emptiness.
8. Inappropriate, intense anger or difficulty controlling anger (e.g. frequent displays of temper, constant anger, recurrent physical fights).
9. Transient, stress-related paranoid thinking or severe dissociative symptoms (breakdown of memory, perception, awareness or identity).

At least five of these factors must be present for someone to be diagnosed with the condition. In some ways it is possible to draw very clear parallels between these BPD criteria – including self-mutilating behaviour, self-damaging impulsivity and an unstable sense of self – and the key characteristics of depression.

BPD and depression

One study has suggested that more than eight in 10 of those with BPD will experience major depression.[27] However, it can sometimes be difficult to make an accurate diagnosis of depression in people with BPD as the symptoms of each condition can be difficult to separate. Nevertheless, they are distinct and need to be recognised as such, as each disorder needs to be treated in its own right.

When it comes to treatment, studies suggest that while effective treatment of BPD seems to have a positive impact on depressive symptoms as well, it may not work the other way around – treatment of depression does not have the same positive effect on BPD symptoms.[28] This seems to suggest that taking antidepressants alone is not as effective for depression that occurs alongside BPD as it would be if depression was the only illness present. Instead, a combination of medication and psychotherapy tailored to the BPD is likely to be most effective.

Like so many other mental illnesses, it can be very hard for the person living with BPD to understand exactly what is happening inside their brain and to identify if and when depression has also entered the picture. The path to seeking help can be another daunting mountain to climb. Family, friends and loved ones, I urge you to continue to offer unwavering support, however frustrating and worrying it may be at times. Be an extra set of eyes and ears to ensure that the person you care about gets the most appropriate treatment for their full spectrum of symptoms.

Jo says of how her BPD and depression are entwined:

> Quite often those of us who have BPD as a diagnosis have comorbid diagnoses as well. One of these may be depression. My diagnosis was originally depression before adding in

the BPD diagnosis. A characteristic of BPD is that we feel emotions much more intensely than those without it. This means that when we experience depression, we experience it in an extreme way. When I feel depressed, I don't just feel a little bit low; instead, I am in the depths without any sign of light or hope. I want to end my life over the smallest triggers of my depression. It is an exaggerated depression that can change so quickly. It doesn't creep up on me in the way it may do with other people; instead, I can be high one minute and in the depths of despair the next. There is no in-between. All symptoms of depression are exaggerated. Depression and BPD can be difficult to live with as you never know where one ends and the other begins. Often, they are so entwined that there is no separating them.

Schizophrenia

Schizophrenia is generally a long-term mental illness where someone may have very distinct thoughts and feelings that feel incredibly vivid to them but may not actually reflect reality. They may hallucinate, be disorganised in how they think and speak, and experience thoughts and feelings that are delusional.

The effects of this can be wide-ranging. Living with schizophrenia may make it hard to cope with everyday life and may lead sufferers to feel isolated and lonely. Their illness can make them suspicious of others and reluctant to seek help. The delusional symptoms of schizophrenia may make it hard for them to even see that there is something wrong.

Schizophrenia is not always well understood by the general public. Perhaps due to the negative stories that make headlines in the press, many believe that people with schizophrenia are dangerous. This is not the case for most people with the illness, but can lead them to feeling isolated and misunderstood.

Schizophrenia and depression

Schizophrenia can trigger or be linked to many other mental illnesses, including depression. Around a quarter of those with schizophrenia could also be diagnosed with major depression,[29] which can make it even harder to cope with the effects of schizophrenia and it is thought it can also increase the risk of people with the illness attempting to take their own life.

Families can be a huge help here. By caring for them and listening to them, you may be able to help prevent your loved one feeling abandoned or isolated. You, as the carer, can remind them of the importance of caring for themselves and help them avoid things that may make their illness worse, such as alcohol or drugs. Allowing the person with the illness to talk without being met with judgement can be a really important way of showing that their feelings really do matter.

Families may also need support when caring for someone with schizophrenia, whether the illness is accompanied by depression or not. I would urge you to seek help as soon as you can, as this will enable you to build up your resilience, helping you to remain strong through the more challenging times. Ask about family therapy as this may well contribute to the wider treatment plan for schizophrenia, so helping everyone involved explore ways of supporting someone with schizophrenia.

Alcohol misuse and depression

As alcohol is the most commonly taken drug, its link with depression is worth looking at in more depth. The connection between the two is alarmingly stark, with information from Drinkaware suggesting that people with anxiety or depression are twice as likely to be heavy or problem drinkers. Interestingly, the two seem to share a common footprint, with common risk factors including a family history of alcohol issues, low self-esteem and a propensity to anxiety. Social environment also has a part to play, with someone who has been abused or suffered a traumatic event being more at risk of both.

The overlap between depression and alcohol abuse may be clear, but often it is less obvious which one came first. Some people will drink to blot out the symptoms of their depression, believing they can perhaps relieve their overwhelming unhappiness with alcohol. Others develop the latter as a result of the mood-altering effects from the alcohol. Either way, the knitting together of the two illnesses makes both more complex and harder to unravel.

To understand the link between drinking and depression, it is helpful to understand what happens in the brain when someone consumes alcohol. Having an alcoholic drink alters the chemical balance of the brain which is why, when someone has a drink or two, they may start to feel more relaxed and less inhibited. However, if they continue to drink, the alcohol may quite quickly switch their mood to anger, upset or despair. If this happens on a regular basis, the neurotransmitters in the brain that are essential for good mental health will be affected. Drinking too much also causes the level of the mood-boosting neurotransmitter serotonin in the brain to fall, which ultimately can make the symptoms of depression worse and also lead to a vicious cycle of feeling the need to drink more to find that relief that some people may mistakenly believe that alcohol will give them. Furthermore, the after-effects of alcohol – the dreaded hangover – can create a cycle of dread, shame and anxiety. The social effects of drinking – including arguments with loved ones or trouble at work – can also contribute to depression.

Indeed, for families and loved ones of those with depression, being alert to the signs that someone has an unhealthy relationship with alcohol can be the first clue that they may also be suffering from depression. Behind the arguments, emotional dysregulation, accidents or work or university absenteeism that can be some of the effects of unhealthy drinking, there may be a person struggling with a persistent low mood and crushingly low self-esteem who is filled with despair about the future. Recognising and understanding that may be the first step towards getting them the help they need for both illnesses.

Lucy shares the experience of her mother:

> When my parents divorced, my mum went into a really out of character routine of drinking alcohol every night. It started with one or two but turned into binges whereby she wouldn't wake up for work; she couldn't get out of bed. Her head was all over the place. My uncle intervened and managed to convince her to get help. She is doing much better now.

So, what can be done? To start to unravel the roots of someone's mental illness, eliminating or significantly cutting down the drinking may be a crucial first step (although of course it is much easier said than done and may require considerable support from both family members and friends, as well as professional services). According to the Royal College of Psychiatrists, many 'depressed drinkers' start to feel better within a few weeks of cutting out alcohol.[30] If that is the case, it will help to highlight whether the drinking has triggered the depression or the other way around. The latter is more likely to be the case if the symptoms of depression do not lift once the drinking has stopped.

In either scenario, tackling both the depression and the drinking at the same time is likely to be the most successful course of action. This may include – as outlined in Chapter 4 – talking therapy, complementary therapies and, possibly (under the strict direction of a doctor) medication. Getting help to stop drinking or resolve depression is not a sign of weakness or failure; finding the strength and resolve to recover is just the opposite. With the right intervention it is possible to tackle both and make a significant difference to the person's overall mental health.

Drug misuse and depression

Alcohol is not the only substance that can play a part in someone's experience of depression. There are other substances that can do so too. These can include painkillers, laxatives and also recreational drugs. Essentially, anything that alters the chemistry in the brain can exacerbate the risks to someone's mental health, particularly in those who are perhaps more prone to, or at risk of, this kind of illness.

As with alcohol, the interplay between other drugs and depression can be complicated and multi-layered. Some people will take drugs to escape the difficult and painful feelings that plague them. However, underneath the 'disguise' of the drugs, these problems still persist and the side-effects or come-down from taking drugs may simply make the situation even worse.

In other cases, heavy drug use can lead to the kind of chaotic lifestyle that creates a fertile base for mental illness to take root. Taking drugs can cause financial problems, relationship issues and/or risk-taking behaviour, all of which could contribute to the onset of depression.

Getting the right kind of help when drugs are involved alongside mental illness can also be particularly challenging. A doctor will need to try and work out how much the substance itself – or the withdrawal symptoms from it – is responsible for how someone is feeling and how much is part of an illness such as depression.

Take cocaine for example, which is now a commonly used drug by many people; it may initially cause a high, but once the effects start to wear off, users have a come-down where they may feel low and lacking in energy. For many these feelings will soon pass but it can be much more prolonged in people who use cocaine regularly and could contribute to a depressive illness.

If possible, the best way forward would be to try to support the person to get their drug use under control or, better still, stopped (sometimes easier said than done) and then a doctor can try to tackle the symptoms that remain with the appropriate treatments for that individual. Seeking help from a GP, drugs advisor or helpline is an important first step towards taking back control and getting a true picture of a person's mental state and what further help and support they need.

Maty, who suffers from depression and other mental illnesses, describes how he turned to alcohol and drug use:

Using drugs and alcohol helped me in the short term, but in the long run made everything worse. When I was extremely low and down the first place I went was the bottle.

Inhibitions lowered and feeling more depressed after taking a depressant (who would have thought it?), for me the answer was to escape. Stimulants would force a chemical smile to appear, only for me to feel 10 times worse when they wore off. Psychedelic drugs took my mind away from itself but created psychotic worlds to open up to me; I had to be careful.

Eventually, becoming psychotic came with everything I took: voices were amplified with alcohol, visions and delusions with stimulants, extreme paranoia was an everyday thing and depression, well that had a new friend to destroy me with, hangovers and come-downs were depression's Trojan horse.

That's when I sorted myself out for the better. I've been clean for a long time now but there's nothing I crave more when I'm depressed than alcohol and any type of high but I know the next day it won't be worth the extreme lows.

These substances helped keep me safe from myself but in the end made me more dangerous to myself. I would be dead now if I'd carried on how I was going.

A lot of people say they will never do it again when they stop, but not me. If I needed to, although I know they're taxing on my mind and body, sometimes a crutch is needed to lean on while you figure out your next move.

I hope that after reading this chapter you have a better understanding of the better-known and more talked about psychological illnesses, and of the possible inter-connective and complex nature of mental illness as a whole. Very rarely do symptoms fall into one neat, generic category, so for the majority it is hard to distinguish one illness from another. However, again I cannot stress enough the importance of following your instincts and arming yourself with as much applicable knowledge as possible to help you and your loved one find the right recovery path together, remembering always that recovery is possible and sustainable, provided the sufferer really wants it.

Depression and physical illness

Depression may be an illness of the mind. However, the connection and interplay between depression and some physical illnesses is undeniable and can often add a further complicated dimension when treating an illness that patients, carers and even doctors may sometimes struggle to fully recognise and/or comprehend.

Understanding is crucial, not least because we know that when someone has depression or any other mental illness that accompanies a physical condition, their journey towards recovery can be much more challenging. One of the reasons for this is that mental health issues can make it much more difficult for someone suffering to play a part in managing their own health. Those living with depression may find it harder to motivate themselves to follow a healthier lifestyle or to be able to stick to treatment plans. Even attending doctor's appointments can be a struggle.

Although it can be hard in many cases to work out which came first, the depression or the physical condition, the figures below, taken from the King's Fund Report,[31] demonstrate the scale of the connection between the two:

- Depression is two to three times more common in a range of cardiovascular diseases, including cardiac disease, coronary artery disease, stroke, angina and congestive heart failure, or following a heart attack
- People living with diabetes are two to three times more likely to have depression than the general population
- Mental health problems are around three times more prevalent among people with chronic obstructive pulmonary disease (COPD) than in the general population
- Up to 33% of women with rheumatoid arthritis, and more than 20% with all types of arthritis, may have co-morbid depression.

The figures may be stark, but the role depression plays in physical illness is complex and differs depending on which condition someone has and the individual circumstances they face. While it can affect anyone, with any illness, for the purposes of trying to gain a greater understanding of its role within this book, I have broken it down into three very broad categories.

Firstly, there are illnesses where depression takes root as a result of the stress and strain of dealing with physical symptoms and the limitations that illness can place on someone's lifestyle. This can be the case with almost any illness and can particularly play a part in progressive conditions, such as Parkinson's and arthritis. There is also considerable evidence that the toll of tackling illnesses such as cancer or a stroke can also trigger depression.[32]

The second category is those illnesses where depression is one of the symptoms of the illness itself, or a side-effect of the medication being taken for it. Falling into this category are very common thyroid disorders, as well as other conditions such as dementia and, again, Parkinson's.

The final group of illnesses are those that are actually triggered by the depression. There is evidence to suggest that those who suffer from a mental illness may be more susceptible to certain conditions, such as chronic pain or even heart disease. Lou, a chronic pain nurse specialist, shares her professional thoughts:

In my other caring role I currently work as a chronic pain nurse specialist and I also had 12 years' experience working in palliative care before that. I think it is important to recognise how our mental and physical health are inextricably linked. I have noted that for many people with long-term chronic illness, they also suffer from depression, and those suffering from long-term depression appear to develop physical illness as a response to the depression. When we are depressed for long periods of time, we produce high levels of the hormone cortisol as a response to stress. While cortisol is helpful in fuelling our fight or flight response in a crisis to keep us safe from danger, persistent high levels can cause physical changes such as increased blood sugar levels, calcium loss from bones, suppressed immune responses, high blood pressure and risk of heart disease, digestive problems, increased fat accumulation, sleep disturbance and even loss of cognitive function. All of these changes can lead to long-term physical illness. I also recognise that living with such illnesses takes a toll on mood and stress levels, often contributing to depression.

Throughout the rest of this chapter I will be looking at these three categories of physical illness in turn, with the hope of helping you to understand the part that a mental illness, such as depression, can play in them and what can be done to tackle it. Of course, few conditions will fit neatly into these categories. Mental illness can seep silently into so many lives that it is virtually impossible to cover every permutation of its relationship with physical illness, but I hope this chapter will nevertheless give you a greater understanding of that interplay.

Depression that accompanies a physical illness or ailment

A serious physical illness does not just take its toll on someone's body. Every area of their life can be affected, from the sufferer's home life, to their relationships, to their career. It can leave them feeling isolated, fearful and anxious about the future and not in control of their own life. All of this can leave a huge emotional mark on those most vulnerable to mental illness, particularly those at risk of developing depression, but virtually anyone can be affected.

It is thought that depression affects up to 20% of patients with cancer, compared with 5% of the general population.[33] Nevertheless, depression is often poorly recognised as a complication of this life-changing illness, even though it can affect someone's quality of life, how well they cope with and pursue treatment and even their ability to deal with and ultimately survive the cancer.

It is perhaps not surprising that it can be hard to recognise depression in cancer, not least because it may look a lot like the sadness, worry and fear which one would expect to accompany such a diagnosis. However, if that feeling persists and deepens, it is definitely worth raising it with a doctor as soon as possible. It is important to spot the signs of depression early so you can help to keep it from affecting the person's quality of life, and, possibly, even how they take up and respond to their treatment. As I have touched on before, it can be much harder to manage a physical condition when also coping with depression.

As Maureen says:

> I went through a long and emotionally draining struggle with cancer last year. It really took all my energy and positivity about life away from me. At first I tried my best to stay on top of it and be light-hearted, but it soon got the better of me. I ended up being extremely depressed and suffering from cancer at the

> same time. Thankfully now, because of the help and support of
> my friends and family, I am in a much better place.
> Anyone who is going through this struggle, I think it is so
> important to have emotional support around you, not just
> medical or physical support.

Almost any illness can trigger depression. Losing life skills
after a stroke, or struggling to walk after a heart attack, and
coping with the restrictions such change can place on everyday
life, such as altering working life or forcing the sufferer to give
up once loved hobbies, can be very hard. This in turn could
change their role at home and affect their self-esteem, with all
these things potentially contributing to the onset of depression.

Unsurprisingly, those who suffer from a long-term chronic
condition, such as diabetes, arthritis, heart disease or kidney
disease, all of which could all lead to a huge change in someone's
lifestyle, are particularly at risk. According to the World Health
Survey 2007, those with a long-term condition are two to three
times more likely to develop mental ill-health, while people with
two or more long-term conditions are seven times more likely to
experience depression than those without a long-term condition.
A chronic illness can prevent people from going out, enjoying
activities and socialising with friends, which is one of the risk
factors of depression.

Seeking help can also be a huge and challenging step to take.
Firstly, it may be hard to recognise depression within yourself
when you are also coping with and battling a physical health
issue. It can seem to be a part of the physical illness that many
people mistakenly feel they should put up with. They may be
unwilling to 'burden' the medical team with 'yet another issue',
worried they may seem ungrateful or complaining when the
doctors and nurses are working so hard to tackle their physical
symptoms. It can also be very hard to admit that you are struggling, particularly if your body is beginning to heal and you

feel you should be counting your blessings and grateful for the medical help and support you have received from loved ones.

Friends and family can have such a crucial role to play here, both recognising if someone is battling with mental health concerns, and also in reassuring them that to seek help is not a sign of weakness but rather part of their overall treatment plan. Encouraging the sufferer to open up and talk about how they feel is an important first step. However, if the feelings persist, there should be no hesitation in coming forward and telling their doctor or medical team. It can be so tempting for someone to try to keep busy in an attempt to push away and bury these feelings, but it is paramount to remember to be kind to yourself when you are unwell. If you know someone is suffering, encourage them to lighten their load, to eat well, take gentle exercise and pursue the hobbies, interests and friendships that have always made them happy, and to raise their concerns with a professional. No harm can come from doing this and it could provide a crucial piece in the puzzle of their recovery.

Eliza, who suffered from depression alongside diabetes for many years, shares her experience:

> For the first 10 years of being diagnosed with diabetes depression has to have been the biggest problem for me. I was on the wrong medication for a long time and didn't realise how much the wrong type of insulin had affected me emotionally. Diabetes and depression are very closely linked for me and I believe for many others too. You can live a good life with diabetes but you must control the sugars. No need for crash diets, just balance your life.

Depression as a symptom of physical illness

Sometimes depression can be a symptom of a physical illness. It may be one of the ways that the body notifies a person that there is something wrong and that they need to seek medical help. This is another reason why depression should never be ignored, and why we should not wait to see if it lifts. We would not – or should not – dismiss pains in our chest or a lump in our breast and in the same way we should not ignore a persistent feeling of gloom or hopelessness, issues with sleeping and/or an unexplained negativity towards things that once made us happy. If those feelings of depression are present, a GP or doctor should first of all do tests to rule out any other underlying medical conditions that could be linked to this change in mood.

One of the most common conditions to be related to symptoms of depression is hypothyroidism (essentially an underactive thyroid gland). Depression and hypothyroidism share some symptoms, such as sluggishness and a feeling of wading through life, so a doctor could diagnose depression without realising the symptoms could be connected to your thyroid gland. However, if this mood change is accompanied by other symptoms, including weight gain, thinning hair and/or sensitivity to the cold, the doctor should also test for thyroid disorder with a simple blood test. Then, if low levels of the thyroid hormone thyroxine are diagnosed, medication should be able to treat the symptoms, including depression.

Parkinson's disease is another condition where depression can play an active part. As I have already explained, the toll exerted by this degenerative illness and the limitations it puts upon the sufferer's life can be very stressful and may trigger depression in both people with Parkinson's and those who care for them – but more on that later. In addition, it is also thought that depression can be one of Parkinson's many symptoms, along with the more well-known effects such as tremor and muscle rigidity. Some research suggests that this may be because a lack of the neurotransmitter dopamine, which causes the symptoms of Parkinson's, can also be a trigger for depression, worry and anxiety.[34] Some people may even experience depression before they notice any other Parkinson's symptoms.

Working out exactly what role depression plays, and how it can be treated, is an ongoing challenge for those with the condition, as well as their medical teams. However, the connection between Parkinson's and depression is undeniable. Julia, who has lived with this condition for nearly 20 years, explains the part that depression plays in her illness:

I believe the depression is part of my Parkinson's as it kicked in for the first time in my life straight after my diagnosis. For around six months I could barely get off my sofa and it is only looking back that I can see I was depressed. While I believe it is part of the illness, I also think it is accentuated by difficulties of dealing with Parkinson's. It puts you in a constant state of mourning. Every week you find things are a little harder than they were the week before. The relentless march of Parkinson's takes its toll on your mental health.

Over the years, the depression has come and gone. It never really goes away, but I can generally keep its effects at arm's length by being a very positive person and keeping very busy. When I feel myself 'going down', I become much more self-centred. It becomes all about me. Usually I really enjoy going out, but I become very insular. I can become pre-occupied with thinking about death and what my death might be like.

Instead of fighting it or punishing myself and making myself feel worse, I allow myself to feel the depression, to accept it. I remind myself that it can be part of Parkinson's, that I will get through it and that it will come to an end. In particularly bad spells, I go to my GP and get a short prescription of antidepressants, usually for around three months, which I have found do help.

I find that keeping active helps to keep my mental health on a more even keel. I walk my dog each day, do Tai chi and I also sing in a choir that I set up for people with Parkinson's. I try to keep a positive attitude and remind myself it will not last forever. There can be a stigma around depression, but I'd urge others not to suffer in silence.

There are other illnesses where depression can be part of the condition, as opposed to being triggered by the stress of dealing with it. The exact relationship between the two often remains cloudy and unclear, but research continues into the overlap between other conditions, such as dementia and multiple sclerosis (MS), and depression. With dementia, for example, while the effects and limitations of the illness may lead to depression, it may also be the case that damage to nerve pathways and chemical changes in the brain caused by the dementia, may also play a part.

Depression can feel like a particularly cruel extra burden for those already dealing with a life-changing diagnosis. As if it is not hard enough that their body is being put through the mill, their mental health may also be affected. I think the important thing to remember is that there is still hope – and much that can be done – even where depression is bound up in a wider physical illness. People with Parkinson's, MS or dementia do not need to accept it as an inevitable part of their condition that they just have to put up with. Lifestyle changes, such as staying active and continuing to maintain friendships and interests, can improve depressive situations. As Julia's experience shows, medication can also be effective as long as it works in harmony with any other treatment that has been prescribed for the wider illness.

Illnesses triggered by depression

The third connection between depression and physical illness is where the former may play a part in the onset of the latter. While it makes complete sense that someone's state of mind can have an impact on the health of their body, it is often not appreciated how strong the link is between the two.

For people who suffer from depression, being diagnosed with a physical health condition on top can often feel very unfair and as if everything in life is against them. However, this type of dual diagnosis is more than just coincidence; researchers are increasingly realising the close connection between psychological and physical issues.

Consider this: one report found that depressed people over the age of 50 were considerably more likely to develop vascular dementia and Alzheimer's than people who were not depressed.[35] With diabetes, just as people with the condition are more at risk of depression, so those with depression are more likely to develop the type 2 form of the illness.[36]

This connection is partly down to a change in the way that people with depression might behave. Being less motivated to eat well or exercise regularly, for example, or having issues sleeping, can have a clear physical impact. However, it is also thought that the link could run deeper and in some cases may be associated with physiological changes in the body that can occur in people with depression. The neurotransmitter serotonin, for example, is not only responsible for regulating a person's mood, but can also affect their sleep pattern, appetite and digestion, among other physical processes, and could be linked to digestive problems, such as irritable bowel syndrome.

Nothing demonstrates the link between depression and physical illness more clearly than one of Britain's most deadly illnesses, heart disease. Studies show that people with depression may be twice as likely to develop circulatory disease.[37] In addition, when depression continues after recovery from a heart attack, the risk of death increases to 17% within six months as opposed to 3% among heart attack patients who are not depressed. The link is thought to be partly due to the fact that those struggling with mental ill health may be less likely to stick to their treatment plan or healthier diets or exercise regimes. However, in addition, doctors believe that physiological changes may happen in people with depression and these may be a factor.

Ed Lovern, a senior physiotherapist, explains how depression can be closely linked with physical pain:

Depression and persistent/chronic pain are two of the most debilitating disorders worldwide. The clustering of the two is very common with prevalence between often being cited.[38] *Although there is no guarantee of getting chronic pains if you have depression, it's important to take note there is an increased likelihood.*

Long-term depression can cause an increase in inflammation within the body, causing a heightened sensitivity of the nervous system.[39] *On top of this, people with depression, understandably, tend to be less active, which has also been seen to cause an increase to pain sensitivity, either through chemical mechanisms or a poorer mental state.*[40] *This can not only cause an increase in the chances of 'non-specific pain' (pain without damage), but also increase sensitivity-slowed healing rates of injuries.*[41]

Pain is an unpleasant sensory and emotional experience associated with actual or potential tissue damage, or described in terms of such damage.[42] *This definition has been perceived as narrow as it does not take into account feelings or the impact it may have on lives. Pain can and often does occur without any damage, examples being headaches and menstrual cramps. The amount of pain a person may have is directly correlated to their brain's response to any particular threat/damage. The body constantly monitors itself and sends information up to the brain via the spinal cord. A message of pain will only be signalled if the information being scrutinised by the brain is perceived as threatening.*[43]

Within a good healthcare system/model, the approach to any pains a person may have should begin with viewing the issue at a whole-person level. A model developed by Engel in 1997, called the 'Biopsychosocial Model of Health and Illness', describes some of the domains that healthcare professionals may look at. This links a person's biology (bio), psychology (psycho) and social (social) aspects of life – in other words, where their thoughts and behaviours will directly affect how they perceive feelings of pain. A pain, whether there is physical injury or not, relies on these three stimuli to get better. Where poor mental health and decreased social activities both occur healing rates and duration of pain can equally be prolonged.[41]

Acute pain can be caused by an action like rolling your ankle. Damage to local tissues causes cells to release chemicals which trigger the nervous system to start sending messages to the brain. Chemicals released by the damaged cells cause messages to be sent up to the brain; this causes the healing process to begin; it will start with swelling and inflammation.[43] *Pain in and around the damaged tissues will normally also persist to remind you to try to protect the area during the healing phase. The brain can inhibit these pain messages, if it is preoccupied or does not see the 'injury' as threatening at the time.*[43] *Say you roll your ankle and a bus is coming towards you at full speed. Priority number one, get out of the way! Pains can come later. This example shows that pain can be situation dependent and your brain will respond to certain stimuli around you to control what you do to react. This, in part, is why there is a link between depression and pain.*

The question is, how do we hope to help prevent pain? And how do we wait for pain to go before trying to get back to normal life? Is it all hopeless? Absolutely not! It's a case of graded exposure and taking everything step by step; it's a marathon, not a sprint.

Surround yourself with people whom you love, and who make you happy. Do something daily that makes you or someone else smile. And keep yourself as active as possible to keep your body happy. Think of what you can do to help issues outside the biological pains. Try to start exercising; getting yourself more active and stronger not only helps decrease the chances of pain, but helps release chemicals in the brain which are stronger than any drug, to make you feel happier.[44]

It is important to note that if you do have any issues you are worried about, you should consult a health-care professional. We are always here to help and reassure you. We can ensure you have a safe way to get active and provide any information you may need.

Depression when you are caring for someone with an illness

Whether you are supporting someone with a mental or a physical illness, caring can take its toll. Being on hand for someone around the clock and often putting their needs first, leads to around three in five carers facing depression themselves, according to the charity Carers UK.[45]

Of course, caring for someone can have huge positives. Helping and supporting other people gives many a real sense of satisfaction and fulfilment. Giving so much to someone else can be a wonderful act of love that gives many carers a feeling of having a deeper sense of purpose. Having cared for and supported my own daughter through her battle with mental illness into recovery, I know at first hand how rewarding it can be to be able to help someone you care about and to see the positive impact your love and understanding can have on them. But equally, I also know how challenging and difficult it can be.

My Samantha looks back and says:

> Without my mum's unconditional love and support, I know I would not be who and where I am today. She gave up her life so I could have mine. At the time I did not realise just how much she had given up. I wish she had taken time out for herself as, looking back, she needed it, but hindsight is a wonderful thing.

When giving their all to someone else, carers can naturally often neglect their own needs. Carving out time for themselves, without being dogged by a feeling of guilt or failure, can be very hard. In addition, facing the illness and the possible deterioration of a loved one or close friend can be difficult to bear. As a result, carers can be plagued by anxiety and stress, constantly worried about their loved one and overwhelmed by question marks about the future for all involved. The limitations of the illness can lead to feelings of isolation, which is one of the many trigger points for depression.

In addition, carers often have little or no time for themselves. Their own interests may go on hold and their relationships with others can suffer. This may also have an impact on how they look after their own health. Finding time to exercise, prepare healthy meals or simply do something that they once enjoyed can often be a real struggle. Add in money worries, lack of sleep and perhaps turning to alcohol or food to cope with these difficult feelings, and it is easy to see how caring can be a real risk factor for depression.

The temptation for carers is just to plough on. They may tell themselves that their own problems or issues are minor compared with those of the person they are supporting and they might find it difficult to ask for help, worried that their loved one might not be properly looked after if they cannot do it themselves. However, this selfless attitude – laudable as it is – can put someone at risk of depression; as with all types of mental illness, as soon as you become aware of any symptoms (or ideally before), you should ask for help.

Please remember, this is not a sign of weakness. Like that often-used analogy of the oxygen mask on the plane, it is important for carers to get their 'mask' in place and be breathing easily in order to be able to help others.

There are many avenues to go down to seek support. Firstly, opening up to others and being honest about these feelings is an important first step. Some people find it easier to speak to friends or family members; others find it less daunting to open up in a support group or online forum. At the same time, seeing the GP is crucial. GPs are best placed to put a treatment path in place, which may include talking therapies and/or medication, and also to help make contact with other agencies that may be able to offer support or provide respite. All carers in the UK have a legal right to a carer's assessment, so that social services can work out how best to support them in their role.

At the same time, trying to carve out some time for yourself as a carer is essential, reminding yourself that you need to be healthy and happy in order to be able to provide your loved one with the care that they want and need. Eating healthily and doing some physical activity – even just a daily walk – can be helpful. Finding some way to relax is also vital. For some people, that might take the form of meditation or mindfulness; for others it might be doing crafts or painting. Whatever brings you pleasure, trying to find time for it, even when there are so many other demands on your time, is vital.

Jonathan, who cares for his mother who suffers from depression and multiple physical illnesses, describes how reaching out for help was the best thing he has done:

> I have been my mother's carer for many years. The past few have been the most difficult. I found it really hard to open up about my struggles and just had a 'get on with it' attitude towards myself. I spoke to a close friend, and they suggested I reach out to other family members for help and support so I could live my life a little more. I find I am able to cope a lot better now and still care for my mother, but the help makes it so much easier.

To conclude

This chapter demonstrates how all-pervasive depression can be. Where there is any kind of weakness, be it mental, physical or emotional, there is the risk that depression can move in and take root. For that reason and for the best chance of recovery, it is crucial to be alert to its effects and to act on them as quickly as possible.

However, that is not to say that depression is an inevitable effect of illness or caring for someone. Many people will not be affected and those who follow a healthy lifestyle and look after their own well-being are more likely to have the strongest defence against it. For those who do develop depression, maintaining that healthy lifestyle is a key tool in helping to tackle it.

The question of how to deal with depression is particularly important when you consider the part it can play in the development of other conditions. Seeking help for the debilitating symptoms that may leave sufferers isolated, anxious, and unmotivated is crucial, not only to tackle the depression, but also as one defence against wider health issues.

Depression does not automatically accompany other illnesses, but it *can* occur alongside some of them. Bearing this in mind and remaining alert to the potential of depression is an important line of defence for sufferers and carers alike.

Chapter 7

Depression and the risk of suicide

Suicide
By Samantha Crilly

Imagine being so mentally tormented
Everything the illness has taught you is so cemented
That the only place to hide
is by suicide.
The only way to silence your mind, is to not exist
It becomes the only solution you can see on your list
Imagine your body hurting so much you just
want to be dead
Now transfer all that pain and agony to live
inside your head
Imagine the thoughts of something like cancer, wiring
through your brain
The destruction, the evil intention, and most of all the pain
Because sadly both mental illness and cancer
can end up the same
The only difference being mental illness has
our exterior to hide behind.
If we are lucky we can see a by-product but often,
we are blind

The growth, the threat, the damage can be
impossible to find
Even though their battle to us is invisible
We need to break the stigma, they are being tortured, not
just miserable
The strength it takes to just exist with these
battles in one's head
Should not be stigmatised, they should be
listened to instead
To believe in something we cannot always see
I know, will one day, save somebody.

The title of this book is *Hope with Depression* and that sentiment is meant from the bottom of my heart. There *is* hope with depression and the vast majority of sufferers will find a way forward with their illness, treating it successfully or finding ways to manage it as part of their day-to-day life.

However, the statistics remind us all too often that some people's illness takes them down a very different path, when sadly they may see taking their own life as the only escape from the agony they are feeling. The deaths of so many people in the public eye remind us that no one is immune from depression or despair.

If we can keep in mind that, rather than being about choosing to die, suicide is about wanting to stop hurting, it may help us understand a bit more why it is such a risk for those suffering from mental ill health. For some, it may seem the only escape route from the feelings of self-loathing and hopelessness that continually overwhelm them.

Figures from the charity Samaritans make sobering reading. They reveal that in 2018, over 6500 suicides were recorded in the UK (6507 to be precise) and 352 in the Republic of Ireland (a rise of 11.8% on 2017),[46] with a far higher number attempting to end their own life. While not all those people who died by suicide will have had depression, research shows that those with a diagnosed mental health condition are at a higher risk of attempting and carrying out suicide,[47] with more than 90% of suicides and suicide attempts having been found to be related to a mental illness. Across the world, the highest rates of suicide were linked to depressive disorders.[48] The statistics purely for men are even more alarming, as I will discuss in the next section. (The figures above are for men and women combined.)

Despite these shocking figures, it still feels that there is a stigma around talking about suicide – even more so than opening up about mental illness itself. While of course it is very hard to even think about a loved one taking their own life, it is also important not to bury your head in the sand and hope the danger will go away. You might be afraid of bringing up the subject or be unsure how to do so, but talking openly about suicidal thoughts and feelings can help save lives.

Depression and suicide in men

Although there has been a decrease in male suicide, according to the Samaritans Suicide Statistic Report from 2018 (published September 2019), British men are still three times more likely to take their own lives than women, with the highest rate being among men aged 45 to 49. (In the Republic of Ireland, the rate is highest in men aged 55 to 64.) I never fail to be shocked and saddened by the frequently reported fact that suicide is the biggest killer of men under the age of 50, with more men taking their own lives than dying from cancer or being killed in road traffic accidents.

The over-arching conclusion from this must surely be that men do not ask for help in the same way that perhaps women tend to. The macho stereotype pervades, making many men feel that it is somehow a weakness to ask for help, and while progress is being made, many men still believe they should be 'man enough' to handle their emotions themselves. The message that depression is a treatable illness, rather than a sign of emotional weakness, has yet to reach many.

Furthermore, men may not be able to recognise their mental health issues. All too often they focus on a physical issue instead, such as insomnia or sexual problems, or they may become angry or aggressive or indulge in risky behaviour, such as drinking too much or gambling compulsively, without realising that all these things may be a manifestation of underlying depression.

Nikki, whose husband was in a very dark place and contemplated taking his own life, says of the warning signs that alerted her:

Now that I think back on my husband's depression, the warning signs were all there. I just didn't put two and two together. Everyone has different signs, but I now know that his are: drinking a lot more alcohol, including daytime drinking; angry outbursts; not wanting to be at home; saying that I'm 'putting him down' when that's not reality; staying up very late and being very tired the next day; and poor personal hygiene.

Men need to know that they can open up without being judged, that talking about what they are going through can be helpful. That means knowing who they can turn to. Making sure the boys and men in your life are aware that they can come to you and that when they are ready to talk you are ready to listen, will give them the green light to start getting help.

Garry, who suffers from clinical depression, shares his advice for anyone suffering:

Keeping it all inside is a recipe for disaster. I should know! Talk to someone, anyone, even the cat! Saying it out loud does help.

Men also have a responsibility to each other. Between the banter and bravado that fuel so many of their conversations, there also needs to be more honest space and when men ask each other 'How's things?' they should be prepared to listen to the answer and that means looking beyond the usual response of 'Fine' to spot any unspoken clues.

Jody wishes his best friend, Darren, had talked to him instead of trying to deal with it on his own before taking his life:

In the notes he left behind, he felt he had not led a good life. He could see no point in his work, hobbies, social life or, indeed, life itself. All this was heart-breaking to read and although it explained his actions, it made no sense to me – it was not the man I knew.

I keep asking myself 'Why didn't he talk to me?' I thought we spoke about everything, but he couldn't or wouldn't talk to me about the things that were troubling him most and that made me question our friendship and the importance of the history we'd had together.

Since his death, I've tried hard to raise awareness of mental illness, especially among men, and I have changed my approach to my male friends, breaking down the male bravado and trying instead to dig deeper and check in on how they are feeling, as well as talk about my own emotions more.

How to support a loved one who is having suicidal thoughts

Most people who feel suicidal do not want death; they just want the pain to stop. The most powerful thing you can do is be there for them, showing that you care, that their life matters and helping them find an alternative way forward.

Most people who attempt suicide will give some clue or warning, so it is vital to take those clues seriously, even if they are made/said casually. They may talk or write about death or harming themselves or they may seek out things that could be used to take their own life, such as weapons or drugs. However, there may be more subtle signs: hopelessness, self-loathing and self-destructive behaviour should all be taken seriously. Be alert also to those who seem to be getting their affairs in order or saying goodbye to people as if they will not see them again. It sounds obvious, but all too often the clues are missed.

If you spot any of these signs and are worried about someone you care about, it is natural to question whether you should say something. But the best way to find out is to ask them. Showing you care should not push someone towards suicide, rather it will give them an opportunity to voice their fears and feelings which could in turn help them to see that there is another way forward.

While talking is crucial, so is listening. Allow your friend or loved one to unload their despair and listen without judgement, remaining calm and accepting of how they feel. Reassure them that help is available and tell them how important they are to you. Avoid arguing with them or appearing shocked.

Angela shares her experience with her own son, who is now recovered:

> It got to a point with my son's depression, after he opened up about his suicidal thoughts. I did not know what to do next. I needed help! I could not tell anyone as the trust between us would have ended. I could tell he was in such a dark and desperate place. I spoke to one of my close friends, who works as a counsellor, in confidence about my worries he might take his own life. She suggested that I approach him about my concerns with openness and honesty. This was such a turning point for us. He honestly felt that no one would miss him and once he saw the agony in my eyes, I think he realised that we did care.

Help the person who is feeling suicidal to find professional help, and be proactive in keeping in touch with them – do not wait for them to call you or expect them to ask for help. Instead, be in touch often and continue to be supportive in the long term, even if the immediate crisis appears to have passed. Help them to come up with a plan to follow if they feel suicidal thoughts descend. This may include identifying their main triggers, as well as what may help them to fight through those difficult feelings. The plan could also include a clear list of contact numbers for friends and family who can help in an emergency, as well as details of their doctor or therapist. If you are worried that there is an urgent danger that they might take their life, try to contact their doctor or (in the UK) dial 999.

Never think that it is too late to make a difference. Can I remind you of the story of two strangers who met on London Bridge. One was about to jump to his death, before the other took the time to stop and talk to him, and ultimately saved his life.

The two are now firm friends, both campaigning for better understanding of mental health.

If you can help the person you care about find support, you may be starting the process of their beginning to turn their life around. If you are unsure of what to do or say, the Samaritan's website and the Zero Suicide Alliance website are good sources of information about how to help someone who is having suicidal thoughts.

The three stories told here speak for themselves:

I made my son a promise...

By Stephen Mallen
Bereaved Father
Chair, The MindEd Trust
Co-founder, Zero Suicide Alliance
Member, National Suicide Prevention Group,
HM Government

My beloved son, Edward, took his own life on the railway line which runs through our village, in February 2015.

He died six weeks after his 18th birthday, suffering from the sudden and cataclysmic onset of devastating clinical depression.

There are simply no words to convey the bone-crushing and heart-stopping grief and devastation his loss has wrought on his family, his friends and his community. Four years after his passing, we are daily still confronted with a bottomless abyss of grief beyond reason or comprehension. Some wounds will never heal.

One might expect a devoted father to wax lyrical about a cherished son now deeply missed. As everyone whoever met my son will tell you, however, he was a truly remarkable and lovely lad. Head boy at both his primary and secondary schools, Edward played for the local cricket team, delivered the newspapers in our village and was at the centre of a close-knit friendship group which only village life and togetherness since infancy can nurture. Academically brilliant, with straight As in every exam he ever sat, and an offer to study at Cambridge University, Edward was also a gifted pianist who has the shattering epitaph of having played all of the music at his own funeral via clandestine recordings made by his friends.

Mature beyond his years, Ed was kind, intelligent and self-effacing. It is a cruel irony that he was the go-to person in his circle of friends, helping many in times of need and distress. The eldest of three children and voted by his classmates 'most likely to go on and become Prime Minister one day', Edward was quite simply one of the most promising prospects of his generation. His parents could not have been more pleased, nor more proud.

It is abundantly clear that depression, like most forms of mental illness, is frequently and closely associated with adversity in childhood. Inequality, fractured families, poverty, abuse, bullying, neglect and disability are just some of the well-established contributory factors in psychological trauma and suicidal ideation and completion.

However, in the case of my son – and hundreds of others whose families have contacted me in the wake of his tragedy – it is equally clear that depression is a disease like any other which is indiscriminate in incidence, regardless of wealth, status and stability. Edward was from a professional, affluent and very stable, loving family and had grown up in a comfortable and friendly community. He had never experienced any adversity nor faced any challenge which he was not able to overcome with ease. His death was nothing short of seismic in its impact on his loved ones and his community. His hitherto contented and vibrant family was obliterated forever at seven minutes past 3:00 on that cold, bright February afternoon.

In attempting to alleviate my appalling grief, people have often suggested that my son's death was some terrible accident, a twist of fate or the inexplicable act of whatever god you may or may not believe in. This is not so. He contracted or developed a disease, plain and simple. If, in reading this, you think that this could not happen to you, think again. In the same way that you can develop lung cancer if you have never smoked a cigarette, so can you develop severe depression in the absence of any apparent cause. Nobody is immune from this frequently catastrophic condition. Of course, there are risk factors, and of course one can guard against it, but, make no mistake, there is no immunisation. The sooner we learn this as a society, the better. Depression, like most mental illnesses, is not consigned to some unspoken underclass somewhere far removed from ourselves; it is all of our business and one of the most damaging and pervasive forms of ill-health right across our society. It is also the most often-cited mental factor in both attempted and completed suicide.

The loss of our son was compounded by the horror of its aftermath. Edward's brief passage through the health system was an utter disgrace and, as with countless others that we have lost so needlessly and tragically, an indictment on our society.

Despite an emergency, 24-hour suicide risk referral from a trusted family GP, our dear lad tumbled through a litany of local NHS Trust mistakes and malpractices to end up on a routine waiting list within which he could expect a first treatment consultation within six to nine months. Triaged by a psychiatric nurse in that nurse's first week of unsupervised work, whose entire experience was confined to violent offenders in the prison population, Ed was prescribed medication with a known suicide risk in complete contravention of NICE guidelines. His medical notes were never written up, there was no communication with his GP and his address was incorrectly entered into the system so that he never received any indications of care. The sum total of our beautiful boy's treatment was a couple of website addresses scribbled on a scrap of paper ripped from a notebook by an ambivalent social worker.

Despite telling five different medical professionals that he was self-harming and actively thinking of taking his life on the railway – two of the most powerful and basic diagnostic risk signposts – nobody did anything. Nothing at all. He gave his consent twice for his family to be consulted and involved in his care and yet there was not a single attempt to contact his devoted parents or anyone close to him. We were, of course, aware that all was not well with our son, but we had no inkling of the severity of his condition. A single phone call might have saved his life. The earth-shattering irony of him dying 500 yards from our front door – on the railway – three weeks later leaves me numb with injustice and rage.

Utterly bereft with grief, you will draw your own conclusions when I say that we were then told that the social worker who had seen Edward was suddenly signed-off sick after his death, that he was then miraculously no longer employed by the Trust and that he was then refusing to take part in the investigation into Edward's death. Edward's medical notes do say that, with appropriate care and therapy, he was expected to make a full recovery. Having been emergency referred with pronounced and classic symptoms, our lad was literally dying in front of a set of medical professionals. They quite simply did nothing, not adhering to even basic medical procedure. Edward's incomplete case notes state that he was a polite young man who shook hands and was wearing a clean shirt. His parents remain of the opinion that their son died because they had raised him well. The NHS made a socio-economic diagnosis, not a clinical one... which returns us to the point about depression affecting all corners of society and not just the disadvantaged or the underprivileged.

All of this was forced out at the Inquest into Edward's death, prompting the Coroner to issue a Regulation 28 – Prevention of Future Death Notice, which is just about the most serious conclusion an Inquest can reach before it enters the realms of criminality. Our boy should not have died and the Lord Chancellor, the Chief Coroner and the Secretary of State were appraised of this.

The Inquest process was horrendous and tortuous and something that no bereft family should have to endure in an empathic and truthful society. Having had one Coroner recused [legal term for when a professional is found to be unfit] for gross insensitivity and multiple blunders, Edward's case was eventually fully and fairly assessed by the coronial system. The fact that this was nearly 18 months after his death and was accompanied by more than two years of aggressive legal wrangling involving what was then the NHS litigation authority (now NHS Resolution), says much about how society views depression and suicide.

From personal experience and contact with dozens of other families, it is clear to me that the post-tragedy processes we force bereaved families to endure are both immoral and inhumane. Only the most robust families are able to successfully navigate this hellish pathway when they are most likely at the lowest point in their entire lives. Moreover, opportunities to learn are lost, systems do not improve, mistakes are covered up and millions of pounds are wasted in defending claims which amount to little more than a request for an apology and a contribution to funeral expenses where blatant errors have occurred. Anyone working in mental health will be familiar with phrases like 'parity of esteem' or 'duty of candour'. Sadly, for those living with depression or feeling its aftermath, these words remain little more than hollow rhetoric. Depression kills people. The people left behind are then killed by the way they are treated by society whilst they experience the very darkest depths of the human condition.

In considering depression, we remind ourselves that it is not a perfect world. Mistakes happen, tragedies occur – and they always will. As I stood next to my son's coffin in church, though, I made a public promise to investigate his death and seek reform on his behalf and that of his generation. It is the very least I can do for my boy and the very least he would have expected of me. It rapidly became clear that Edward's death was not an accident or a random mishap. We lose somebody like Ed every single day in this country and we lose a male to suicide every 90 minutes, commonly via depression. The suicide rate has fallen in recent years, but the male rate remains stubbornly high, and tragedies involving young men and women are actually rising. We may never eradicate depression or suicide, but we must try.

In honouring my promise to Ed, I have researched the mental health sector and pressed for reform. In the past four years, there has been much that has been positive. The stigma of mental illness and depression is subsiding as we talk more openly on the subject. The media, celebrities and the Royal Family have all played a vital part and mental health is now ingrained within all political party manifestos where once it was a taboo subject. Current trials within the Department of Education and the long-term plans for the NHS hold much promise, we have a Minister for Suicide and our most senior politicians will now readily take to the rostrum in support of mental healthcare, reaching out to other nations and the international psychiatric community. There is a very long way to go from a sceptical and stigmatising society and a desperately underfunded and fragmented healthcare system, but the direction of travel is at last broadly positive. I will have it that my son will not have died in vain and, in this regard, I stand shoulder to shoulder with the tens of thousands of parents and family members who have lost a child or a loved one to suicide.

From my work, two key themes have emerged. Firstly, what we can do as parents and citizens. As the stigma evaporates around depression and mental illness, it is beholden on us all to improve our knowledge and become more psychologically literate. Whilst I partially blame the health system for the loss of my lad, and I rage in torment over how I myself and my family have been treated in his wake, I also have to accept my part in his tragedy. So do his teachers, his friends and his community. The signs were all there and had I known 10% of what I now know, it is highly likely that my boy would still be alive. I will have to forever now live with the terror of my personal inability to save my own, dear child. Education and openness are key. There is a clear distinction between the trials and tribulations of adolescent life and the mood swings and volatility this gives rise to and clinically recognisable illness. The same is true in adult life. Depression, once established as a clinical condition, rarely abates by itself and intervention, preferably as early as possible, is usually essential. We must recognise the symptoms, talk openly and sensitively, seek care and engage. Medical evidence has now established that talking empathetically about suicide does not increase its likelihood and is often the road to salvation for those experiencing the darkest of thoughts. How many of us have worried in silence about the apparent depression and negative thoughts of a loved one, friend or colleague, and not acted appropriately through a combination of shame, worry and ignorance?

Depression usually presents via the sustained coalescence of several factors which typically include: disturbed sleep, disturbed diet, lack of engagement, loss of confidence, a withdrawal from previously enjoyable activities and interests ('anhedonia'), a reduction in achievement, faltering speech, self-harm and an overall predisposition towards negativity. Edward exhibited all of these in the weeks before his death. Depression has been termed the 'curse of the strong'. High functioning and previously accomplished sufferers frequently soldier on with their lives (sometimes, although not in Ed's case, anaesthetised by substance abuse or aggression), fighting a battle they cannot win whilst exhibiting a combination of these symptoms to varying degrees. I cringe in anguish and in pain with the realisation of the agony that my boy was going through. It is all of our responsibility to understand depression, see how it presents itself, appreciate its impact and take action. Doing nothing is not an option.

My second theme and concluding remarks relate to the healthcare system. The decentralised, self-governing and incredibly fragmented nature of the health service in the UK makes system-level reform and improvement near impossible to achieve with any depth and speed. The levers that were once pulled in Westminster now have little to connect with. All is guidance rather than mandatory, and national policy is now translated by local power structures into wildly different neighbourhood models and applications. Money from central government rarely finds its way to its intended targets and the whole system lacks accountability. This is why we have a postcode lottery in all forms of healthcare and, most especially, in mental health, for decades the poor cousin of physical health.

Marching down Whitehall does not achieve what once it might have done owing to the devolution of government and the decentralisation of health- and social-care services into largely autonomous entities. Whilst there may be sound reasoning behind the localism agenda, its principal drawback lies in the emasculation of central government in the face of the need for wholesale improvements to crisis care – which is exactly what is required in mental health.

Thankfully, the government has just recently started to recognise this in addressing the mental health challenge. Despite my own shockingly negative experiences with the healthcare system, shared by hundreds if not thousands of other families, it remains the case that, across the country, there are excellent local services, good examples of innovation in mental healthcare and best practices involving technology, local communities, the charitable sector and private enterprise. There are also many excellent and dedicated clinicians and professionals.

It is simply not acceptable, however, that people should die in one locality when they might so easily be saved by the enhanced but unmigrated services of another locality, sometimes just across the county boundary. In honouring my promise to Edward, and with the help of some outstanding mental health leaders, I have co-founded the Zero Suicide Alliance (ZSA). Recently validated and funded by the government via the Prime Minister and Secretary of State, the ZSA, at the time of writing, has approximately 160 NHS Trusts, Clinical Commissioning Groups, Public Health Directorates and Emergency Service organisations as its membership base. Although complex, the aims of the ZSA might be summarised as simply doing what we already do best everywhere, dispelling forever the stigma of depression and mental illness, whilst simultaneously innovating new methods and models for those in need of care, especially those in crisis. A significant proportion of the healthcare system now agrees with this vision.

A great deal has changed since I lost my son to depression, much of it positive. Frontline services, however, remain woefully inadequate and that must be our next project. Until I am confident that, were my son to walk into a mental health hospital today the outcome would likely have been positive, I will stay standing squarely next to his coffin. Likewise, until I am confident that we have all understood the nature of depression as an illness and how to alleviate the suffering of the millions it affects, my promise will remain unfulfilled.

In correspondence with Downing Street after Edward died, I

said that I would tear open the sky to bring my boy back. This I cannot do. Collectively, however, we can and we must tear up the hopelessly outdated rule-book on depression and suicide, start over and build a better future.

The Grace Dear story

by Hope Dear
Co-founder of The Grace Dear Trust

The Dear family has set up a charity, The Grace Dear Trust, to remember their daughter Grace, who took her own life in 2017. Her sister, Hope, is working with her family to challenge and break the stigma around mental illness so that young people can access the help they need before it is too late.

I was a bit in awe of my sister, Grace. She was such an outgoing and bubbly person, always out with her friends and seeming to have a good time. She loved dancing and drama, and for a long time there was no outward sign of the trauma we now know she was battling with. Everyone who met Grace seemed to fall under the spell of her bubbly personality.

It was my 16th birthday, Grace was 21, when I first realised that something wasn't right. She got very drunk and her perfect mask slipped dramatically. Instead of my happy, beautiful sister, I saw a person who was out of control, screaming that she was ugly and fat. A lot of people have moments of feeling that way, but Grace's behaviour was really extreme. Sadly, it was the first of many times that I saw her like that.

I later found out that Grace had been struggling with her mental health since she was 13. She'd never opened up, probably because she didn't understand how she felt or was afraid to admit it. If only she had felt able to talk to someone, she might still be here now.

I liken Grace's illness to cancer. If we'd known about Grace's illness at stage one or two, I think her chances of recovery would have been strong. Instead, we didn't find out until stage

218

four and by then, despite treatment and the love and support of our family, it was too late.

Grace was a master at covering things up and, even though she began drinking more, she was seen as the life and soul of the party. As her behaviour became more erratic – emotional or even aggressive, especially after those nights out – she'd wake up the next day and act so normally that she almost convinced others that nothing had happened.

Grace had so much going for her – great friends, a loving family, a good job with supportive employers – but there were also clues that she was vulnerable. When relationships ended, for example, she took it particularly badly and very personally. The hurt and rejection she felt would affect her very deeply.

But even after the worst of break-ups, she always seemed to bounce back. We had no idea how much pain she was really in until she attempted to take her own life when she was 23. Typically though, she brushed it off, carried on as normal, and made everyone else feel they were making a bit of a fuss. She rejected all our efforts to help her.

She made another suicide attempt a few years later, which was terrifying. I think by then Grace had begun to realise how serious things were. Even though she thought she could cope without treatment, she let Mum accompany her to the doctor and shortly afterwards we got her admitted to a private mental health hospital, realising she needed help as quickly as possible.

Unfortunately, things didn't go as we'd planned. We put our faith in the doctors, believing they knew best, but Grace's mental health issues escalated rapidly. As a family we felt shut out by the medical team, and for Grace, being separated from us only made things worse.

Prescribed a huge amount of medication, the bubbly sister I'd once idolised so much disappeared. Instead of her being the big sister looking after me, I was the one constantly looking out for her. In the hospital, the one place where she should have been safe, she continued to harm herself. One day, when I had popped outside during visiting hours, she called me, saying 'Sorry.' I raced to her room and found her in the bathroom in a pool of blood. This was yet another attempt to take her own life, indicating just how desperate she must have been feeling.

She was discharged after three months when the health insurance had run out. She was offered three months' outpatient support, which initially helped. Sadly, after a few months, her consultant forgot about her and she felt suddenly abandoned, which is why we think she took a massive overdose of her prescribed medications.

She began to receive support from the NHS community mental health team and we did see some improvement. We started to see the old Grace again. We got her a little dog, Dora, whom she adored, and her medication was reduced. We do feel that her meds were not reduced soon enough and we believe this was because of the transition from private to NHS after the insurance funding had run out. She began to talk more, opening up about her demons, telling me how she had felt this way since she was 13. Throughout this time, though we, her family, were fully aware of what was going on, only a handful of her friends knew. She made it her own battle and barely asked for help.

Unfortunately, the problems persisted. She'd miss her appointments and, because she was an adult, we, her family, wouldn't be told this had happened. Once she said that she didn't feel she was living for herself anymore. Instead, she was keeping herself alive for us, her family. She would say, 'You have to let me go.' From then we knew it wasn't a case of 'if' she took her own life, but 'when', although of course we did everything in our power to change that.

Grace attempted to take her own life at least four times from the age of 23 and on 17 February 2017, she lost her battle with mental illness.

The pain of losing her has been agonising. We all did so much for Grace but it wasn't enough; she just couldn't be fixed.

We're now campaigning to open up the conversation around mental illness and suicide. We've set up a charity in Grace's name, the Grace Dear Trust, and we promote work in local schools to challenge and break the stigma around mental illness. Additionally, we are funding school counsellors to help get youngsters talking about their problems at a younger age, no matter how big or small, before they become more entrenched and harder to treat.

Why the focus on schools? Because if we'd managed to pick up Grace's problems at that stage in her life, her outcome might well have been very different. We know now, for example, that Grace self-harmed when she was at school and some of her friends suspected something was wrong, but they didn't know how to talk to her – or us – about it. Perhaps if there had been more awareness in schools, they would have opened up or her teachers might have noticed something was wrong and alerted our parents, allowing Grace to get help sooner. This is why we've chosen to work with local schools, to provide funding for specific mental health training courses so that staff can develop their knowledge surrounding mental illness. We also deliver monthly assemblies with guest speakers, improving mental well-being and encouraging young people to speak out about how they are feeling.

We are also striving to change the system for treating mental illness. My parents asked for an inquest after Grace's death so the issues in 'the system' that we had encountered as a family would be formally investigated and made public. We still question how she could have come out of the private hospital, where we believed she was getting the very best care, worse than she went in.

We are pushing for closer links between schools, the NHS and other stakeholders, including families, so that everyone works more closely together to tackle mental illness. It has to work better that way.

The charity's slogan is 'It's ok to not be ok'. No one should feel they have to suffer in silence.

My postnatal depression story

by Nikki Blissett
Mental health advocate, blogger and freelance writer

I'll never forget the day I discovered the depth of my depression. It was the summer of 2010 and my baby boy was 5 months old. I was walking the dog along the canal.

As I pushed the buggy, my baby slept, unaware that his mummy's soul felt crushed. I couldn't go on any longer feeling like a failure as a mother. I had wanted to be a mum for such a long time. But now I felt empty.

As I walked under a bridge, I paused. I stood by the edge of the water and watched as it rapidly flowed down stream. 'No-one will miss me,' I thought. I could leave the baby and the labrador together, safely near the bridge wall. It was a busy route, someone would come by soon and find them. It was as if my mind was being sucked down a plug-hole. Thoughts spiralled out of control. Luckily, within minutes, a couple walked past. They glanced at me briefly, which was just enough time to pop the plug in and stop the thinking. I turned around and walked straight back to the car, filled with guilt and hopelessness.

After that incident, I made an urgent appointment with the GP and was diagnosed with postnatal depression (PND).

Pregnancy and motherhood weren't anything like I had imagined. I'd read so many magazines. But I didn't glow or look cute with my bump. I was bloated, blotchy and had a painful condition called 'symphysis pubis dysfunction' (SPD). I didn't walk, I waddled. I practically needed a sling to hold my huge bump up.

Childbirth wasn't what I'd imagined either. They didn't quite explain the details in the NCT classes I attended. In fact, the classes had been more of a social exercise to meet 'mummy friends' instead of preparing you for what was about to happen.

Labour was frantic. My mum still says she'll never forget the look of terror in my eyes. I was at the hospital for just under two hours when my son ripped through me in a desperate attempt to escape. The whole thing was traumatic, including breastfeeding. I tried to feed him naturally, because it felt like anything else was frowned upon. But my baby couldn't latch. And the crying started.

He cried for three months. He had colic and was inconsolable. The crying became, and still is, an anxiety trigger. I didn't know what was wrong. I felt detached from my own baby. I went through checklists to make sure I hadn't missed something. But I felt helpless. I couldn't even feed my own baby. I felt completely out of control.

My thinking changed. Negative thoughts began to crowd my brain and I became extremely anxious. I'd never had a panic attack before, but they started becoming a regular occurrence. I became obsessed with my baby. I wouldn't let him out my sight. I hated anyone else watching him and was convinced I was the only one who could care for him, even though I also thought I was useless. I obsessively kept him clean. As he started weaning, the mess was unbearable. I kept wiping him. Washing his hands and face before he even had chance to learn what squashed banana felt like.

After I was diagnosed with PND, I felt relieved. I wasn't losing my mind. I thought I would take the antidepressants the GP had prescribed and the pain would disappear. But it didn't. I had a terrible reaction to the first antidepressants I tried. My anxiety became so bad that I trembled. I couldn't leave the house without help and I started having panic attacks in the car, making it dangerous for me to drive.

Even after changing medication, I was getting no better. The suicidal thoughts worsened. One day I handed my baby to his father, got into bed, pulled the covers over my head and gave up. I physically could not do life any longer.

I was taken to a psychiatrist who referred me urgently to a psychiatric hospital. I was terrified. I could only imagine what you saw in the movies. White cells and straitjackets. But worst of all, I had to leave my baby.

I spent two months in three different hospitals. I was pumped with high dosages of antidepressants and diazepam ('Valium'). I spent all day either crying or screaming. I moved from one group therapy session to another, feeling like a fool as I spoke about myself like this pathetic excuse of a mother. The depression got worse until one day I really did try to end it all. I still bear the scar on my arm today.

After eventually finding a medication that worked, ruling out psychotherapy and focusing on cognitive behavioural therapy (CBT) instead, I started to improve. I learnt how to start challenging my thoughts. I learnt about my core beliefs and deep-seated feelings I hadn't realise I had. As if the curtains opened on the first day of spring, light finally started to shine through. I started to engage in more positive therapies like art and writing therapy. I grew hopeful that I would eventually get better.

I look back now at my experience with postnatal depression and it sometimes feels like it wasn't me. I can't imagine thinking those darkest thoughts and acting on them. I'm so grateful I was rescued in time. It took me a long time to recover enough to consider having more children. But I'm blessed that, even though it was seven years later, I now have two beautiful little boys. I didn't experience postnatal depression with my second son. I was determined not to. I was under the watchful eye of a perinatal care team and had regular reviews and CBT sessions to challenge any worrying thoughts.

Even though I still have anxiety, PND did leave me with something positive – a renewed passion for writing. I am now a freelance writer, blogging about my own mental health experiences and encouraging others to open up about their own.

Depression is a lonely illness, but you don't have to go through it alone.

To conclude

As these stories show, suicidal thoughts and actions can affect anyone, regardless of their age, gender, social background, race or sexuality. If you are concerned about a loved one, please refer to the resources section at the back of this book for helplines and support.

Dear Suicide
By Samantha Crilly

If we fly away together, can we go as high as we can
So far away we'll lose sight of this land?
I have to admit it scares me ever so slightly
I know life on this earth isn't given out lightly
You've said it will be more peaceful where we'll end up
however, I've been told here many times I have too
much to give up
I hope you're not lying as word says you're a thief
Wearing a mask of purity to cover the muck underneath
You've made me swear not to listen to tomorrow
But it keeps telling me love still has time to grow
That there is happiness down here still waiting for me
That one day I will have the strength to set myself free
So therefore I've decided to pull out of our deal
I know I'm worth so much more than how you feel
Goodbye, I hope you keep your thoughts to yourself
and I'm looking forward to sharing tomorrow
with everyone else

Chapter 8

Depression in the under 25s

Peer pressure
By Samantha Crilly

I have never really fitted in with the 'norm'
Though I spent all my teenage years feeling under pressure
to conform
I worried so much about what everyone thought of me
I failed to be truly happy
I felt like I was uncool because I didn't do what
the 'it' girls did
I couldn't possibly just say I'm staying in tonight;
GOD FORBID!
I would sit and watch a movie which I would
normally have enjoyed
Yet I was too busy thinking I should be at all the places
I'd tried so hard to avoid
And even if I did go, I never enjoyed it anyway
I just wish I could go back in time and tell myself, it's okay
Stop being paranoid about people wondering
why you're not there
Because, truth be told, most of them don't really care
They are too busy living their own lives to be that
worried about you

So make sure you pursue whatever you want to do
and to be whoever you want to be,
because that is the only way you will ever be truly free.

We would all like to believe that someone's school days are the happiest of their life and, for many, even in today's increasingly pressured society, that does remain the case. However, for a significant number of young people, mental ill health is a reality that will sadly forever taint their experience of growing up, whether dealing with concerns at primary school, coping through adolescence at secondary level, making the hard transition to university or heading out into the 'real world' at the end of it all.

Given that the earlier we identify and help those with depression, the better their chances of recovery are, it is imperative for parents, carers, teachers and friends to have their eyes open to any potential issues that could arise during these life stages. Sadly, the statistics are alarming. Some studies show that almost one in eight young people will experience a mental illness before they are 19 years old,[49] and almost four in five teachers said that in the preceding year they had seen a pupil struggle with a mental health issue.[50] While anxiety is the most common of them all, nearly half (45%) of the 300 teachers surveyed by a mental health charity (stem4), have also encountered at least one pupil with depression.[50]

With a huge pressure on Child and Adolescent Mental Health Services (CAMHS) in many areas of the UK, there can often be a long waiting list for help and support, leaving many vulnerable young people battling on with issues that could have serious consequences for their ongoing health and happiness. It is devastating to think that young people are not getting the support and help that they need, and the impact this can also have on already over-stretched parents or carers and hard-pressed teachers.

If a child's behaviour is giving cause for concern, try not to ignore it and hope it will go away or sit back and accept the potential long wait for help and support. The longer it goes on, the more likely it is to disrupt your child's life and could potentially develop into something more sinister and result in long-term issues.

Jenny Craig, who has taught in UK schools and is now currently working in an international school in Hong Kong, says of the rise she has seen in mental illness among young people:

> I would say the depression among young people has always been there and it is due to the rise in awareness and the desire by many to address it that the issue appears more prevalent. With mental health ambassadors and so many in the public eye advocating the need to address depression and mental health, it can only be a positive to helping us all understand and be more sympathetic and proactive in addressing issues.

Depression in young children

As a parent or carer, if you think or feel something is amiss with your child then you are probably right. As a mum myself, I always say that there is nothing more powerful than a parent's intuition and love, so do not be afraid to follow and act on your instincts.

The causes of depression in young children

Depression rarely has one specific cause but is usually a combination of biological, psychological and environmental factors. It may be that a child has a biological vulnerability towards mental illness which is triggered when they experience a difficult, traumatic or confusing life event. There are some situations and events that are of particular note, which I will now endeavour to explain in more detail.

Chapter 8

Bullying

We tend to think of bullying as someone ganging up on a child in the school playground. Sadly, this is only one aspect of the issue. Bullying can happen in and out of the school environment, in a school club, online or even at the hands of a family member. Whoever it is dishing out the demeaning behaviour, the effects on the person they are targeting can be profound, making them feel isolated, worthless, lonely, anxious, angry and/or lacking in confidence.

Caroline shares the experience of her daughter:

> We have no doubt in our minds that our daughter's depression was brought on by some low-level bullying which went on over a sustained period of time, often under the teachers' radar. This made her feel low and then we believe that feeling was exacerbated by social media and before we knew it we had a 13-year-old who was suffering from mild depression and anxiety.

The crucial way to tackle bullying is to break the silence that so often surrounds it. Keeping quiet about being targeted will not stop it from happening. If you suspect a child you care for is being bullied, ask them about it and encourage them to talk about it and then to report it, whether to the school, their parent, club leader, youth worker and – in the case of online bullying – to the website or social media platform.

Arun shares his experience of how his depression was linked to childhood bullying:

> I was bullied as a young man and no matter how much I tried to avoid the topic, I realised this was the main cause of it all. I never really addressed it from a young age because I felt it was normal and my fault.

Feeling 'different'

Young people do not need to be actively bullied to suffer from low self-esteem and self-worth which could, if left unchecked, trigger a mental illness such as depression. For a fragile young mind, simply feeling 'different' may be enough to leave the person feeling adrift. It may be something visible that makes them feel at odds with others, such as a physical condition that, in their eyes, makes them different. Alternatively, they may sense a cultural separateness that they cannot ignore. Either way, this otherness can grow from a small seed of disquiet into something that dominates their life and potentially their mental health.

Sophia, who suffers from a birth deformity, shares her experience of when she was younger:

> I was never able to do what everyone else was doing or join in on most group activities. I felt this really isolated me from others. What was worse though was the feeling that I was different from everyone else and that no one wanted to be friends with me. I now know this was not the case, but at that young age I just could not help but feel that way. It really caused me to be down and have quite dark thoughts. I thankfully now am able to accept who I am.

Of course, that is not to say that 'difference' is anything to be ashamed of. Quite the contrary in society today, individuality and diversity are rightly embraced and celebrated. However, for a young child, particularly one with a poor sense of self, 'fitting in' may be something they aspire to and if they feel that they fall short of that, it could trigger difficult feelings that, in those already more vulnerable to mental illness, should be taken seriously.

Family problems

Sometimes family problems or traumatic events at home can contribute to the onset of depression in young people. It is very hard for a young brain to process some of the difficult feelings surrounding divorce, family disputes, bereavement or illness; they could bottle up those confusing emotions, possibly for fear of upsetting other family members or thinking they might somehow be making things worse. Each of these traumatic events will affect children in different ways, and there are individual organisations that can support parents in helping their children to make sense of them. If you are in the UK, organisations such as the NSPCC and Childline carry a wealth of information on their websites about how to help youngsters through these challenging times and events. Both have helplines where children and adults will find a sympathetic ear. The key for a parent or carer is not to cross your fingers and hope your youngster emerges unscathed. Instead, try to be proactive in seeking information and support and remain vigilant for signs that a child could be struggling.

Marcus shares his experience:

> My journey and struggle with depression, I have no doubt, started when my parents got divorced when I was 14. I really struggled with coming to terms with it and felt so unlucky that it had happened to me and my family. I became really jealous of all my friends whose parents were still together, and lost a few friends from this. I look back now and see I had isolated myself, making my low feelings even worse. My parents were still very united in supporting me and my older brother and got me some help, which I am so thankful for.

Social inequality

Growing up in poverty, or in a financially struggling household, can have a significant impact on a child's mental health, with some research suggesting that children in the poorest households are 'three times more likely to have a mental illness than children in the more well-off households'.[51]

Children whose families struggle to afford many of the things in life that others take for granted can grow up feeling that they are somehow a failure and inadequate and that the future is hopeless. They may feel less able to enjoy time and activities with their peers on an equal footing, leaving them feeling 'different' as discussed already. They may also feel misunderstood by others and marginalised by society as a whole. All these things can leave an early impression on a child's mental health.

Liam shares his experience:

> I grew up in quite a low-income family; a lot of my friends were from the same area and no one really had any motivation to get anywhere. I would go so far as to say that many people suffered from depression. I did too for a time, but I was one of the lucky ones and managed to get some help through my college. This was a turning point for me and I have managed to get somewhere with my life. I do feel growing up in a low-income family and being around others who have more does take a toll, especially when you are little and don't understand.

Depression and learning disabilities

Children who learn differently can be more at risk of mental illness, with up to 40% of young people with learning disabilities having a diagnosable mental health issue.[52] This is in part due to the fact that the issues that can affect anyone's mental health can be felt particularly keenly by those who have a learning difficulty or disability. Social isolation, insufficient support, feeling different from peers – as described above – and fears for the future can all play a part.

A further issue may be that symptoms of mental ill health may not be recognised as separate from the learning disability and some individuals may not be able to express those depressive feelings in the same way as others. For example, challenging behaviour may be seen as part of the learning disability rather than resulting from another cause, such as depression or anxiety; this then goes uninvestigated. Even a GP may attribute symptoms to the learning disability rather than raise concerns about mental illness.

Depression and autism spectrum conditions

People with autism are more at risk of mental illness, with suggestions that half of autistic adults have had depression.[53] This may be in part because of the challenges that many people with autism have interacting with the world around them, which can of course start from a very early age. In addition, those with autism and other related conditions, who often rely on a predictable routine, can be particularly prone to anxiety if the structure to their life is altered or upset. If this anxiety is not addressed, it could trigger further issues, including depression.

Many people find it hard to talk about their mental health and this can be even more challenging for people with autism, who may struggle to recognise their feelings initially and find it particularly difficult to communicate them. Even visiting the doctor can be a source of great stress and anxiety to people on the autistic spectrum and so accessing appropriate help and support can sometimes be an even harder mountain to climb.

Autism is a lifelong condition, so these issues are not simply a concern of childhood. However, it is important for carers to recognise the increased risk of mental illness in both adults and children on the autistic spectrum so that they know what symptoms to look out for and what help is available. Organisations such as the National Autistic Society (autism.org. uk) for readers in the UK give more detailed information.

Faith, whose son has autistic disorder, says of how her son struggles with low mood:

His low moods began when he started in education and being around other children. He struggles to communicate properly and other children tend to be wary of this. It is so hard, as a parent, to watch; I can see when he is trying to interact with other children and they dismiss him, the sadness in his face is devastating; he can retreat to his room when he is at home and get into a depressed state. He is getting help, which seems to be working. I just hope he can find happiness in who he is.

Talking to your child about mental health

Due to their immaturity, most children suffering from depression will have difficulty in knowing how to talk and communicate about what is going on inside their head. They may be confused, embarrassed and unable to process and understand the content of their thoughts. The most effective way to help them is through communication.

If your child is finding it difficult to verbalise their thoughts, encouraging them to draw or write down how they are feeling can sometimes be used as a different form of communication which can be just as effective as talking. This could help both of you to develop a better understanding of what is going on inside the young person's head.

Another way to help your child open up is to use role play. Pretending to act out a difficult scenario, perhaps with the adult taking the place of the child and demonstrating what he or she would say in certain situations, can help children understand how to react to difficult situations in their life.

Through drawing or acting, or even singing a song or making up an expressive dance, you can give youngsters the confidence to open up about their feelings and emotions that may be connected to, or could lead to, depression. With this in mind, it is important to pick the right moment and location and it should be at a time and in a place where they feel relaxed, safe and secure.

Depression in teenagers

The causes of depression in teenagers include the factors already covered when discussing younger children: bullying, social isolation, problems at home, learning difficulties, autism and social inequality, as well as having other mental illnesses as covered in Chapter 6. There are, however, further issues relevant to teenagers that could have an impact on their mental health. These include:

- pressure to succeed
- sexuality and relationships
- abuse and neglect
- drugs and alcohol
- acne, and
- dealing with the pressures of social media.

All of these are exacerbated by the maelstrom of change caused by puberty. Caroline shares the start of her daughter's depression:

She had managed to settle into secondary school well and was a happy, well-adjusted 13 year old but half way through her second year at senior school all of this changed. One of her close friends started being unkind to her. It really was just childish things: speaking to her one day and not speaking to her the next; making snide remarks to her in the classrooms; a little bit more rough in sports lessons than she needed to be; putting her down in front of others; cutting her out of conversations. All of this went on over several months and our daughter started feeling displaced at school and insecure about herself.

We knew it was being at school that was making her feel low because during school holidays she would bounce back and be her usual self. However, over time this started changing and it was taking longer and longer in the holidays to get her back to feeling herself. She went back to school in September a little anxious but generally in good spirits and the same behaviour started again with this one girl.

Some time over the next couple of months she decided to open up a social media account. She started comparing her life with others' on there and was able to see when others from school had got together and she hadn't been invited along. She started feeling insecure about her body. She didn't feel she looked as good as all the other girls. She became very critical of herself and then over the next couple of months she went downhill very, very quickly. It hadn't really crossed our minds that she was suffering from depression.

Puberty

Teenage angst is a very common issue in pubescent young adults as they struggle to get to grips with the rapid hormonal and physical changes that their bodies are being subjected to. Someone who was once a sociable, relatively happy and engaging child can quickly become subdued, dramatic, over-sensitive, self-conscious, short-tempered and distant. These are all normal shifts in adolescence, as teenagers naturally try to find their own platform and independence, detached from the usual securities of their family unit.

At the same time, huge hormonal and brain changes are underway, often throwing logical reasoning off-kilter and opening the door to confusing and sometimes irrational thought processes. Most teenagers will experience short-lived episodes of angst as they navigate their way through the challenging cross-over from childhood to being a young adult, and emotions such as sadness, anxiety and frustration will occasionally come to the fore. Problems at school or with friendships and relation-ships can often be the main culprits, but usually these periods of anguish only last for a short period of time.

It is incredibly hard to differentiate between what is normal behaviour for a teenager and what is not, but generally any prolonged and repeated episodes could be early warning signs of a more chronic problem, such as a mental health issue.

Charliee, who suffers from bipolar disorder, echoes this:

> My school notified my family that they were concerned about my low mood. I first self-harmed when I was 13 and every school I attended (four secondary schools) ignored the symptoms of what was a very obvious mental health illness. I was 'tested' for ADHD three times as they believed that I was just 'badly behaved' rather than trying to discover the underlying problem. I don't really remember being aware of depression but looking back I can see that it wasn't normal behaviours for a teenager of that age.

Pressure to succeed

The pressure to conform to a certain ideal is felt particularly strongly during adolescence, and not least because young people can feel that success has to be achieved, no matter what the personal cost. Elaine, who suffers from severe depression, looks back on the pressure she felt to succeed from a young age:

> I had both anorexia and clinical depression at age 13 onwards. There was always pressure in my family to succeed and nothing less than perfection was good enough. I was a people-pleaser and put others before myself. I started to withdraw and only went out of my house if I really needed to. I closed the curtains and would stay there where I felt safe. When around others I put a show on and was the life and soul of the party... the funny one... but this was an act.

There can be pressure to get good exam results, to achieve on the sporting field, to get into a certain school set or to move onto a particular college or university. Not achieving these things can leave a young person feeling that they are somehow lacking and that they must be to blame.

Michael, who has suffered depression, anxiety and PTSD, speaks of the pressure he felt:

When the exam results came through, the shame and embarrassment on my conscience were unbearable. This was the earliest memory of maybe feeling or experiencing depression, which was more than feeling sad or upset. Day after day, week after week, ruminating about wishing I could have done better; but I couldn't – that was my best. But I felt a failure in my parents' eyes, a feeling which I still hold to this day, though to a lesser extent now.

Sexuality and relationships

It is hard to escape the subject of sex in today's society. For teenagers trying to understand their own sexuality at this time in their lives, it can for some feel unsurprisingly overwhelming. Coming to terms with sexuality, relationships and early heartbreak are among the most testing teenage experiences. For those with low self-esteem or who are vulnerable to mental illness, issues around sexuality can add significant extra pressure.

The situation can be exacerbated for those questioning their sexuality or their gender. Although society is becoming more understanding and accepting of sexual diversity, there is little doubt that those who are gay, bisexual or transsexual face greater challenges to their mental health. In an NHS survey, more than a third of young people aged 14 to 19-years-old who identified as gay, bisexual or with another sexual identity had a mental disorder, as opposed to 13% of those who identified as hetero-sexual.[54]

Aaron shares his own experience:

My depression has been such a bumpy ride. I first noticed it when I was at secondary school; all through college, I just couldn't pin-point what was wrong with me. When I went off to university, I came to realise that it was because I was living a life that was not me. I was gay, I just didn't 100% know it, or I didn't want to admit it. I actually found a partner at university which really helped me with my own feelings. The thing I was most worried about was how to tell my parents. I had formulated a scenario in my head that my parents would disown me and I would be left with no one. This caused me to fall into a pit of depression. I saw a therapist at university who really encouraged me to speak with my parents, which finally, after two years, I did. I have not looked back. They were very shocked but it felt like a massive weight off my shoulders... My low moods and dark thoughts gradually faded.

Abuse and neglect

If a child is being physically, mentally or sexually abused, the effects will manifest themselves in different ways, one of which may be as mental health problems. Someone who has been abused can often struggle with depression as an adult in later life, but of course, the impact can also be much more immediate.

Lia, who has suffered from major depression and anxiety from the age of 15, shares her own experience:

My parents hated each other and the household was an abusive one from the day dot. Suffering through this alone rendered my childhood different and this, alongside having to conceal such abuse and hardship, led to an explosion that manifested itself through depression, anxiety and anorexia in later life. With my parents not caring when they did discover my suffering, and treatment not working for so many years, the suffering has been prolonged, continuing to where I am today.

If you have concerns about a child and you are in the UK, the NSPCC website has lots of good advice about what you can do. The most important thing is to keep lines of communication open, taking the child's lead in the conversations you have together. By showing the child or young adult that they can talk to you and that you will listen, you are giving them the green light to open up further as and when they are ready.

Kimberly Lucas, personal advisor for social services, says:

Working with care leavers who have experienced a lot of different types of trauma and mental health problems, I can see so clearly how young people have slipped through the cracks. The complexity of the individuals who come to my attention often means that they cannot sustain support for their mental health through agencies, often because they cannot remember appointments or their chaotic lifestyle means that they struggle to engage. Although conversations are being had around mental health and the focus is on early intervention, there is lack of resources to meet everyone's needs as it cannot be that one size fits all; this leads to many young people having their cases closed after a referral, which means they often begin to use negative coping strategies, including substance misuse, which can increase their experiences of mental ill health.

Drugs and alcohol

It is natural for teenagers to want to try new things, to push boundaries and to take risks, and as such many will experiment with smoking, drinking and taking drugs. Individual families will have their own views on this, but if you are worried about your child or feel they are using alcohol or drugs as part of a mental health issue, it is paramount not to ignore it.

Parents who can talk openly and honestly about alcohol and drugs, making it part of everyday chat rather than a huge one-off conversation, will be showing by example that their door is always open and that the subject is not taboo. Discussing all aspects of drinking and drug-taking, including how mental health can be affected by drinking too much or using drugs, will help them to make safe and healthy decisions.

If you fear your child is making unhealthy choices around substance use (including alcohol), do not hesitate in seeking help. Your GP should be a good first stop and they should be able to point you in the right direction of another organisation that can help.

As a parent or carer, it is also important to bring your own knowledge about illegal drugs up to date, including the effects of taking them, so that if necessary you are able to talk from a position of some authority. Nikki, who has suffered with dark thoughts from the age of around 15, looks back at when they started:

> When I look back, the negative thinking and suicidal thoughts started when I was around 15 or 16. It did coincide with me starting to smoke weed with my friends. While I am not 100% sure whether the two are linked, I was an outgoing, chirpy young child until I hit my teenage years and then my mind started becoming darker.

Acne

According to the NHS, acne affects around 80% of teenagers and young adults age 11 to 30 in the UK, and in some cases it is severe and can continue into adult life. Around 5% of women and 1% of men over the age of 25 suffer from acne. Anyone who has suffered from a skin issue will most likely say that it is much more than just skin deep.

A study has shown that the risk for major depression was highest within a year of an acne diagnosis,[55] this is a 63% higher risk compared with individuals without acne. The outcomes of this study signpost how important it is that both professionals and the loved ones around the sufferer monitor mood symptoms in those with acne and initiate treatment if the sufferer is displaying signs of depression or another mental illness.

Carla shares her experience of suffering from severe acne when she was a teenager:

> My acne started flaring up from the age of around 11 or 12. It wasn't just a pimple here and there, but was all over my face. I used to wake up everyday with five new spots. They were also very painful, and it got so bad I could barely open my mouth to eat. I was on antibiotics on and off for eight years; every time I went to come off them it came up again almost overnight. It

was just awful. People used to stop me in the street and ask what had happened to my face. My heart would drop and I would feel so small and disgusting. I also handed in my notice at work because I was so embarrassed about how awful my skin was. It really affected my confidence and caused me to not want to leave the house. I finally went on a stronger medication, but one of the side-effects of the medication was depression... however, I was already depressed, so what did I have to lose? It took around three months to work, but as soon as I started seeing a different in my skin, my mood started lifting. Acne is so much more than just a physical thing; it affected my whole life.

Social media

There are few teenagers who are not in thrall to social media. Fuelled by their desire for approval and admiration from friends (and strangers) as well as a very 21st-century 'affliction' known as Fear of Missing Out (FOMO), from when they get their first smartphones – often around the age of 10 or 11 – many spend hours on social media sites every day.

While on the one hand the sense of community and shared interaction with others can be beneficial, there are also undoubted downsides to heavy social media use, with a link to poor mental health being one of the key concerns. We will explore this in far more depth in Chapter 11, but suffice it to say that teenagers, with their fragile egos and frail self-esteem, are particularly vulnerable to the feelings of inadequacy that all of us, of any age, experience when faced with the seemingly perfect lives that people post online. Furthermore, the time they spend on their devices scrolling through these styled images and carefully curated posts is time they are not spending having the face-to-face conversations that are vital for mental well-being.

Jenni Philipps, deputy safe guarding lead at Oak Academy in Bournemouth, says:

Young people are becoming addicted to social media and being 'in the loop' with their peers. With a smart phone, you can be contacted 24/7 and you can't escape it unless you delete your account or return back to an old school Nokia 3210!

We now have a culture where it is socially acceptable to document your entire day on your Snapchat or Instagram story and show 'highlights' of it. The reality is that some young people don't always have a highlight to their day that they deem acceptable to post as they may fear they will be made fun of by their peers.

Hannah Arbuckle, a primary school teacher, shares her thoughts on younger children and the effects on them of awareness of depression on social media:

I think the internet and social media enable children to see more on depression – what it is, what it does and some websites. I feel it also glorifies depression somewhat and children are very influenced and use the term more openly and freely, not fully understanding what true depression actually entails. On the other hand, some children are more encouraged to discuss their inward battles which can be a good stepping stone to helping to cure or support any issues they are experiencing.

Signs to look for

When looking for signs of depression (or anxiety or another mental illness) some valuable things to consider include:

- Have you noticed a sadness or low mood that does not seem to go away?
- Are they irritable and have they lost interest in things they used to enjoy?
- Do they go out less with their friends?
- Do they seem to be exhausted a lot of the time?
- Do they have trouble sleeping or sleep more than usual?
- Has their confidence taken a dip?

- Do they talk about feeling guilty, worthless or hopeless, or seem lacking in emotion?
- Do they talk about hurting themselves or show any signs of self-harm?
- Are they having problems at school or playing up, getting themselves into trouble?

How to talk to your teenager about mental health

The difficulty in separating and identifying a mental illness, especially in a teenager, is that teenagers can seem reluctant to openly communicate with those closest to them, thus making an accurate diagnosis quite challenging. Confronting them head-on and throwing specific questions at them, such as 'Are you depressed?' or 'Have you self-harmed?' may be counterproductive, causing them to clam up, run away or shout back. Instead, creating an environment where they feel trusted, safe and respected is much more likely to help them open up.

This means making mental health a subject that you talk about little and often. It is just as important as physical health and if we can begin to talk about it in the same way as we do other illnesses it will not be pushed to one side and potentially get worse. It also means that youngsters are less likely to bottle it up because they will not have fears about how you may react.

There will be times when you have specific issues to address and where and when you to do this is up to you, but choose a place to talk where they feel relaxed and unpressurised. Some parents find that a car journey can be a good place to conduct tricky conversations, allowing youngsters to talk without the full glare of their parents' attention on them. Adults too may feel more at ease than they might do facing their teenager over the kitchen table or in the naturally defensive environment of the teen's bedroom. Talking on a car journey also makes it harder to slam doors or storm out!

Sometimes something you read in a magazine or see on TV will provide the perfect starting point for a conversation. It might be a character on a soap opera highlighting an issue, or a report on the news about the stress young people are under. This is when the media can be used to positive effect as the starting point for a chat about mental health.

Wherever and whenever you decide to talk, start the conversation without accusation or assumption (not least because you may find that you have jumped to the wrong conclusion) and try to ask open questions rather than homing in on specific issues. This might mean opening up the conversation by saying something like 'You have been very quiet lately... is something troubling you?' or 'You do not seem yourself recently, is there anything wrong?' Their answer may not come during that conversation or even soon after, but by opening up the discussion you are showing to them that you are there to help, whenever they feel ready to talk. When they do feel able to open up, the key is to listen. Do not assume that you know what they are going to say or leap in and pretend you have all the answers. Instead really hear what they are saying about their own situation and equip them to find a way forward with your help.

Abigail talks of when she spoke to her son about his mental health worries:

> The first time I tried to speak to my son, I regret that I think I jumped in too quickly to a conclusion that he wasn't ready for. I then slowly planted seeds so he knew he could talk to me when he was ready. It was an extremely slow and painful winter; however, he then came to me and said he needed to talk, we had a very open and honest conversation and agreed we would look into getting him professional help. I am so pleased I decided to then give him the space and time to come to me himself, I do however think if it had gone on much longer, I would have needed to intervene somehow.

It is important not to judge your teenager, even if you do not necessarily agree with what they are telling you. Even though your mind may be racing and your heart hammering, it is important to stay calm. When they are looking to you for guidance, showing panic will only unsettle your teen further. Perhaps you can share a situation in your own life where you felt worried or stressed to show them that their feelings are understandable and natural.

It often helps teenagers to feel that they can help themselves, so part of your role may be giving them the tools to do this. Once they start talking to you, help them identify what they can do to help. Say to them: 'When you feel that way, what kind of things could you do to make things feel better?' and you can perhaps help them think of sports, hobbies or other activities that they find calming or confidence-building. You can also point them towards books, websites, podcasts and health information that they can read and digest in their own time, filling them with knowledge that in time they can use to feel more in control of their own well-being.

I make it sound relatively straightforward but, of course, when teenage hormones are mixed with the maelstrom of emotions that accompany any mental health concern, there will be many twists and turns and cross words along the way. Remembering that teenagers often hit out at those that they love and trust the most – especially when they feel confused, scared and unsure about the future – may help you to stay calm during the most testing times.

At the same time, do all you can to increase their resilience to the pressures they are facing. Help them sleep better, eat well and take regular exercise. Encourage them to spend less time on their devices and get out and about, continue to see family and friends and make time for doing things together, even if it is just taking the dog for a walk or making a cake together.

And finally, do not forget yourself in all this. The role that you play, as a parent or carer, can be one of a child's most important defences again mental ill health. Make time for yourself and get support from friends, family, loved ones or colleagues, and your GP if necessary. Looking after yourself and acknowledging how you feel is vital for you to be able to support your child.

Teachers are well placed to spot the early signs

Depression can affect anyone regardless of age, gender, sexuality, social background and / or ethnicity; however, families and carers should be particularly alert during adolescence. It is essential for us to try to understand how the secondary school years can have an impact, and how head teachers, teachers and support staff are in a pivotal position to recognise the signs and symptoms and in turn, the potential onset of depression, enabling them to trigger the early intervention which is so key in tackling this and other mental illnesses successfully.

Hope Dear from the Grace Dear Trust tells us why they are concentrating on giving teachers training in recognising mental ill health symptoms:

Grace [Hope's sister] had been suffering with depression and anxiety from the age of 13, but hadn't felt she could reach out to anyone to help her make sense of her feelings.

Not knowing why, she suffered in silence for many years. Eventually when Grace spoke out, we tried to give the best help possible, but unfortunately it was too late.

We are working collaboratively with local schools, to educate and inform teachers on the signs and symptoms of mental illness and what to look out for. As Grace was in school for the most part when she was suffering, we feel that if those around her were more educated on what to look for, her suffering could have been picked up much sooner than it was.

Of course, teachers are in school to teach and with increasingly stretched budgets and the pressure for their students to perform, their jobs appear harder than ever. However, they are also human beings and if faced with a student who they are concerned about may have a mental illness such as depression, few would, I am sure, turn their backs. However, they are rarely mental health experts – and no one expects them to be.

Melissa Helliwell, assistant vice principal at Oak Academy in Bournemouth, shares her thoughts below:

Schools are no longer only places for education; they are the main hub for all multi-agency support referrals. Increased funding cuts, pressure for progress and achievement, sparse training for all and a lack of time do little to support mental health concerns within some schools.

It may therefore be helpful to note the signs of depression that may become particularly noticeable in the school environment. Causes for concern may include the following. The teenager may:

- perform less well, dropping grades or struggling to complete their work
- display poor timekeeping or increased absentism.
- appear lacking in energy
- start to isolate themselves
- struggle to concentrate in class
- show signs of tiredness and irritability
- show signs of low confidence and self-esteem
- set themselves unreasonably high standards.

How teachers can help

School staff can not only play an important role in noticing the signs of depression, which can hopefully lead to early intervention, but also a trusted teacher could be the person that a student confides in if they are worried about their own mental health. With around three children in every classroom affected by a mental health issue,[56] it is a good first step for a teacher to make sure they are familiar with their school's mental health policy, if indeed there is one. That way they will know what to do if the issue arises with one of their students.

Former college lecturer, Nicholas Warburton, shares the experience below of how best to support a pupil with a mental health issue:

I would speak to the student to initially confirm any suspicions of depression. This might be during or after a class, or in a personal tutorial. If already diagnosed with depression, then it will depend on the education establishment's policies and procedures as to the level of involvement at which staff can assist the student.

If there is an Action Plan in place set by the college, then the staff member will follow those particular guidelines. At an individual level then it will be a case of being vigilant as to any changes or extremes of behaviour, observing class interaction/ dynamics and also any changes in quality or quantity of work produced. It will also depend on how much is kept confidential. Communication is key.

If you are a teacher and a student does open up to you about a mental health issue, the most important thing to do is take the time to listen to them. It may have taken them a long time to muster up the courage to approach you and so it is vital to demonstrate that what they are saying matters. If you need to tell someone else about what they have told you, try to let the student know who that person is and explain why you need to talk to them so that the student will not feel that you have betrayed their trust.

Jenni Philipps, deputy safe guarding lead, Oak Academy in Bournemouth, confirms this:

Within my role I currently support many young people struggling to manage their mental health and those with a diagnosis of depression. I always offer a judgement-free and safe environment for them to come and speak to me if they would like to and regularly link with their families and exter-nal agencies to develop a support package tailored to their needs.

Good days needs to be celebrated and on the darker days, the safety net of support is always available and I believe it's vital that young people know the support is consistent.

I also believe it is important for someone with depression to know that it is ok not to be ok and to feel listened to. The pain they are experiencing is frightening and at times can be overwhelming so to feel that others are there is vital and cannot be taken for granted.

In some cases it may be necessary to seek extra help outside the school community and that could include a referral to Child and Adolescent Mental Health Services (CAMHS). Each school will have a policy on this and will have a staff member assigned to make a CAMHS referral if necessary.

Jane Tomlinson, inclusion manager at a secondary school in the UK, shares her thoughts:

There have been many opportunities for me with regard to training, as this is pivotal to my role. I have received training for specific conditions such as OCD, Eating Disorders and ASD [autism spectrum disorder] and the impact that these conditions have on the person.

I would describe the training as basic and the idea is to raise awareness and spot specific signs. In order to fully support the children, I liaise very closely with CAMHS and the school nursing/GP service.

My concern is that teaching staff within their training receive little infor-mation on spotting the signs of mental health and I do feel that many become reliant on the expertise and experience of others in school who support in a pastoral/welfare/safeguarding role.

Lessons in prevention

A school's role is not just to act when they are concerned or worried about a pupil. It is also to educate, inform and support them throughout their education, helping to nurture their confidence so that they can grow up with a strong sense of self. Good self-esteem and a confidence in one's own abilities is a powerful defence against a mental illness such as depression and schools have an important – and wonderful – role to play in strengthening that armour that will protect their pupils throughout their life.

Melissa Helliwell, assistant vice principal at Oak Academy in Bournemouth, confirms this:

> I personally take an interest in this area of our young people's lives as without understanding this, we cannot help students to achieve their potential or encourage them to understand how valued they are. Many believe that they are not 'worthy' and as a result then hurt themselves in a myriad of different ways; sadly, both physically and psychologically.

There are many opportunities throughout the curriculum to help young people grow a knowledgeable, confident and resilient attitude towards themselves. From PSHE lessons through to PE, there are many opportunities to discuss good mental health and well-being.

Through involving pupils in discussions about mental illness, schools can help all young people to be aware of these issues which can both help them recognise and understand problems in themselves or in their friends.

Jenny Craig, who has taught in UK schools and is now currently working in an international school in Hong Kong, finishes with her passion:

> I have come across many students who have suffered from mild to severe depression. With families who have also suffered from long-term mental

health issues, I am acutely aware of how important it is to support as much as possible the child and the family. The lack of support from the school and from medical services when I was younger angers me, but spurs me on to ensure that nobody in my care should ever be left to manage without support.

Depression among teachers

Bigger class sizes, increased paperwork, budget pressures and a workload that feels relentless, are all factors that can take their toll on teaching staff. As a result, the number of teachers with mental health issues is reaching worrying levels. In 2017, 3,750 teachers were signed off on long-term sick leave, because of the pressure of work, anxiety and mental illness.[57]

Many teachers would claim that the most obvious way forward is to reduce the workload placed on their shoulders, leading to better retention of their colleagues and less pressure of those in the profession, but they also know that change may be slow to come.

In the more immediate future, teachers can take steps to cocoon their own mental health, nurturing their own well-being to make them more resilient to the pressures exerted by their work. Measures can include:

- Increasing the amount of exercise they take
- Decreasing the level of caffeine, sugar and other artificial stimulants they may consume
- Finding a relaxation exercise that they enjoy and can maintain
- Getting rest at home, with time away from both work and technology
- Eating well-balanced meals
- Prioritising time for fun and hobbies away from work (I know this may be easier said than done!).

The leaders in a school have an important role to play in both recognising the pressures their staff are under and responding to that stress with practical measures that foster a supportive environment. Examples of better practice may include leaving a week or two each term free of meetings to give teachers extra time to complete their work. As often as possible meetings could be held within the working day rather than before or after school. Regular forums where staff can honestly air issues may be helpful. It should also help if emails sent in the evenings or at weekends are kept to a minimum so that teachers do not feel compelled to respond during their hard-earned free time. With all this in mind, the happier and more positive the teachers feel within themselves, in theory, should create a more optimistic learning atmosphere for the students.

There is more information about how to cope with the pressures of the teaching profession on the website of the Education Support Partnership, a charity providing health and well-being help to those working in the sector.

Nicholas Warburton, a former college lecturer, and former sufferer of depression, says the below:

> Does depression apply to every teacher? The answer is No. It will depend on the person's character, their working environment and their home environment. The more that is understood about depression, the more chance we have to recognise the signs and avoid it. This is something that can be put in place relatively easily for both staff and students, but I fear this is still a long way off.

Depression at university

The move from school to university can be a difficult one to make, involving leaving home for the first time, meeting new people, facing unknown experiences and having to take control of their own finances – and own life – for the first time. It is no wonder that this can be a particularly challenging time for those with mental illness or those vulnerable to developing one. In a survey by the Mental Health Foundation, possible clinical depression was found in 12% of male and 15% of female students.[58]

While some students adjust with apparent ease to the transition, others may feel overwhelmed with the new responsibilities they face. Most expect university to be the best days of their life and if it feels very differently, they may find themselves struggling.

Pete shares his experience of being at university:

I can now see that I started to experience symptoms during my first term at university in 1991 and that those symptoms came and went frequently during my time there. I could sense for years that something was wrong but couldn't quite work out what it was. It was as though the black dog was following me but ducked out of view whenever I turned round to look at it. It was not until 1999, at the age of 26, that I received a diagnosis of depression. At the time, I knew very little about the illness and it was very difficult to talk about at work and with friends and family.

All this can be made worse by the move away from home and the seismic change that this brings to all areas of their life. Without the support circle of family and established friendships, it can be easy to feel very isolated. Furthermore students are often drinking too much and may be experimenting with drugs. They are likely to be anxious about money and feeling pressure to justify the huge cost of this investment in their education and they are also facing the weight of expectation that university days are supposed to be the best days of their life. All this can make a pretty perfect recipe for anxiety and/or depression.

It can also be very hard to find someone to trust and confide in, within the new and unfamiliar environment. Which can mean that those battling a mental illness can often find themselves suffering in silence, their anxiety or dark thoughts steadily gaining control often without anyone really noticing.

Chapter 8

Universities have increasing awareness of their responsibilities towards students with mental illness; however, the nature of college and university life, where individuals can so easily slip under the radar, makes providing a safety net for the most vulnerable students more challenging.

I would urge parents or carers who have a niggling concern about their loved one not to ignore it, even – or maybe especially – if they no longer live at home. Make regular visits to your child, talk to them often, encourage them to share their worries or concerns, and follow your instinct if you feel that something is amiss.

Encourage them to take part in university life – to go to lectures, get involved in clubs, hang out in the library or coffee shop, where others are. Locking themselves in their small student room could only make things worse. Also remind them that there is life outside the university walls and urge them to find out what else the city where they are studying has to offer beyond that slightly unreal bubble of student life.

It is also helpful to remember that every university will have a counselling service which is usually free and which is very used to listening to students facing some of these challenges. Encourage them to seek help or visit their GP to tackle their concerns before they escalate.

Trainee teacher and current university student Alice gives her advice:

Often student teachers are put under extra pressure as they have to study full-time for the teaching degree but also spend time at school placements learning about new subjects and plan classes under observation. This can be challenging on your mental health, so it is crucial for student teachers to be able to talk to each other about their difficulties and also take advantage of the mental health well-being services available to them at university.

Finally, remind your student son or daughter that university life often does not live up to the hype, that it is not unusual to feel sad, lonely, homesick and/or excluded. However, at the same time, do not write off those feelings as 'normal' in case that stops them from seeking help. Encourage them to keep talking to you about how they feel and give them the details of the university counselling service so that they know there is somewhere they can go to for help.

Depression after education

While going on to further education can be hard, so can leaving school or university for the 'real world'. Without the shared experience that education can give someone, it can be all too easy to feel alone and adrift. Problems can feel unique to them and that the battles they face appear to be ones they must tackle alone. However, while it may feel that way, it is possible to find the people who can walk forward with us and help make us feel less alone.

Arun shares how he found the university to 'real life' transition difficult:

> I become fully aware of my depression once I graduated from university and it was time to become an adult and live in the real world. I realised I had neglected myself, what I had gone through and began to lose focus and stop myself from crashing and burning.

It can be particularly testing for those who are looking for work. Many graduates find themselves living back with their parents, often feeling that they have lost the independence and freedom that they built up away from home. Friends may now be a long way away and it can be easy to wallow in that old mental health adversary, loneliness. Without the structure of school or university, the days can seem directionless. Without a job, it can feel like the months stretch on ahead with no real plan. This emptiness can be very hard to get to grips with.

Patrick shares his experience when he was due to finish university:

> Uni for me was a great experience, there was not too much pressure on my course, I had my student loan, I didn't really have to worry about much. I was coming towards the halfway point of my final year and it suddenly hit me: what am I going to do when it is all over, a job isn't guaranteed, I have to go back home and live with my parents, it was almost as if I was going back 3 years. I really struggled with completing my final course work and dissertation, I felt as though all my motivation had gone, I just couldn't stop that feeling of emptiness after university was over. My parents realised something had changed in me, which I am grateful for as they really helped me to work out what the next steps were, which ultimately was what I needed to move on with my life in a good and positive way.

Even for those who do secure a job, the reality of working life can be very different from the fantasy they may have harboured for many years. In place of the great pad and smart wardrobe, maybe a dingy flat-share and living on a starting salary, yet more money worries. After years of dreaming about being grown-up, it can often be a shock to find it is not as they had imagined. If you add in the stress of possibly moving to a new city, meeting new people and probably burning the candle at both ends, it can be easy to understand why these years can be difficult to handle.

As always, the role of family and friends is never-ending. Instead of assuming you have got your loved one 'off your hands', check in on them as much as you can. In these years when they are learning to 'run' without your hand to hold, they may find themselves 'stumbling' or even 'falling over'. Reminding them they are not alone, acknowledging how difficult this time of their life can be and showing them where they can find help, is essential for nurturing their mental health and helping them deal with difficult thoughts and feelings. If you have real concerns about their state of mind, encourage them to talk to their GP or seek further professional help, and monitor them as closely as you are able.

To conclude

It is essential that everyone involved in the life of a young person or indeed anyone suffering from depression employs compassion, understanding and patience. In this way, home, schools, clubs, colleges and universities can become an effective part of the caring network for young people struggling with depression.

Throughout this book I have been careful to emphasise that depression does not affect just the young. However, sometimes the underlying issues can begin to develop and form at this crucial age. Schools, colleges and universities are all environments where depression can take root. Where schools can, they should incorporate self-esteem into their programme – and preferably from an outside speaker. I say this not because I believe teachers are ill-equipped to deal with the issues, but because I know that young people will often open up to a stranger, safe in the knowledge that they will never see that person again.

There is much more work being done to challenge and break the taboo around mental illness. My Samantha, a recent drama graduate, has joined with friends to develop a funny and thought-provoking sketch show challenging and breaking that stigma. Through her work with 'My Mental Life', she is turning the illness that once tormented her on its head, using humour to educate others.

I applaud her and all others working to support those tortured by mental illness including depression, and hope that many more people will take the opportunity to understand how sufferers feel, and find out more about what they can do to help.

Chapter 9

Depression in the home

Modern everyday life can be incredibly stressful. Every generation that has ever existed has probably said the same thing; however, that does not make it any less true. Today, the expectations of what family and personal life should be like are completely different from how they were even 30 or 40 years ago.

The planet is forever changing, technology is advancing, and the population is continuing to expand. In the UK we undoubtedly have more freedom of choice and are less confined to the traditional gender roles than in previous generations. Whilst these advances are generally to be embraced, within relationships and the home environment, some of the realities of contemporary culture may prove to be inadvertently damaging.

We cannot control the challenges and misfortunes that come our way, but we can control how we deal with them and how we allow them to affect our relationships with those around us. Generally, everything is okay in moderation. We do not have to allow ourselves to be glued to our devices 24/7, we do not have to allow ourselves to make the wrong dietary choices for our brain's well-being and balance, we do not have to allow ourselves to be made to feel inadequate by the riches of others and, whilst we would like a better future for our planet, we need to try to understand that it is a global effort, not the weight of the world on one person's (our) shoulders.

How we navigate our lives greatly affects how we manage our relationships with others. Within a family/partnership, it is quite normal to have fraught and challenging times as individuals, all with different personalities and needs, jostle to find their own voice and be heard, all together, under one roof, and this is without having someone with depression, or indeed any mental illness, thrown into the mix.

When living and coping with the dreadful effects of a loved one who has depression, it can put an enormous strain on personal and professional relationships and the toll it can take on all concerned can be devastating.

Amber, whose husband has now recovered from depression, shares her journey:

> My husband went into a very dark part of his life. He wouldn't speak to any of us and wouldn't come home until gone midnight every night. We all really wanted to help him, but he seemed to have turned into someone none of us knew anymore. He gradually lost all his friends and the relationship with his children was impacted. Thankfully one day there was a turning point; none of us know what caused it to happen, but he gradually began to come back to us and we are so grateful for this.

Every day within my work I see the shattering effects that mental illness can have on the sufferer and their loved ones and every day I am continually confronted by the pain and trauma that mental illness can bring to the home environment and everyone in it. I have seen and experienced at first hand how it can rip families apart and drive a wedge through once solid relationships, bringing them crashing to their knees.

I will never forget when Samantha was in the throes of her eating disorder and OCD, my husband Kevin described our everyday family life as being like someone was picking our house up each morning and giving it a good shake, bringing mindboggling chaos and turmoil with it for the rest of the day, until bedtime once again restored the peace and calm... until the next day when the whole cycle would begin again! Equally, I can speak at first hand from my own experience and that of my daughter Samantha, that with the right support, understanding, patience and unconditional love, the damage can, in time, be repaired and family dynamics restored, bringing family members closer together, more united and stronger than they had ever been. My family is a real example of this.

I do though recognise that when 'depression' comes into your life, trying to live in a united household can seem very much easier said than done. It is true that family life will be disrupted and everybody within it will have to make some changes and sacrifices to accommodate the ongoing recovery of the person suffering from depression.

How people act and react around someone with depression can also be an important part of the sufferer's recovery. Trying to strengthen family relationships and promote genuine acceptance, understanding and co-operation within the household can be a challenging task – especially for the person trying to facilitate it. I have listed below some suggestions and ideas to help cope with the many challenges of living with someone who has depression or who may be at risk of developing it.

Recognise the warning signs

As we already know, depression is a serious mental illness, which, is not always visible or easy to identify. Being alert to any early warning signs can be of paramount importance to the sufferer as the sooner your loved one/friend receives the right help, the more positive the outcome is likely to be for all involved, particularly the person with depression.

In my personal and professional opinion, behavioural

changes are one of the biggest signs that something is amiss. As busy as family life can be, it is vital not to dismiss any changes that could quite easily be passed off as 'just their personality'; with hindsight, looking back, many carers say that their loved one became withdrawn, forgetful, emotional, angry and/or pre-occupied before their illness became obvious. This is important because these are the outward signs of the turmoil that the sufferer is fighting in their head.

Depression can develop slowly over time, with the changes in someone's behaviour and outlook happening gradually. However, with time, it can advance into something much bigger and more sinister.

Maty, who suffers from depression, shares his advice:

> The warning signs are important. Sleeping all day and being awake all night, not eating or eating too much, can all be well recognisable signs that depression is taking hold of a loved one. Then there are more signs that are well hidden, in my opinion: becoming withdrawn from family and friends and small comments like, 'It would be better if I wasn't here' should not be taken lightly.

Some signs to be aware of include a person:
- expressing sadness, helplessness or hopelessness over a period of time
- shying away from social situations or activities they usually enjoy
- struggling to sleep, or sleeping more than usual
- being unusually intolerant of others
- showing persistent signs of anxiety
- eating more or less than usual
- having unexplained aches and pains
- seeming to be less motivated and lacking more energy than usual.

Eve shares her advice to carers:

> When someone argues more than they laugh, when they don't
> clean the home or feed the pets or even cook the dinner or do
> the washing up – try not to take over these things. Encourage
> your depressed loved one to do them. When these things start
> to slide, it is a big warning sign.

Do not pretend things are fine

The temptation may be to pretend that everything is okay, to
dismiss some of these signs and symptoms as not important
or at least to decide just to keep an eye on them rather than
acting on them right away. The taboo that sadly still exists
around talking about mental health can often come into
play here. Some people worry that raising the subject of
depression may be somehow intrusive or that they do not
know the right words to use. They may be concerned that
they themselves do not fully understand mental illness and
worry they could somehow make things worse if they say or
do the wrong thing.

All of this is perfectly understandable. We still have a
long way to go to challenge and break this stigma and lack of
knowledge and it is therefore no surprise that many people are
still not comfortable talking about mental health. However, I do
think that being able to be open about it, however clumsily, is
generally preferable to not saying anything at all.

Pete, who suffers from major depressive disorder, dittos this
below:

> One of the things that I've found hard is when there is a
> pretence that everything is fine and people try to jolly me along.
> Sometimes, it is important just to acknowledge what's going on
> and call the day what it is – difficult. I find this recognition much
> more helpful as a way of dealing with a difficult day and then
> trying to get up the next day with a different approach. If there is

a pretence that everything is fine, I often feel guilty and that I'm dragging the mood down.

Not discussing depression or mental illness only reinforces the taboo. It sends out the message that it is something that should not be talked about out loud and, to the person coming to terms with their own mental health struggles, the message they receive can be that it is something to be ashamed of and kept to themselves.

The opposite is true. Talking about depression removes the stigma surrounding the illness. Raising the subject sends the message that it is okay to talk about it. Having the conversation can remove a large chunk of the shame and embarrassment which can and may accompany depression. By letting someone know they are not alone in their illness you can reduce the isolation which is so often bound up in it.

Dr Ian Drever, psychiatrist and founder of the Academy of Mental Fitness, reinforces this message:

It's okay to talk about it – you wouldn't pretend things are fine with any other illness.

The most important reason for not pretending things are fine is that, if left unchecked and undiscussed, the depression could get worse. Mild depression could escalate to a higher level, ultimately increasing the more serious risks, such as suicide. So, the message here is, please do not be afraid to talk about it, to raise the subject, to ask if someone is struggling and to offer your help. Showing you care will not make things worse but may make it easier for someone to seek help, thereby putting them on the path to recovery. For the person who may be wrapped up in their depression, unable to see a way out, you – as someone who cares about them – can often give them the priceless gift of hope.

Say the right thing

It can be really hard to know what to say to someone with depression. You do not want to ignore the illness, but sometimes you just do not know if you are saying the right or wrong thing. With the help of some of the wonderful people who have taken the time to contribute to my books, I have put together a list of some of the things that could be helpful to say to those with depression, and others that are best avoided.

What not to say

Whilst all of the types of response listed below are completely understandable; the manner in which they are said is often not helpful for the mind-set of someone battling depression and they are more likely to make them feel misunderstood.

- Try not to apportion blame or show anger by saying things like: 'Why are you doing this to us?' or 'Look at the effect this is having on the rest of the family.'
- Try not to minimise the problem by saying: 'What do you have to worry about?' or 'This is all in your head.'
- Try not to ask someone to 'Snap out of it" or 'Pull yourself together.' Depression can be a complex, deep-rooted issue and cannot be switched off at will just like that
- As hard as it is sometimes not to say 'How can you be so selfish?' or 'I cannot see why you cannot just ignore it', we have to remember that depression is a serious mental illness and, like any physical illness, it is not the sufferer's choice.
- Try not to judge the sufferer, whatever they confess to you. Instead, tell them, 'I respect your viewpoint' even if you do not agree with what they are saying.
- Try not to say, 'I do not know how to help' as they are looking to you as someone to take their pain away.

All the above phrases can potentially create a barrier between the person experiencing depression and the person trying to help them. Getting cross and shouting will only make everyone feel worse, including you. No matter how frustrated and disheartened you may be feeling, it is important to try and put those feelings aside when talking to your loved one. It is vital not to belittle their feelings, as they will seem overwhelming to them; it will only exacerbate the anxiety they are feeling.

Throwing around positive clichés, however well meant, may also not be helpful, coming across as empty and worthless. Instead, try to tie your comments and thoughts to their particular situation, praising them for specific steps they have taken forward or reminding them of their personal attributes that you love and admire so much.

What to say

When a family member has depression, communications can, at times, require extra effort and patience. Effective communication serves as precautionary care, reassuring family members that they care about each other and appreciate each other's efforts. Good everyday communication can also make it easier to bring up issues, make requests when needed and resolve conflict when it arises. Open, non-judgemental communication should, however, always form the basis of the approach.

As I have said, it is not always easy to know what to say and how to say it, when talking to someone who is struggling with a mental health issue. Every person has their own preferences, but here are a few ideas that you may find helpful:

- You might ask questions such as: 'Can you tell me what is happening?' or 'Do you feel you would rather talk to someone else?'
- Give the person space and time to express themselves,

asking: 'Would you like my advice or would you rather I
just listened?'
- Encourage your loved one by saying something like: 'There
  is nothing you can say that will stop me loving you.'
- Praise them for every small step forward by saying: 'This
  must be hard for you, but you are going to get through it,'
  or 'I am so proud of you.'
- Help by taking away their fear by telling them, 'You are not
  alone and I would like to help you in any way I can.'

A lot of the time, simply just listening can be helpful. It is
important to talk to the sufferer in the same way you have always
done, remembering they are still the same person that they were
before the illness.

It can be useful having certain code words between you. These
can be words that the person with depression can use to demonstrate when they want to talk or when they are struggling, or
they may use their words to talk about their depression and how
they are feeling without actually naming the illness. Perhaps this
is where the 'black dog' or 'dark cloud' can be useful, as it can be
hard to say the words 'I'm depressed' or 'I need help'.

Dr Ian Drever, psychiatrist and founder of the Academy of
Mental Fitness, gives us a useful tip for both sufferers and family
members:

*Often it can be difficult and complicated for sufferers to explain what sort of
day they are having, especially if they're feeling low and flat. Family members
can then become more anxious, feeling left out, wondering how they're feeling, and pushing for a discussion which the sufferer doesn't feel up to.*

*So, just give a simple one-word snapshot of how the day is going, using
a one-to-10 point rating scale, with 'one' being life is terrible, this is the
worst I could possibly feel, and '10' being perfect. The sufferer can then say
that today is a 'four' or whatever, so that in one word, the family at least
gets a sense of how they are – and, if the day before was a 'three', then*

they'd also have the comfort of knowing that things are moving slightly in the right direction.

A simple, 'rough and ready' little trick can make life a bit easier for sufferers and those around them.

Create a positive home environment

Those living with or close to someone with depression may well be able to have a positive impact on their well-being. Creating an environment within their home which is conducive to a positive, emotional balance can be pivotal for the person suffering and the family as a whole. This is about both the ambience in the home, and the way people interact within it.

One effect of depression can be that people lose interest in their surroundings. They may lack the motivation to look after themselves and feel disconnected from the environment around them. Yet at the same time, they may struggle to get out, losing interest in activities they once enjoyed and instead spending long periods of time behind closed doors. While no one would claim that clearing the clutter around them or keeping the house clean will directly change their depression, not doing so could well contribute to their negative state of mind.

Rachel Kelly shares the kind of support she valued the most:

> I think one breakthrough was to realise that someone suffering from a mental illness needs much of the same support in the home as someone suffering from a physical illness. The support I most valued when I was unwell was the friend who brought round the fish pie so I didn't have to worry what was for supper; the relation who emptied the dishwasher without asking and changed my sheets ... That kind of domestic help made a huge difference, just as if I was suffering from a physical illness.

There are certainly benefits to having access to natural sunlight, so opening the curtains or moving a chair outside into the garden may be helpful as part of a wider treatment plan. Surrounding the sufferer with things they love could also have a positive impact. Framed photographs of happier times, candles scented with mood-boosting fragrances, blankets and throws that make them feel secure and comforted and activities that may stimulate their interest, such as art materials, jigsaw puzzles or music, can also be helpful.

Eating a varied and broadly healthy diet is important in the treatment and prevention of depression and of course someone's home life is absolutely key to this. Working together with the person who has depression to find out what they feel like eating, and making this as nutritious and enjoyable for them as possible can be really important, especially if they have lost interest in their diet or preparing their own food. Helping them understand the foods that can play a part in lifting their mood, versus those that offer no benefits or may even make them feel worse, can also be really valuable.

Avoid making personal criticisms

The way in which you react to your loved one's depression can have a big impact on them and how they feel. While their bleak mood and apparent lethargy may be frustrating as well as upsetting, showing exasperation or anger is unlikely to be helpful. It will not 'jolt' them out of their depression and instead is more likely to fuel even more feelings of guilt and/or shame.

Try to detach yourself from the way the sufferer is acting and the effect that may have on their wider circle of family and friends. Instead, remember it is part of their illness and that the person you love and care for is still very much there inside. Hopefully, doing this will enable you, the carer, to connect with the sufferer, rather than becoming alienated from them.

Jessica looks back at when her daughter was suffering from mild depression:

Before I really understood what was wrong with my daughter, I just presumed (very naively) that she was being a 'typical' teenager, not wanting to get up and sleeping for a lot of the day. On many occasions I called her lazy and said she needed to sort herself out. I feel so awful now knowing that this actually reinforced how she already felt about herself – that she was worthless and good at nothing.

Acknowledging small steps forward

Most people thrive on praise and those with depression are usually no different.

The road to recovery from depression can be a long and complex one. It can often feel overwhelming, and never-ending at times, to both the sufferer and their carers. The recovery process may involve medication, therapy and lifestyle changes, as well as a willingness and courage on the part of the person with the illness to follow the path recommended to them. Frequent encouragement and praise will help to give them the strength to take the next step on this journey, and this is where friends and family can step in as a supportive back-up team.

Dr Ian Drever, psychiatrist and founder of the Academy of Mental Fitness, shares his professional thoughts:

It is useful to know that this is a bumpy ride – there will be good and bad days, often in no particular order; there can be mood dips out of the blue and these can be really alarming and dispiriting for sufferers and family members alike. But it doesn't mean that things have unravelled and are back at square one – it is just part of the very up and down ride which often characterises a recovery from depression. When there are good days – or even just a few good hours – these are like the clouds opening up and a ray of light coming through. Even though it may be very transient at first, it's actually a very good prognostic sign, because it shows that the illness is (slowly) shifting and that things aren't completely stuck and immoveable.

It is important to acknowledge seemingly small accomplishments along the way. From the very first step, which may simply be the sufferer admitting how they are feeling, the reaction of loved ones can be a powerful motivator, encouraging them to keep moving forward and not give up. Through visits to the GP, keeping appointments for therapy, sticking to prescribed medication, recognising each of these steps can help motivate them.

You can also support them by encouraging them to set small goals, breaking down larger tasks into smaller, more manageable steps. For people who struggle to get out of bed, setting goals like having a shower and a healthy meal are accomplishments in themselves that should be recognised and praised. They may then be able to move on to meeting with friends or being motivated to revisit a once-enjoyed activity. Acknowledging these achievements lets them know that their hard work and attempts to recover are worth all the effort they undoubtedly took.

Maty says of his steps forward:

> Something that is hard to do as a sufferer is to compliment yourself. But forcing yourself out of bed and into the shower after three days is a massive achievement, not a small step. After that achievement personally I used to force myself out of the house to have a small walk to the shops to buy a little treat or a walk with the dog at the end of the day. You may still want to cry yourself to sleep but with the help of the people around you and yourself realising what you have done, these actions can make your world seem less claustrophobic.

Be as kind as possible

Irrespective of their age, or position in the family, allowing the sufferer the time, space and security they need on their recovery path will also enable them to open up and relax a little more around those closest to them. By vocalising and acknowledging to the sufferer that you accept and understand how difficult and challenging things are for them, empathising and reassuring them that there is nothing they could say or do to make you stop loving or caring for them. This will help to give them the courage and the confidence they need to continue in the right direction.

Paige talks of her experience when her close friend was suffering from depression:

> The smallest act of watching a film together or talking to them about other things like work, will mean a lot to that person as they feel that they are being included in your life and they know they have someone there who will support them and wants to keep them in their lives, no matter how they are feeling. I think people who suffer from depression often feel they are a burden to others and that nobody will want to talk to them as they can appear to be uninterested. But it is really important to make sure that they know that they are significant to you and that you want to keep them involved in your life.

By keeping the boundary walls down between you and the sufferer, you are perpetuating the recovery cycle and creating an open, non-judgemental environment for them, which is exactly what they need to be able to keep challenging themselves and move forwards. That feeling of working together can be immensely valuable to someone suffering from depression. It helps them to feel understood and trusted, giving them a gentle boost to their self-esteem, which is so important to recovery.

India says of her partner Amie and how kind she has been:

> At first Amie was a bit impatient with me, because I hadn't opened up to her and actually told her what was wrong. Ever since she has known, she has been so patient with me, which has helped me want to recover, not just for me but for her too.

Encourage self-care

When someone has depression they may lose interest in both their surroundings and themselves. Smothered by their illness, looking after their own well-being can sometimes feel exhausting, unnecessary and out of their reach. However, looking after themselves is not a luxury. It can in fact be an important part of their recovery plan and as someone who cares for them; this is one area where your support can have a significant influence.

Dr Ian Drever, psychiatrist and founder of the Academy of Mental Fitness, shares his thoughts:

Even though sufferers may not feel like looking after themselves, do it anyway – as an investment in the future – their body will need to be taken care of for when they come back to life.

Encourage them to adopt good sleeping habits, to eat well and to take exercise – anything from walking or cycling to yoga or dance – and perhaps join them in doing so. All of these have been proven to be valuable mood-boosters. Help them make a list of the things they enjoy or make them feel happy (or have done in the past), maybe a good book, long bath or their favourite funny film, so that they recognise the things they can pursue to improve their own mood. Encouraging them to set mini goals can help provide a really positive focus and give them something to strive for.

If someone is struggling, you might feel like you should take care of everything for them. While it may be useful to offer to help them do certain things, like keeping on top of the housework or cooking healthy meals, it is also important to encourage them to do some things for themselves, as Eve said on page 263.

Stay in touch

Relationships with others are essential to all of us, especially those with a mental health issue, but having an illness like depression can make it even harder to maintain those crucial bonds. If friends, family, carers and/or loved ones can keep in touch – even if that contact can sometimes feel one-sided – it can make a huge difference to the person who is wading through the weight of the illness. Just knowing that they are being thought about can make a big difference to how someone feels.

It is likely that the person you know with depression seems to have withdrawn and it is easy to mistakenly interpret that as them not wanting contact. However, the opposite is likely to be true. It is the depression that prevents them from reaching out, going out, or accepting invitations and they may fear and mourn the isolation that their illness brings. Try not to take it personally if someone seems to rebuff you or does not keep in touch. That is a symptom of their depression, not a reflection on the relationship between you and them or how much they value you as part of their life.

Even when it does feel one-sided, sending a message, email or letter to someone, or picking up the phone to give them a call is likely to be much appreciated. Reminding them of their strengths or recalling happy times together can give them a real lift and help them remember how special they are. Depression destroys self-confidence and self-worth so hearing that someone genuinely still believes in them can be very powerful, particularly at a time when they may not believe in themselves.

Going out and meeting up with a friend with depression requires a good dose of understanding. They may cancel plans, leave early, or simply say 'no' to well-meant invitations. Remember this is a reflection of their illness and not the way they feel about you as a person. Many people like to continue to be invited to things, even if they rarely go, because it makes them still feel part of things. However, always be patient and do not force them to come out if they are not ready.

My daughter Samantha's best friend, Zoe, sums this up beautifully:

In truth, Sam suffering from mental illness does add a complication to our friendship. It is a subject that I try to comprehend, but often can't fully. There's almost an unspoken agreement between us, I won't always understand what she's going through, and she won't always be able to commit to doing things. We don't have to talk about it, but we can when she wants to. The end result is a best friend who is great in so many other ways and her challenges are an accepted part of that friendship. It's similar to a friend in a foreign country or a friend with a new baby; it can be difficult to maintain a connection sometimes. But stand by a friend with mental illness, because when they are ready, they will be one of the most tenacious, courageous people you will get to have the honour of being friends with.

Find the humour

Depression is certainly no laughing matter, but that does not mean that humour has to be banned if someone is ill. While being able to laugh together when someone has depression can sometimes feel like an impossible task, trying to see the lighter side of certain situations can normalise them and help everyone weather the storm of mental illness.

That is not to say that having a joke or a giggle is suddenly going to bring a suffeer out of their depression, but doing something to make your friend or loved one laugh may be helpful in lifting their mood. Just make sure the person with depression feels respected and is not left out of the laughter.

Maty says of the positive impact humour can have:

Humour is fantastic, but it can be a touchy subject, especially when aiming jokes towards a depressed person. If you have the right level and timing I'm a great believer that you can change someone who is majorly down into cracking a smile and even having a little giggle.

Keep your family routine 'normal'

It can be easy to let the depression take over, to feel as though you constantly have to tread on eggshells and allow everyday life to revolve around the person who is ill. However, where possible being able to maintain a normal routine can be really helpful, both allowing the wider family to carry on and also helping the person with depression to have some control over their own life.

Establishing a routine with someone who has depression can be a key part of their self-care. Setting daily targets for getting up, having a shower, doing exercise and achieving other small goals can provide a series of crucial stepping-stones which may well aid their recovery. That said, you cannot force them to do things; they have to want to do them for themselves. There will be times when they need to sleep and when they cannot motivate themselves to set goals let alone achieve them. Allowing them those times without making them feel guilty about it is okay too.

For parents, partners, friends and loved ones, maintaining your own everyday life is also essential. Make time every week to do something you or your family particularly enjoy, together or alone. It could be listening to music, reading a book, going to the cinema or simply going for a walk. Setting aside time to do your favourite activities can help relieve family tensions, whilst reinforcing the bond.

My Charlotte adds:

> It was so important to all of us to still try to spend some time all together, even just going for a walk or sitting and watching a movie at home. It gave us all a small sense of normality and kept us going.

Remember, there is life outside of the depression, for everyone.

Offer hope

When someone is engulfed in the fog of depression it can be a dark, lonely and hopeless-seeming place to be. That famous 'light at the end of the tunnel' can feel constantly out of reach, with the darkness so deep that it can seem impossible to find a way out.

If, in someone's bleakest times, you can continue to be a friend and to care for and about them, you may just provide that glimmer of sunshine that they may be struggling so hard to find. Telling them that you are there for them today and will be tomorrow, that you believe in them and will never stop doing so, that they are ill but the illness will pass, may just give them the glimmer of hope they need to keep going.

Look after yourself

Supporting others can be mentally and physically exhausting. As a parent or carer, you probably spend a lot of your time focusing on everybody else, always putting everyone else's needs before your own. However, looking after your own well-being is just as important for you, your loved one and the whole family, as they can only be as strong as you are. You may not be able to take a break every time you need one, but it is important to have some time that is yours, whether it be going for a walk, meeting a friend, doing a relaxation class or simply reading a book or a magazine. By doing this, it will enable you to recharge your batteries, so that when you are by the side of the person you care about, you are there with renewed energy and focus.

Jeff Brazier, life coach, supports self-care whilst caring for others:

Sometimes in life we become so busy looking after everyone else we forget to adequately care for ourselves. Regardless of how noble the cause, the problem with this is that if all is not balanced within us, our ability to tend to the needs of others is diminished as a result. We must first give to ourselves if we are going to give openly to others.

Depression in the homeless

While this chapter is entitled 'Depression in the home' I also very much realise that many of those without a home also experience depression and are, indeed, more vulnerable to mental illness. It is believed that around four in 10 rough sleepers have a mental health issue.[59]

Mental ill health can be a contributory factor to someone losing or leaving their home. It can also be made worse by the stress of not having a roof over their head. Put simply, mental illness is both a cause and consequence of homelessness and the support services for people in this situation, some of the most vulnerable in society, often struggle to keep up with the demand.

It is sobering to reflect on this strong link between mental ill health and homelessness and to realise how hard it must be, when everything in your life feels so precarious, to find a path back to good health. Adrian tells us of his journey:

> I went through a very traumatic divorce which resulted in my getting extremely depressed and eventually losing my home. I ended up sleeping rough as I could not work and had nowhere to go. On a more positive note, after a while I found myself and managed to get back onto my feet. I think the depression contributed a lot to me getting into such a bad position of becoming homeless. Once I got the help I needed to work out how I was feeling and I was put on antidepressants, my life seemed to turn around.

To conclude

There is no definitive, right or wrong way to work together as a unit in the home; every situation, every sufferer, every family unit and every home environment is different. But by everyone sticking to the basic fundamentals and working closely together, for the benefit of everyone involved, you will all be on the right path.

Chapter 10

Depression in the workplace

Depression in the workplace is an area of increasing concern, partly because of the effect that someone's working life can have on their overall mental health and partly because of the huge disparity in different companies' approaches and attitudes towards this kind of illness. What is clear, however, is that millions of employees in any one day will be struggling with their emotional well-being; after all, around 16 million people in the UK, at some point each year, will suffer from a mental illness.[60]

Those who struggle with depression at school or university may continue to battle with mental illness when they are in the world of work. Others may find that their depression actually develops when they are older, possibly as a direct or indirect consequence of their working life. There are many thousands more people at work today who will be desperately juggling the demands of their employment with the stress of caring for a loved one with a mental illness, such as depression. The health and productivity of all of these people may be being compromised, making it essential that employers play their part in creating a working environment which is both knowledgeable about mental illness and supportive of those who are affected by it.

Mental health in general is currently a hot topic, and employers are starting to recognise their responsibility for supporting employees with this kind of issue as much as they would someone with a physical illness. However, it is questionable whether the many words that are spoken on the subject are matched by actual action. The fact that 15% of employees who disclosed a mental health issue faced demotion, dismissal or disciplinary procedures and that less than a quarter of line managers surveyed had received any training in mental health shows just how much still needs to be done.[61]

This suggests that there is a long way to go to educate employers, managers and human resource teams about depression. Having a vague working knowledge gleaned from articles in the press or anecdotes from friends is rarely enough. There are so many myths that pervade society about depression and associated illnesses that it is not unreasonable to ask companies to have a policy around these and provide regular training for those who oversee teams of employees. After all, 91 million working days are lost to mental illness in Britain each year.[62]

Promoting a respectful and understanding environment at work is also important. Feeling able to open up about a mental illness, such as depression, and believing they will be supported for doing so, could be absolutely critical in helping someone you work with get the help they need. Carl, who has suffered from situational depression, shares his positive experience of being supported at work:

> I really struggled with an ongoing family situation which made it more and more difficult to get up and face people at work every day. After a period of time I gained the courage to talk to my line manager about the situation and they allowed me the flexibility to work from home when I was having a really bad day. I am now back working in the office most days and am so thankful for the support I received from work. They encouraged me to seek help, which I did, and found very beneficial.

Chapter 10

Work stress versus work depression

It is important to note that feeling stressed, irritable, upset and/ or demoralised at work is very common. We all have days when everything seems to go wrong or times when we struggle to get along with our boss or colleagues. Those difficult feelings may even escalate to the point where they have an effect on our life, leaving us questioning whether we want to continue in our job or even leading to Sunday-night dread about going to work the next day. Though those emotions are very real and can be hugely challenging, they do not necessarily equate to depression. Generally, if tackled – by changing jobs, improving work-life balance or finding solutions at work – the stress can be lessened.

By contrast, depression seeps into every part of a person's life, leaving them feeling hopeless, adrift and unable to find a light in their darkness. Their bleak feelings are unlikely to lift when they finish work and their home and social life are also likely to be affected by their dark mood.

The two are different and that distinction should be made. However, it is also important to recognise that work stress can escalate into depression if left unchecked or not acted upon, and, if something else happens in a person's life that they struggle to cope with, it can further aggravate an existing mental health issue. This can often make it hard to separate stress from depression. Whether problems at work per se can actually cause depression remains under debate, with some arguing that people either have to be predisposed to a mental illness or subject to major stresses in other areas of their life for depression to deveop; however, what is undeniable is that work – where we spend so much of our time – is a key piece in the puzzle of our mental well-being.

Claire shares her experience of how work stresses were detrimental to her mental health:

> With help I achieved some of my dreams but, after suffering an accident in 2006, I had to completely rethink my career. This is

why I ended up in a support position for the last three years. I was offered the opportunity for promotion to a management role in October 2018 and took this as I thought it was the next logical step.

However, since Christmas my anxiety levels, mental health and emotions have taken a battering as I have found it increasingly difficult to cope on a daily basis. I find I am feeling sick, not eating properly, crying, being horrible at home and not enjoying holidays knowing that I have to go back to a job I am not cut out for.

I do not feel I have the capability or confidence to move the role forward. I am sick of feeling stupid in front of others and always thinking I have something to prove to everyone else when really it should be about me. For this reason, I have today spoken with my manager and put the wheels in motion to make changes.

The causes of depression at work

There is little doubt that many aspects of working life can heavily impact someone's state of mind and that this can in turn progress into an illness such as depression. From being bullied by a manager to feeling financially trapped in an unfulfilling role, there are many ways that pressures at work can have a negative effect on someone's self-esteem and self-worth. While the list of possible work triggers for depression is virtually endless, I will endeavour to discuss some of the main issues here.

Bullying

Bullying can take many forms, from overt put-downs to so-called 'gas-lighting', where a person's perception of reality (for example, how they are performing at work) can be insidiously distorted by someone else. Being bullied at work, where your professional credentials are under attack along with your own sense of self, can have a particularly brutal impact, making you feel worthless. It is in the nature of 'office politics' that reporting bullying can feel hard, with employees worrying that by doing so they will risk further damage to their standing in the workplace.

It can be hard to know what to do to stop a bully at work. It may be helpful to keep a diary of incidents as they happen, so there is a record to refer back to, if further action is taken. Talking to a colleague or manager is also important to break the silence that bullying thrives on. Also, consider calmly addressing the issue with the bully themselves. Their actions may not be deliberate and they may be shocked by the effect they are having.[63]

Sandy, who suffered from depression after an intense phase of bullying at her work, shares her experience:

> At first I tried to brush off the negative comments aimed at me and thought to myself that I was stronger than to retaliate or let them get to me. But after a while, without realising it, the bullying got more and more emotional and turned into blackmail and got quite nasty. After about six months of this going on and getting myself deeper into a pit of depression, I told my husband about it and he spoke to my boss at work. My boss was amazing and looked into it; the person bullying me got a 'disciplinary' and from then on stayed away from me. I feel that it got as far as it did because I let it, and let them get away with it.

Low morale in the workplace

Often bullying can develop alongside a culture of general low morale at work. Like the playground bully, someone who mistreats their colleagues often comes from a place of feeling undermined, undervalued or vulnerable themselves. That does not excuse their behaviour, but it may suggest that the problem is more to do with the unsupportive or demanding culture of the workplace than the unpleasant actions of one individual.

Like a persistent black cloud hanging over you, low morale at work can have a real effect on your well-being. Those who find that the pervasive negative culture of their workplace is having an impact on their mental health, should not ignore those feelings, especially if they persist even when they are at home. Instead, they need to take steps both to look after their own well-being (for example, through exercise, diet, taking breaks or even seeing a life coach or counsellor), and to try to deal with the issues at work, which may mean raising them with a manager or the human resources department.

Former college lecturer, Nicholas Warburton, tells us of his experience in the education sector:

> Having worked in the education sector for about 20 years, I have seen and experienced depression. With relentless workloads and continual budget cutbacks, teaching staff are put under more and more pressure to cover the other jobs, like those of administration and support staff who are made redundant. Naturally the teacher's workload increases exponentially. The teacher still has to arrive at a class in good spirits, be professional and consistent and wear the mask of everything being okay.

A wrong-fit role

There are times when a job that looks amazing on paper or seems impressive to others can feel anything but that to the person who is doing it. Feelings of being trapped or at odds with your own personal values can fester and grow. Couple this with other pressures, such as needing the salary or of working-parent guilt, and it can soon begin to have a negative effect on your mental health.

Working-parent guilt or work-life imbalance

Most people spend many hours at work. However, it is essential to have a good balance between working time and leisure time. This balance can feel even more important if work is taking you away from your children, especially if your workload keeps increasing, robbing you of time at home even more. It can be such a hard balancing act, knowing you have to work to keep a roof over your head but still wanting time to spend with people you love or doing the things you enjoy, which are both vital to good mental health and well-being. For parents in particular, guilt can be an ever-present burden, which is often misplaced. However, even if unjustified, its effects can be very real, causing people to dread going into work or leaving them really struggling with the dual demands of their career and family.

Ted looks back at the time when he feels his depression started:

> I really enjoyed my job. It earnt us enough money to live on, the hours were great and I had been there about seven years. We then got bought out by another larger company and my work-life changed. I had to fit so much more work into my day, which meant I was working 12 hour days, leaving home at 7 am and not getting back until around 8.30 pm. I missed our children going to school and coming home from school; I was tired and could barely play with them. I often had to catch up with work at the weekends and so missed out on their play dates and sports days. I felt so alone and as if I wasn't really part of the family anymore. I ended up deep into a pit of depression, before I even really knew it.

Financial struggles

There may be an assumption that people in work do not have financial pressures, but of course, in reality, that is rarely true. To a greater or lesser extent, everyone feels the stress of having to provide enough money and ensuring they continue to have enough in the future. Many people feel they have to stay in a job that they do not like to be able pay the bills. If this situation continues over a long period of time, it can put a very stressful burden on someone's shoulders, eventually affecting other areas of their life. Their relationships with loved ones may start to suffer, they may struggle to sleep, or they may find themselves turning to alcohol or drugs as a release, so in turn putting more pressure on their mental health. It can also be a vicious circle, affecting how well they do their job. The fear of losing that job can further exacerbate their feelings.

The way forward can often seem unclear, but talking about these emotions with loved ones or a professional can help. Concentrating on your own well-being is also essential to weather these difficult times.

Petra shares her experience:

> We were young and decided to buy our very first house together. I think we were very naive and stretched ourselves way too far beyond what we could actually afford. We struggled to get by week to week and I also hated my job but had no other option than to stay there. We didn't even have a family yet and still we couldn't even afford to look after ourselves; I couldn't see a future or where we would be in six months' time the way we were going. After a very stressful year, my partner and I finally spoke to each other about how we were feeling (both of us were pretty depressed) and made the decision to move to a less expensive house. It is the best thing we could have done. Sometimes now I still get dark thoughts, but I am in a better position to fight them off.

Working in certain industries

While anyone can be affected by depression, regardless of what work they do, there is evidence to suggest that working in certain sectors can increase the risk of suffering mental health issues, including suicide. One UK report highlighted the significantly increased risks of suicide for:

female nurses

women working in culture, media and sport

both male and female carers

teachers and

construction workers.[64]

For the latter, for example, men working on a construction site are three times more likely to take their life than the average male. Working long hours, often away from home on a building site for weeks at a time, with fears about job security, can all play a part. Couple this with the traditional macho culture of the building trade, where asking for help and opening up about emotions do not come naturally, and the reasons behind these statistics become clearer.

In reality, anyone can become depressed in any job, from a farmer to a musician, and each industry in an ideal world should have organisations who can help people deal with any issues triggered by their work. Each profession will come with its own set of concerns, whether that is undue pressure, isolation, a machismo or sexist culture or other issues, and specific unions, trade bodies and charities can all be supportive at times of significant stress or worry.

Mason tells us of his struggles being in a 'macho' working environment:

I work in the building industry as a scaffolder. We all know before we start that banter is part of the job. This was all well and good until I felt the depression come over me. There were days when I couldn't get up for work and I'd pretend I had been out the night before, so I sounded like I was hard, but the truth is I was depressed. I thought if I told the truth I would get ripped to pieces. It was so difficult as I needed to work to keep myself going. In the end, I spoke to one of the guys on site that I am closest to and he was really supportive and said that he had also been through it himself. I still thank him now.

Depression when you're struggling to work

When talking about work it is really important to acknowledge that depression can render many sufferers unable to take on or maintain a job. While for many the routine of getting up and going out to work is a crucial part of their armoury against the illness, for others it is simply not possible to commit to regular work and all the demands and expectations that entails.

There is evidence though that working can help you cope with depression and that not working for a long period can sometimes make it worse. Therefore, perhaps finding the right kind of work is paramount. Negotiating shorter hours or flexible working times could be key for those who want a job but cannot cope with the full-time commitment it may involve.

Arun shares his experience of benefiting from his work environment:

> Currently, I work in an open environment involving hundreds of people on a daily basis, so I have learnt to channel my energy into a more productive, helpful manner.

It is helpful to remember that, by law, employers must make 'reasonable adjustments' for workers with disabilities or long-term physical or mental health conditions, such as depression, so you do have the right to ask for help if you want to return to work. Such adjustments can be adapted hours, for example.

For those not in employment or who cannot return to their previous job, another possible route may be volunteering. This can be a valuable way for people to re-establish a routine and to see how well they are able to cope with having an ongoing commitment to others. Beyond that, it can also be great for self-esteem – especially if it involves helping others – and can give people a focus away from their own challenges. It can also improve their chances of getting a paid job when they feel ready and able.

Maty talks about how he found voluntary work helped him in a positive way:

> I unfortunately can't work in a 'proper job' but do have voluntary work every week, with 150 to 200 disabled people a week for a special-needs/disabled disco and club.
>
> I often find my depression means I don't want to go, get out of bed or sometimes even get ready to go and I will put it off till the very last minute, but in reality it's really helped me to get out of a semi-selfish state and help other people who are worse off than me.
>
> Voluntary work along with a few other things has really helped me become a stronger person and I personally recommend it to anyone even though I didn't want to go there to begin with.

Spotting depression at work

Many people spend eight hours a day, five days a week – or more – at work. That is more time than some of them spend with their families. It means that colleagues are well placed to identify – and possibly help – those with depression. However, even if someone suspects that a person they work with may be struggling with depression or any other mental illness, they often do not know what to do about it.

I have already covered in earlier chapters the signs and symptoms of depression. These all still apply. At work, however, there are a few other things that colleagues can also look out for. These could include:

- poor job performance or increased absenteeism
- difficulty concentrating and/or making decisions
- lethargy, constant tiredness and/or poor time keeping
- frequent mood swings; self-esteem issues; problems with food or compulsive behaviours
- withdrawing from social activities, such as not joining

colleagues for after-work get-togethers when once they used to.

Dr Ian Drever, psychiatrist and founder of the Academy of Mental Fitness, shares his advice:

Depression can adversely affect functions like memory, concentration and ability to interact socially, all of which can make work performance tail off and the office/place of work feel like a more daunting place. All the more reason, then, to have a chat with your line manager if possible and share what's happening – it's hard to believe how, when someone opens up about their depression, suddenly other people feel much freer to share their experiences too – 'Oh yeah, I've had that too/my wife/brother/neighbour etc...'

The effect of depression on someone's working life can be immense. They may find it hard to concentrate on their work or interact with colleagues. On the other hand, for some, having a routine and being in a different environment from their home, can work in a positive way towards aiding recovery.

Charliee shares how her work is her escape:

I'm currently in full-time employment and this is my way of managing stress. I often over-work and work excessive numbers of hours, which I use as my escape. I had a long period (six months) off work a couple of years ago and found it extremely hard to return to work once I had been off for a while.

It is also important to remember that depression can affect anyone. As I keep repeating, it does not discriminate on the basis of gender, race, sexual orientation, ethnicity and/or age. Being aware of the signs and acting, no matter whether the sufferer is male, female, young or old, could make a real difference to the outcome of a colleague's illness.

How colleagues and employers can help

It is one thing to be concerned about someone at work, but quite another knowing what to do about it. Remember that everyone at work has the right to privacy and, regardless of your relationship with them, sharing your concerns with others may breach this confidentiality. If your company has a human resources department, this may well be the best place to take your concerns.

Pete looks back to when he was struggling at work and shares his thoughts on what could have helped him at that time:

> Ultimately, the most valuable response would have been knowing that I could have spoken to someone about what was happening to me, without fear of judgement. If that person could then have reported back to managers to advise that I was struggling so that support could be given, that would have taken away a lot of the fear and worry. Being judged was something that I really feared because I spent so much time passing judgement on myself. My confidence was often so low that my judgement was never favourable.

If you are close to the sufferer and consider yourselves friends as well as colleagues, then you may feel able to broach the subject with them directly. If that is the case, it is best not to accuse them of having a mental illness. Instead, tell them how you are concerned and there for them if they would like to talk or get further help. Encourage them to speak with a professional.

Ron, who has suffered from major depression, shares how one of his colleagues approached him and offered his support:

> I had been at my company for quite a long time and so some of my colleagues knew me quite well. One in particular was a massive support during my journey. When I was having a really bad day but did manage to get myself into work, he opened up a conversation with me. I honestly cannot tell you how

> much this meant to me. He enabled me to talk if I was feeling particularly low and supported me when I was having good days.

Whether or not someone in the team shows any sign of depression, or indeed of any other mental illness, employers should feel a responsibility to make the workplace as open and supportive as possible – and that means doing the right thing as well as saying the right thing. Employers, line managers and human resources teams should, if possible, send out a strong signal that their staff's mental health and well-being are valued, and that people can feel confident that raising concerns about related issues will be supported and not discriminated against.

There are many ways that employers can demonstrate this. Simply by encouraging an environment where people are listened to will help to build trust. Allowing employees to speak up, to voice ideas, to play a part in the direction of the company, will reassure them that what they say matters. If and when in future they need the support of their employer, they will feel more confident that they are likely to get it.

Being a considerate employer, creating opportunities for learning, and encouraging regular one-to-one meetings and mentoring will also help build trust and give employees somewhere to turn to and raise concerns if they need to.

If an employer or manager finds out or suspects that an employee has depression, the first crucial step is to give them the chance to talk honestly and openly, and this should continue should they take time off sick.

Emma, who suffers from depression, shares her experience of her employer opening up the conversation:

> I didn't tell my boss for ages about my diagnosis. Other staff members started picking up on the fact that I was unhappy at work, possibly three months after I had seen the doctor. (I didn't

think I was acting any differently.) Then my boss rang me to see if everything was okay and said, 'A little birdy tells me you're not very happy. Do you want to talk about it?' So, I went round, sat in her lounge and again cried my eyes out at something I didn't understand. Why was I so unhappy? I enjoyed my job.

Employers and managers should ask what their employees need, such as an extra break, or time off for counselling or medical appointments, and make reasonable adjustments to help, such as flexible working hours. It is also important to remember that everyone's experiences of mental health issues are different and the support provided to employees should – as much as possible – be tailored to that individual's needs.

It is not an employer's job to be a therapist to someone in their team. Instead, they should provide the individual concerned with access to information which they can use to get the support they need. This may include details of a confidential telephone service or of one-to-one counselling sessions with a qualified therapist.

One relatively new concept that is gathering ground is training employees to become Mental Health First Aiders. Candidates undertake Mental Health First Aid training courses that teach them how to identify signs of mental ill health and to guide people towards getting support. The first aiders are not trained to be therapists, but they are empowered with the skills to listen and respond, sometimes in a crisis, but ideally before a crisis happens. By providing this training for their teams, employers are helping to break the stigma around mental illness and giving their staff the confidence to talk about these issues, thereby helping those in need to get support earlier. In the long term it helps build the foundations of a positive attitude towards all aspects of health and well-being.

As Mary, who suffers from situational depression, says:

I have trained as a Mental Health First Aider in my current job and am lucky I currently work for an organisation that supports its employees in this way. The only negative is that I have had to work hard to see myself as an equal to other people who appear to have more confidence than I do. I think sometimes people do treat me a little disrespectfully as I am not a confident person and I care what others think of me.

Promoting well-being at work

It is important to remember that those who suffer from mental illness are, by law, entitled to protection at work. In other words, employers cannot discriminate against people with depression, based on their depression.

In addition to providing an open and supportive environment at work, employees – and businesses themselves – will also reap the rewards of a workplace that actively promotes and encourages well-being. From providing strong managerial support to introducing well-being activities such as yoga or meditation, a responsible and caring employer can have a truly positive impact on their team's mental health and happiness.

Petra shares her experience:

When our financial struggles were lessened I was able to find a new job in a smaller company that seemed to care about its staff a lot more. Once every couple of months they bring in life coaches, or yoga teachers etc... I really find it helps everyone to feel a little better and more connected.

As well as looking at the messages that their attitude gives out, employers should also consider how the work culture of the office may affect those struggling with depression. Are colleagues encouraged to leave their desks or is there an unspoken expectation of not taking a break at all? Do employees have their own 'safe' space in the office or is there a hot-desking policy (which a recent study suggested may be detrimental to mental health[65])?

Creating a work environment that promotes a good work-life balance is absolutely vital for overall good mental and physical health. Recognising when someone feels over-worked, under-valued, lonely and/or disrespected reflects an employer that cares about its workforce. Promoting discussions about well-being and good mental health is also important. It shows that these are not taboo subjects and means employees will feel more able to raise their own issues or concerns more quickly.

Supporting those caring for someone with depression

It is not just those who are suffering from a mental illness that need a supportive employer. People who are caring for, or affected by, someone else who is struggling also need understanding at work. Supporting a loved one with depression can be emotionally and mentally demanding and it can also take up a lot of time. Employers who can recognise this and who can make the adjustments that an employee may need will be rewarded in thanks and loyalty by their workforce.

Carers and loved ones should be treated with the same care and respect as an employee who actually has the illness themselves. They should be afforded privacy and confidentiality, and be asked what adjustments would help them balance the demands of their work and home life. Pointing them towards professional help and support should they need it can also be valuable.

Claire shares her experience over the years of struggling with depression at work and how understanding has evolved and changed:

> Very early in my journey with this very dark friend, I didn't understand what these feelings were. No one talked about mental health; no one told you these self-harming, suicidal

thoughts were normal for a lot of people. When you wanted to talk about how you were feeling, the thoughts you were having, people stopped listening. Comments like 'Just snap out of it' or 'Can't you see how lucky you are?' were the response I got. If it was that easy, didn't they think millions of people would do just that? Work did not appreciate the tears mixed with lack of emotion. The thoughts of not being able to cope. If I couldn't do the job, just leave. So, I did.

I cried as I felt I had nowhere to turn to. I struggled for many years bouncing from feelings of euphoria to total depths of despair. I lost friends and relationships because of how I was. Only many years later did I find out this had started with postnatal depression that I had managed to hide well from my health visitor.

Over the last few years, I and my family have suffered some heart-breaking times. My 'friend' [depression] came to visit again. This time as well as suffering my own health issues, I was dealing with work, ill husband, ill father and trying to cope. As part of the pain management I was receiving, I was seeing a psychologist and I honestly feel he saved my life. He made me realise that all the blame I had placed on myself was not healthy – that everything I had gone through made me the strong woman I am today. My manager at the time gave me time off each Tuesday to go to my appointment. I was conscious I had to rush back, but was told to use the sessions well, to help me get past some issues. I was referred to a company health scheme to see if I could access any other help and support.

The difference between employers and their attitudes was amazing. My manager was honest and said, 'I don't understand, but I can see you are suffering and I will do whatever I can to help you.'

To conclude

We spend so long at work, it is little surprise that our working environment can have a big impact on our mental health. Because of the hours people spend there and the connections they make, workplaces and the people in them have an absolutely crucial role in recognising depression and other conditions. The way that employers and fellow employees react to a colleague with a mental illness can also play a part in determining how supported or abandoned their struggling workmate feels. There is growing recognition that companies with an enlightened and positive attitude towards mental health will reap the rewards in terms of the happiness and productivity of their employees, and the more firms can build on this, through schemes such as Mental Health First Aid training, the more change they can bring about in terms of society as a whole's attitude to those living with depression.

Chapter 11

Depression and the online world

Welcome to Society
By Samantha Crilly

Hello and welcome to society, we hope you enjoy your stay
We will make it as relaxing as possible as long as you do
things our way
First of all, and most importantly, make sure you
fix up your exterior
If you slack at any point we will soon make you feel inferior
Secondly, your life will be controlled by pieces of paper
We will count these up and decide how important
you are later
Thirdly, we want you to make your time here look
as perfect as possible
Even if you're having a bad day this is not optional
Fourthly, make sure you post everyday on social media
One is fine at first, but we'll soon get needier
In fact we can guarantee we'll be getting greedier and
greedier
Oh, and in terms of your meals,
We tend to advertise things to make you ill
Keeps our drug companies going if you will

Trust us, the more pills you pop, the better you'll feel...
Lastly, just so you know, our planet is on its way out
But it has to keep up with our needs so that's not something
we talk about
So good luck and we hope everything is clear
Oh and don't smile too much, people will think you're
weird.

Caring effectively for someone suffering from depression takes hard work, determination, perseverance, patience and compassion from everyone involved. It is essential, where possible, to provide coherent and consistent support to counter the destructive force of the illness.

Any cracks in that support strategy could allow the depression to worm its way in, so it is crucial that you, the carer, do everything in your power to make sure that does not happen. However, one of the things that could infiltrate your support network and potentially undo all your hard-won progress is... the internet in general, and social media in particular.

The perennial question of whether the internet is a force for good or for ill continues to be debated and this discussion can get particularly heated when it comes to issues around mental health. Perhaps because of the relative infancy of the online world, evidence about the influence of social media use on our mental health is often contradictory. For example, while one 2018 study from the University of Pennsylvania found a link between social media and lower mood,[66] another study from Oxford University in 2019 concluded that social media has little effect on the happiness levels of teenagers.[67] The truth, I suspect, is that the influence of the online world on our mental health is complex and depends on a number of factors, from how long each individual spends on particular sites to the strength of their own self-esteem and many other considerations besides.

Vivienne Barnes, well-being coach at Woolston Well Being, shares her thoughts on self-esteem and social media:

Within my talks and workshops I include where self-esteem comes from. This is such an important element of everyone's human dynamics. In essence, self-esteem needs to come from the 'Self'. If a person relies on others to provide it then this neediness will haunt them all their life.

The internet can be a valuable source of help and encouragement for sufferers and carers alike, linking them to people enduring similar situations throughout the world and creating a mutually supportive, positive online community. However, the internet's ability to unite like-minded people can be both a blessing and a curse. While few of us could function without it, it can, at times, be misleading and should be used with the same degree of caution that you would use – and advise your loved ones to use – in the real world.

Melissa Helliwell, assistant vice principal at Oak Academy in Bournemouth, shares her thoughts:

Parents have the foremost duty of care for their children but are often baffled by the world their children live in and 'what they could possibly be depressed about'. Generally, this is due to a lack of knowledge of the effects and impacts of the world on the young, as viewed almost wholly through a screen, and then of how to deal with the aftermath of those impacts. Social media is not a total enemy; indeed, there are many excellent platforms that seek to support and encourage healthy lifestyle options, but, for every positive voice there are also negative ones that seek to control and manipulate impressionable minds. Our young people need exposure to what are safe online practices in order to understand where they can turn for support and what constitutes a negative influence.

People have their own opinions about whether the positive impact of the media (raising awareness, highlighting support and, in terms of responsible bloggers and influencers, being a source of empathy and understanding) outweighs the negatives.

It may be helpful to understand just what a potential minefield this is by explaining the most extreme viewpoints. In the red corner we have the people who claim that mental illnesses are intensely private and emotionally driven so it would be irresponsible to claim that factors such as our celebrity-worshipping culture, airbrushing, fashion and irresponsible 'influencers' could possibly be at their root. Meanwhile, in the blue corner we have those who argue that it is impossible to ignore other people's portrayal of their 'perfect' lives along with increasingly unrealistic and artificially enhanced beauty paradigms, fuelled by the immense pressure to conform to these, and that this is enough to drive anyone to a mental illness.

Paige, who is in recovery from a mental illness, says of how the portrayal of the 'perfect' life on social media makes her feel:

I am trying to get better and avoid listening to what the media says and make my own choices, but sometimes it is unavoidable. I feel this especially with how I should look instead of my own personal taste. I feel I should have a great body, exercise all the time, eat the perfect diet and travel the world whilst also having a good job and a brilliant relationship. In reality, these things aren't easy to have and/or balance, but they are constantly pushed in our faces and I feel this adds a lot of pressure into my life.

As I have said, like so many things in life, the online world can exert both a positive and a negative effect. I hope the rest of this chapter will help you understand how to maximise those upsides while recognising and avoiding many of the pitfalls.

The good

Just a decade or so ago, someone living with a debilitating

mental illness might have felt as though they were the only one battling in this way and they might have struggled to know what they could and should do to try to move forward. Nowadays, simply typing a few words into Google will introduce them to a whole community of help, support, understanding and empathy – immediately, right when they need it, without having to make an appointment, go on a waiting list or even venture outside their front door. As quickly as they can type the website address into their browser, the internet will take them to the blogs of people who understand their depression and show them stories of those who have gone on to live and love in a way they can only imagine when they are stuck in a self-destruct cycle of the illness.

Through blogs, social media and positive chatrooms, anyone can share their experience. They can provide the insight of real people in real situations and give people the 'virtual hug' they need when the going gets tough.

Pete, who suffers from major depressive disorder, shares his positive experience of online support:

> The upside has been the amazing support and encouragement I've received through some Facebook forums, most notably RED January [a community initiative that encourages you to support your mental health by doing something active every single day]. Sometimes, you can offload more easily on social media because you don't feel like you are burdening your nearest and dearest, and sometimes that can be a good thing and you can be very open. I got loads of supportive messages after having a panic attack on the way to parkrun in January. It really helped me.

That kind of support is absolutely invaluable and many with mental illness will credit the solace they find through the internet as a key part of their journey to rehabilitation. Some people find it much easier to reach out and ask for help online than they do face to face. The anonymity afforded by the internet can remove the stigma and shame that stops some people seeking support in the offline world.

Michael, who has suffered from depression, anxiety and PTSD, shares his thoughts:

> Social media can be a useful reference for people who may be scared or initially reluctant to seek medical advice or help and support. It can provide links to relevant NHS websites and those of partner agencies and charities. MIND, for example, provide a list of many mental health conditions, causes, symptoms and ways of treating that particular problem. They also include patients who have shared their mental health conditions and their subsequent journey through treatment.

Being able to communicate online can also break down one of the factors that can perpetuate the cycle of depression – namely, isolation. The internet and social media also allow both carers and the person they are caring for to keep connected with friends. For those struggling with a mental illness, this can be a very important reminder of the life that exists outside the illness they may find themselves imprisoned in. Staying in touch with friends on social media provides that tunnel to the light to the outside world and, if they are connected with people they perhaps knew in happier times, it can remind them that their life was once very different – and that it can be again.

It can also be a lifeline for carers' and sufferers' families. They, too, can often feel isolated, and the internet can introduce them to a community that cares and understands, in a way that even their closest friends can often find hard. The advice available online can help carers know what to do and what to say, and above all give them an unbeatable insight into what their loved one is going through. Where would any of us be without being able to search online and find that we are not alone in whatever is troubling us or those we care about?

Summer, whose sister suffers from depression and a physical disability, says:

> The internet has been a complete lifeline for me. I have been able to keep in touch with friends when I need to stay at home and look after my sister. I Skype some of my friends and it is just like being out in a coffee shop and having a chat.

The bad

Sadly, there is a negative and very dark side to the internet and social media. For every positive, inspiring, supportive post, there may be another that is unhelpful, undermining and potentially dangerous.

There are many different environmental factors that may contribute to poor mental health and now social media is close to the top of that list. Used by individuals of all ages and backgrounds, accessible from their handbag or pocket 24 hours a day, it has begun to play a larger part in how an illness such as depression can develop.

While it can be comforting to find people with like-minded experiences online, social media can sometimes prove to be something of a sham sanctuary for those in distress. Popular bloggers and vloggers provide a very easily accessible stage for both the well-intentioned but unqualified influencer and those who intentionally aim to promote negative and potentially dangerous behaviours to the wider public, often targeting the most vulnerable. For those with depression, sites that promote messages of self-harm or that glorify suicide can be very dangerous.

Caroline shares the experience of her young daughter, who has now recovered:

> Our happy, confident 13-year-old daughter's mental health deteriorated and she plummeted into a very dark place. We

couldn't quite get to the bottom of it. We knew she'd had some friendship issues previously and was feeling down because of some low-level bullying that had gone on for a few months beforehand, but our lovely girl gradually became withdrawn from our family unit. She was writing down some very worrying things and her behaviour changed while we were left on the outside desperate to help but struggling to reach her. She'd also recently opened up a social media account and it turned out that a friend had tagged her on a depression site which meant that this site was now following her and bombarding her with new posts and updates throughout the day when her phone was turned on. The posts were quite hypnotic and you couldn't help but look at more and more of these updates and messages. They were also suggesting links for self-harming and suicide sites.

The various social networking sites should also be handled with caution. While these sites themselves may not have any intention of promoting self-harm or suicide, they can unwittingly present an easy and instantaneous way for sufferers to share potentially damaging information.

This was highlighted by the very sad death of 14-year-old Molly Russell who took her own life in 2017. One of her social media accounts was found to contain distressing material about depression and suicide. In the wake of her death, social media companies were called on to do more to remove harmful material and as a result some have banned graphic images that might promote things like self-harm. While it is right for these companies to take responsibility, it is nevertheless impossible to remove or police all the content that may prove harmful. That is why it is essential that we all have a greater understanding of what dangers may lurk around the next 'online corner' and talk with our young people and loved ones about what to do if or when they encounter it (just as we would in the offline world). In the complex (and still much misunderstood) world of social media, we should also bear in mind that not everyone who posts a seemingly 'graphic' photo is seeking to cause harm to others. For some it may be a way of reaching out for help, and, as a result, these social media sites can provide a vital way to reach others.

Dave Davies, manager of Frank Bruno and whose own mother and mother-in-law have had, and still have, depression, shares his thoughts and concerns:

> What concerns me is that social media can be the worst culprit for some sufferers; on a bad day, they may post a 'please listen to me post' in the hope that some of their 'online friends' will say nice things to them, giving them the 'high' that they need for those five seconds. These feelings are of course short lived!

When it comes to the dangers that lurk online, it is important to discuss bullying, with around one in eight young people saying they have been bullied on social media.[68] The particularly worrying thing about this is that it can feel as if there is no escape from it. Without wishing to minimise the pain of bullying in real life, at least in the days before social media people could go home from school or work and have a break from their tormentors. With social media, bullies can now victimise the vulnerable 24 hours a day, seven days a week. Cyberbullying can leave people feeling there is nowhere they can hide, as every time they access social media they have to face unkind comments and criticism; threatening or aggressive messages. Cyberbullies often aim to sabotage friendships and encourage groups of people to exclude or abuse someone, usually for very trivial reasons. At their worst, cyberbullies actively encourage people to hurt themselves or even to take their lives and sadly tragedies have occurred.

While social media sites state that bullying and abusive behaviours (which include harassment, impersonation and identity theft) are and will be banned, sadly this kind of behaviour still continues to proliferate on most of the popular social media platforms.

It can be very hard for someone who is being bullied to see a way out of this torment, but there are things that they and their loved ones can do. Simply by talking about cyberbullying takes some the power out of it. If you suspect that someone you care about is being bullied online, try to broach it with them or suggest they talk to someone else. Encourage them to use the 'block' function available on most social media platforms to prevent further bullying from taking place. Most sites now have a system to report abusive or inappropriate messages and many will take action against users who repeatedly abuse the rules. Use these systems and report bullying messages; meanwhile, remind victims to try not to respond, and instead to delete or ignore such messages.

Thomas shares the experience of his son:

> It was an awful experience. I and my wife were unaware of what was happening to our son; it wasn't until we happened to see a message come through on his phone that we were able to dig a little deeper. We then found out that he was being barraged with negative and nasty messages on his online profile. We eventually managed to convince him to delete his profile and he hasn't looked back since.

I have covered the more 'deliberate' threats to mental health from the online world, but there is also a much more insidious danger, inherent in social media in particular, that applies to all age groups: the effect of social comparison. Accessible to such a huge audience, for those who struggle with low self-esteem, constantly scrolling through 'perfect' photos from friends, celebrities and 'influencers' can greatly exacerbate that negative cycle that they find themselves in. The presentation of a perfect life with photographs of 'gorgeous' people enjoying great times can be intoxicating to many. For those already struggling with low self-esteem and self-worth, it can be all too easy to start believing that if only they had a life like that, they too would be happy and enjoy the same influence as the 'stars' of many of the social media platforms. Impressionable youngsters are of course particularly susceptible, but even someone like myself can on occasions feel the negative emotions associated with such posts, including loneliness, isolation, envy and even worthlessness. For some, these feelings will be fleeting; for others, they will constantly linger in the background. For the more vulnerable, they can have a real impact on their psychological state.

Pete, who suffers from major depressive disorder, shares his experience:

> I find social media encourages comparisons that can leave me feeling pretty rubbish, but that comparison nearly always lacks any depth or context. Most of the time I can rationalise this reasonably well, but on a bad day I just end up feeling worse. I consistently feel that I struggle to keep up with the pace of social media in a way that suggests that I'm just not meant to process information at that speed. A break from my phone and/or social media is vital for me. I have a genuine love/hate relationship with both!

What we need to remember is that this online presentation of perfection, whether it is how people look, where they holiday or who they surround themselves with, is deceptive. Despite how 'perfect' someone's life may appear, everyone has their upsets and battles – they just do not choose to show that side. Their photographs are likely to have been touched-up and filters applied, and the bad days they inevitably will have had, will have effectively been erased from their personal history. These people may not have deliberately dangerous intentions, but for those at risk of mental illness, their false presentation of a perfect life combined with the negative self-perception of those with crushingly low self-esteem may be a recipe for untold damage.

Caroline, whose teenage daughter suffered from depression, says:

Our family was often under scrutiny and our daughter was constantly comparing our family life to others – our table was never set as beautifully as someone else's; other families did much more exciting things at weekends than us; our meals were never quite as spectacular as others'. Then came the photos from social events – some she was invited to, others she wasn't, which led to hurt and upset. Before long she was comparing her body with others' which led to all sorts of insecurities, and even mufti days at school became a nightmare. The night before was always fraught with upset and meltdowns. She had nothing to wear; she felt she looked fat in everything she owned. Others would post photos of what they were planning to wear which just caused her even more anxiety.

Fear of missing out

This can be particularly true when it comes to FOMO, an acronym for 'fear of missing out'. It sounds like a modern-day made-up illness, even something of a joke, but actually FOMO is very real and can have devastating effects on someone's life, particularly if they have a predisposition to negativity and/or depression or are in the midst of other stressful events in their own life. FOMO is the feeling that others are experiencing greater joy or more exciting experiences than you are. While it existed before social media, seeing a carefully curated collection of families', friends' or colleagues' most positive, exciting and interesting experiences reflected in their daily or hourly posts (with all the boring, upsetting or negative bits deliberately left out) can supercharge all those insecurities.

My dear friend, Bobby Davro, who is a professional comedian and has had his own battle with depression, shares his thoughts about social media:

The power and influence that social media has over us does concern me. Whilst it can be great for some being able to keep up to date with things, it can also be very toxic for many, particularly the younger generation. It can give a false

> perception of life, and project the wrong message, which in itself can be very harmful to people with low self-esteem. I always say that if aliens came down to earth and went into our homes and looked at all the happy photographs both online and in the traditional photo frames, they would think everyone was really happy and depression did not exist!

We have all felt this to a greater or lesser extent – for example, when seeing pictures of friends at a party which you knew nothing about or when someone shows off pictures of their amazing holiday that you could only dream about having. However, for someone with depression or who is prone to mental illness, and who may already feel trapped in a cycle of negativity, this extra assault on their self-esteem, when it is part of a wider picture of unhappiness, isolation and feeling unable to cope, can actually be seriously harmful.

Zoe, my daughter Samantha's best friend, shares her wise words:

> I think if you can accept that social media is often a snapshot of one great moment in someone's otherwise ordinary day, then you can use the positives. It can be inspiring and instructive. I often scroll through my favourite fitness and adventure accounts to motivate me if I'm feeling lazy.

What carers can do

Parents and carers can often feel powerless in the face of the onslaught of social media. While the pull of social media is incredibly strong, there are nevertheless still things that can be done to counter its effects.

It can at times feel like just another battle, but setting strong boundaries for online use can be vital. Age limits exist on social media sites for good reason (for most sites the age limit is 13) and you may want to think carefully about your own loved one's individual maturity, mental strength and toughness before you allow them to have accounts on these sites.

It is also vital to keep the channels of communication open with your loved one and to counter the images and influence that they are exposed to with a reminder of the unreal side to social media. Helping your loved one to distinguish the good from the bad in the online world, the life-changing from the life-destroying, is another crucial thing you can try to do to help them. Even while watching TV, discuss whether what you are seeing is really like real life. If you suspect your loved ones might be particularly susceptible to the unhealthy influence of social media, it might be helpful to start talking about that with them. Suggest that they replace the sites and accounts that bring them down with ones that inspire. Have a look with them to find people to follow that make them happy, not miserable or anxious. Encourage them to follow people who post inspirational messages and seek out role models that inspire through their good works or incredible attitude.

Jamie, who suffers from depression and anorexia nervosa, shares his experience and very good advice:

> I'm more mindful of who I choose to follow on applications such as Twitter and Instagram. Don't set yourself up to fail. If you feel there's a chance that following a certain person, or a certain organisation, will harm your mood, then it's better left unfollowed.

The impact of how much time is spent on social media

Part of the potential negative ramifications of social media seem to relate to the amount of time spent on these channels. One study funded by the US National Institutes of Health, for example, found that those who spent the most time on social media sites were 2.7 times more likely to feel depressed than those who spent the least time.[69] There are of course many caveats to this, not least that those already suffering from mental health issues may turn to the online world more readily than those who are not.

It is also noteworthy that one study by the Royal Society for Public Health has concluded that the social media platforms that predominantly show images and photographs – often carefully edited, enhanced or filtered – are the most damaging to young people's mental health, while video-based platforms, where the content is more about sharing information, are the least harmful and may even be beneficial to the well-being of young people.[70] The negative impact of image-based sites is particularly felt by young people, who may contrast themselves with the unrealistic pictures that fill their social media feeds and be left feeling anxious, inadequate and that their own lives don't measure up.

It may also be relevant that time spent on online channels is time that is not being used to exercise, enjoy the company of 'real' friends or do other activities that have been proven to boost mental health. Thus it is crucial for parents and carers to encourage their loved ones to participate in the pleasures and experiences the offline world has to offer, to get them out of the house, off their computers or phones, interacting with others and doing simple things, such as enjoying screen-free mealtimes together or going for a walk as a family. Reminding them of the joys and pleasures of the offline world may sound simplistic, but research consistently shows the positive effects this can have on our well-being.

Jamie shares his advice once more:

If using social media for personal reasons, try to set limits if you are an over-user of such applications. Say, for instance, that you're at an event; don't feel the need to update everyone about it there and then; live in your moment, enjoy your occasion. For personal benefit it's better re-living your moment and sharing your stories and memories afterwards. Life isn't a competition

> about who's got this, who's got that, who's been where, who
> owns this etc.

Away from social media, you can talk together about the things that make you laugh. Ask your loved one about the good things that happened in their day, the acts of kindness they noted or the surprising things that made them smile. Consider keeping a positive diary, either as a family or individually, to arm you all against the negative influences that surround us today more than ever.

To conclude

It is worth remembering that the internet is not an entirely bad influence. There are individuals and organisations, both on- and offline, who want to help sufferers to achieve a healthy mind-set and future, and their positive influence should not be disregarded. You may find that these publications, sites and internet users contribute to your own network of support, providing ways and means of helping your loved one towards recovery which you are unable to do yourself.

The important thing is not to feel that you are powerless compared to the might of the media. Yes, the influence it exerts is strong, but as someone who cares deeply for a person battling depression, your strength and energy also hold huge sway. At times it may feel as if you are swimming against the tide, but please do not give up. With your persistence and love, that tide will one day turn.

As with all elements of effective caring, in this instance, knowledge again is power. Simply being aware of the existence of the dangers that lurk online, in particular being vigilant in checking for signs that what your loved one is accessing is making them feel bad, is better than having no knowledge of them at all. I hope that this chapter has given you some insight into the role of social networking sites and the internet and how they can play a part in both helping and hindering depression sufferers and their carers.

Above all, remember you are not powerless. Yes, the pull of the internet and social media is strong, but the love and care of close, real-life relationships can never be replicated online.

What is recovery?

From my own personal and professional experience, I have learnt and believe that recovery from depression is not only possible, but also sustainable. Throughout the pages of this book, I hope I have helped you to understand and believe that recovery is achievable and that I have given you some of the tools to help you, your loved one and your family and friends move forwards towards that goal.

However, what is not always clear to either the sufferer or their carer(s), is knowing when they have actually reached that place of 'recovery'. They are not only unsure of what recovery should look and feel like, but are sometimes concerned that because they have not got back to being the same person they were before they became ill, recovery has not been achieved. They may feel that they have not and may not ever be able to put the depression firmly behind them.

This is not necessarily true. Again from my experience and that of my family, going through any mental illness can change a person. Therefore, the husband, wife, son, daughter, family member, partner or friend that emerges as they recover will not necessarily be the same person they were before the depression began.

For me, looking back, for more than three years, the depression turned me into the proverbial shadow of my former self and, however much I tried to blow the black cloud away, it persisted in hanging around. Thankfully, with the right help and support, it did start to clear and as that happened, I felt myself emerging stronger and more self-aware than I had been before the cloud first appeared. Over the years this strength and self-awareness have helped me to face and overcome the many challenges that have come my way. Thankfully, the depression has never returned as it was and with time I have learnt to recognise that when the white clouds start to turn grey it is time to slow down and take notice. I have learnt to recognise my limits and triggers and act on them (most of the time!) when needed.

Recovery is not the finishing line you get to at the end of a race. It is a process to go through and an understanding to arrive at. It is an acceptance by the sufferer of who they are and how they want to live, and it is rarely achievable without a lot of effort, support, perseverance, determination and hard work, through set-backs and obstacles, often over a number of months and possibly years.

It is also – and I cannot stress this enough – a completely individual goal. It is a unique journey for everyone who has or has had depression or any other mental illness, and 'recovery' will look different for each and every one of those people. Some will know they have recovered when they never have another dark or distorted thought. Others will acknowledge those thoughts are still there but be able to control them through the coping mechanisms they have learnt, taking the power out of the destructive feelings so they no longer have the effect they once did.

For some it will be about themselves as a person and reaching a point of acceptance of who they are and liking that person. Others will say that being able to enjoy life 'normally' with family and friends is their recovery milestone. For some sufferers, accepting that those destructive thoughts may not fully go away but being able to live with them and control them is a good form of recovery. For others, feeling stronger than the depression itself is a real marker. Some may eventually be able to reach a place where the depression no longer plays any part in their life, perhaps where it feels like it happened to someone else.

Some of the contributors within this book were keen to help you, the reader, understand what recovery looks like and means to them. Their stories show some of the different guises of recovery, but there are many more. Recovery is, as I say, a unique place for each person suffering from depression, which can only be reached when that sufferer finds the right path for them.

A beautiful view

It's a long and winding road. At times a very steep hill. But once you're at the top of it, it's the most beautiful view.

Craig

Every day is a gift

Recovery means the world to me. I feel so lucky that I didn't take my life when I was very low and feeling suicidal. Because of the times when I thought about suicide I regard every day as a gift. I feel that I am now becoming the person I was meant to be and that I am starting to fulfil my potential.

Pete

An opportunity

Recovery is such an individual, unique journey. No two are the same. I've had really difficult hurdles to jump at times and I think of these every day. I'm nowhere near where I would consider myself as 'recovered' but I'm on my way there. It may take months and it may take years, but I've started at least. I see the word 'recovery' as an opportunity to teach and learn. To learn new skills and to teach people that just because we have a chemical imbalance, it doesn't mean we can't be successful. I work as a senior carer and currently manage a team of 23 at the age of 25. I don't hide my diagnosis from my colleagues or anyone else. They are often shocked to hear it and it reminds me that the stigma and stereotyping is very much alive and current.

Charliee

Learning to cope

If I am honest, I don't think there will be a complete recovery, just improving how I cope. But that's not necessarily a pessimistic view, since people with long-term physical diseases, like Parkinson's, learn to cope the best they can.

Garry

Being me

I am me again! I Love Me! I love my heart now, and I love living! I love and enjoy everything about me! I feel good about myself and I have the courage to share with other people my experience; especially when they seek advice or ask me how I managed to get out. The more I've shared, the stronger I've become and the more empowered. It is nothing to be ashamed of. I feel like I won a huge battle for myself. I defeated depression! It has nothing on me! I am Happy!

Linda

Acceptance

I think recovery for me is accepting you are ill and not insane... . In doing so, you acknowledge the problem and begin to move forward. I do not think depression ever leaves you, but you find ways to cope. You recognise the symptoms and signs and are able to seek help and assistance before it gets its ugly little claws into you any deeper. You have to accept you are human, not super-human. I also think that in your recovery you reach a point of helping others to recognise they are ill and point them in the right direction. This is perhaps something you didn't receive yourself.

Claire

To conclude

Never resign yourself to 'this is as good as it gets', because I have learnt, with time, it can always get better. Recovery from depression is possible. It is also personal. Recovery will look different to each and every sufferer and their loved ones. Recovery rarely means getting 'back' the person you had before, but their experiences will have made them wiser, stronger and more empathetic to others. With recovery, they will look forward rather than back, embracing a future rather than harking back to the past.

Recovery is not easy, but it is achievable. Never resign yourself to anything.

Conclusion – from me to you

Over the last 18 years I have fought and won my own battle with depression and have watched my beautiful daughter, Samantha, struggle, gain control of and thankfully conquer her eating disorder and OCD. So, I can honestly say without hesitation, that there is a light at the end of the dark tunnel for most people living with a mental illness and for those caring for them. These powerful and controlling illnesses were so entrenched in my daughter that I did not think it possible for her to make it out to the other side... but she has, as have I. She is free from those crushing, all-consuming shackles and is now chasing her dreams. She has completed and graduated from a stage and media degree, has her own publishing contract and is now writing her own book of very powerful poetry (*Hope Through Poetry*), which is due to be published in May 2020. Samantha is doing and experiencing things that neither she nor any of us ever dared to think possible. I can truthfully say she is the happiest and healthiest I have seen her for many years and every day she continues to challenge herself, taking positive strides towards a future she now knows she has, due in large part to her own perseverance and determination to free herself from the chains of mental illness.

As for myself, I now can say without hesitation that having faced and conquered mental illness and held my daughter's hand as she battled and overcame her own, I have emerged stronger and more confident. Both experiences have set me on a new career path which has enriched my life and still does on a daily basis. Using my new-found knowledge and insight, I have been able not only to help and support other families and their loved ones through to recovery, but to touch many more people's lives through my books, giving them the strength and courage to face and overcome their challenges, just as my husband and I and our daughters have. As a family, we take great strength from knowing that we have been able to turn something so negative in our lives into a force for good, giving others – whether they are the sufferer themselves or their loved ones – the HOPE that mental illness does not have to be a life sentence; that recovery Is possible and sustainable.

I know how it feels to be both a sufferer of depression and a carer for someone who is suffering multiple mental illnesses, so when I say 'Never give up; never settle for this is as good as it gets; and always believe that things can and will get better,' I speak from experience.

I know that caring for someone with a mental illness can be frustrating and exhausting, and can often seem like a thankless task, but please be assured that there is always a way forward. As I have mentioned many times in this book, each and every sufferer is unique and so is their recovery; there is no one-size-fits-all, so finding a course of treatment that is suited to you and/or your loved ones is crucial. If one treatment does not work, do not be afraid to try another and then another… It may take some time before you all find the right path to recovery, but please do not give up. You will find it, remembering always that long-term recovery is possible, provided the sufferer wants it. Explore every avenue you can, ask the professionals as many questions as you need to and do not settle until you are happy with the answers and choices you and your loved ones have made. Keep in mind that it is about the right recovery path, not only for the sufferer but for the family and other loved ones as a whole. Mistakes will be easily made, which is only natural (I made enough of them too), but for every one made, a valuable lesson can be learnt.

Do not be afraid to stand up to the depression or to any other mental illness by staying positive and working together to tackle it. Be prepared for the long haul as any recovery takes time, acceptance and understanding. Patience will need to be exercised at every turn, by everyone involved, but never lose sight of the fact that the person you love is still in there, trapped by the mental illness, waiting for your help to set them free. Your focus should remain entirely on what you can do for them – not what you *cannot* do.

There will also be times when you will need some down-time yourself, so make sure you take time out to catch up with your own friends or to do something else that you enjoy. Spending quality time outside of the restrictions of mental illness will help you to see things with renewed strength and focus, ready to tackle the next challenge that your loved one will face.

And what of the end of the journey, when your loved one has made their recovery? Where does that leave you? It is very common and completely natural to feel mixed emotions at this stage. Your life, which has previously been dominated by your loved one's illness, might feel a little empty and sometimes, as their carer, you might have lost your own identity and direction. I know I did. At this stage, I would highly recommend thinking about some form of support for yourself, such as life coaching sessions. They gave me a new lease of life and enabled me to look forward to a better, brighter future, not just for Samantha but for the family as a whole.

I sincerely hope that, with each chapter, this book has helped you to gain a clearer understanding of this most devastating and sometimes totally misunderstood mental illness and given you the hope that depression can be conquered. Never give up

– families, relationships and lives can be rebuilt. My family is living proof of that.

I will leave you with my guiding principle:

The cure is in the recovery. There is no elevator; you have to take the stairs.

Yours with hope…
Lynn Crilly x

Kevin leaves you with:

I have been around mental illness for years and as much as I have tried I still don't understand it. What I do know now is that if it isn't treated and the sufferer doesn't receive help it's not going away and could manifest into something much worse! Thankfully my lovely Sam is back with us now, from wherever she was.

Charlotte leaves you with:

At times, it can be hard to come to terms with why mental illness chose your family and loved one to hurt. When I look back now, I realise that I wouldn't change anything, otherwise we wouldn't be where we are today. I do feel in the long run it has brought us all closer together, especially my relationship with my sister.

Samantha finishes with her words of HOPE:

I know and believe that everyone has the strength to beat their demons. It won't be easy; it will probably be one of the hardest challenges you will ever face. But one thing I can promise from the bottom of my heart is that when you come out the other side you will feel exhilarated with life, you will see beautiful things around you that you never noticed before and, most of all, you will feel an abundance of freedom and power in yourself. Trust me on this one – you will never ever regret recovery.

Resources

Charities

SANE

Website: www.sane.org.uk

Tel: 0300 304 7000 (4.30 pm – 10.30 pm daily)

SANE is a UK-wide charity working to improve quality of life for people affected by mental illness. It has three main objectives linked to its aims and outcomes:

1. To raise awareness and combat stigma about mental illness, educating and campaigning to improve mental health services
2. To provide care and emotional support for people with mental health problems, their families and carers, as well as information for other organisations and the public
3. To initiate research into the causes and treatments of serious mental illness, such as schizophrenia and depression, and the psychological and social impact of mental illness.

SANE offers emotional support and information to anyone affected by mental health problems through their helpline, email services and online Support Forum where people share

their feelings and experiences.
Registered Charity Number: 296572

Samaritans
www.samaritans.org and for Republic of Ireland: www.
samaritans.org/ireland/branches/
Tel: 116 123 (UK) / 116 123 (Republic of Ireland)

Samaritans offer a safe place for you to talk any time you like, in your own way – about whatever's getting to you. They are available round the clock, 24 hours a day, 365 days a year. If you need a response immediately, it's best to call Samaritans on the phone. This number is FREE to call.

Samaritans is a charity registered in England and Wales (219432) and in Scotland (SC040604).

Pieta House with 18 centres throughout the Republic of Ireland www.pieta.ie/

'In 2006, Pieta House opened its doors in Lucan, County Dublin and since that day we have seen and helped over 40,000 people in suicidal distress or engaging in self-harm, and established fifteen subsequent centres across Ireland... In 2018 alone, nearly 8,000 people came through our doors suffering from suicidal ideation and/or engaging in self-harm, or to avail of suicide bereavement counselling.'

The Grace Dear Trust
www.thegracedeartrust.co.uk
Facebook: @gracedeartrust Twitter: @GraceDearTrust1
Instagram: @gracedeartrust

The Grace Dear Trust is a Surrey-based Mental Health charity spreading and raising awareness around Surrey.

The Grace Dear Trust was set up in memory of Grace, who was a loving member of the Dear family and an amazing friend to many. She died in early 2017 after suffering from mental health problems for a number of years, in part falling victim to the inability to communicate her problems early enough or effectively enough to save her life.

'It's ok not to be ok'
Registered charity number: 1175955

The Frank Bruno Foundation
www.thefrankbrunofoundation.co.uk
0800 368 8196

'We are aiming to bring together the benefits of non-contact boxing with a solution focused well-being programme. The aim is to bring healthy-body and healthy-mind approaches together to provide a holistic and enjoyable approach to supporting people with mental health problems. The aim is to help people to develop a healthier body and a healthier mind, building on their existing physical and emotional strengths and achievements. Our aspiration is that people will use the skills they learn on the programme to develop a happier, more fulfilling and successful future.'
Registered charity number: 1171012

Zero Suicide Alliance
www.zerosuicidealliance.com

The Zero Suicide Alliance is a collaborative of National Health Service trusts, businesses and individuals who are all committed to suicide prevention in the UK and beyond. The alliance is ultimately concerned with improving support for people contemplating suicide by raising awareness of and promoting FREE suicide prevention training which is accessible to all. The aims of this training are: to enable people to identify when someone is presenting with suicidal thoughts/behaviour, to be able to speak out in a supportive manner, and to empower them to guide the individual to the correct services or support.

The MindEd Trust
themindedtrust.org

The MindEd Trust is a Registered Charity which is focused on the prevention of mental illness in young people and early intervention strategies for those experiencing trauma.

The Trust has been established following the tragic death of Edward Mallen, an outstanding young man who took his life on the railway following the inexplicable, rapid and catastrophic onset of severe depression in February 2015.

We mind what happened to Edward Mallen and we will do all we can to avert similar tragedies through the prevention and alleviation of mental ill-health amongst young people.

Via mindEducation programmes, we are minded to improve mental health for young people. Key objectives include:

- To promote and assist in the creation of embedded, whole school mental illness prevention and early intervention programmes throughout the education system.
- To destroy the stigma and guilt associated with mental ill-health so that people experiencing trauma come forward early and openly to seek help. On moral, social and economic grounds, prevention is far better than cure, enhancing resilience and preventing people falling into crisis.

- To actively press for urgent policy and funding reform throughout the education and health system, ensuring that parity of esteem is matched by parity of funding and parity of care.

Please note, this charity does not provide direct assistance. Registered charity number: 1163922

NSPCC
www.nspcc.org.uk

NSPCC stands for the National Society for the Prevention of Cruelty to Children

It means that each of us has a responsibility to keep childhood free from abuse, and we must do everything possible to protect children and prevent it from happening.
- Help for adults concerned about a child – 0808 800 5000
- Help for children and young people – call Childline on 0800 1111
- For donation and fundraising queries – 020 7825 2505

Registered charity number: 216401

Irish Society for Prevention of Cruelty to Children
www.ispcc.ie/contact-us Email info@ispcc.ie Tel: l 01 676 7960.

Parkinson's UK
www.parkinsons.org.uk

Our vision – our ultimate ambition – is to find a cure, and improve life for everyone affected by Parkinson's. The hopes and views of people affected by Parkinson's have helped us form our clear vision for the future. We believe a cure will be found by overcoming the symptoms of Parkinson's one by one.

A registered charity in England and Wales (258197) and in Scotland (SC037554).

Parkinson's Association of Ireland
www.parkinsons.ie / Tel: 1 800 359 359

Professionals

Vivienne Barnes – Well-being coach at Woolston Well Being
www.wellbeing-emotionalhealth.com; email: Vivienne@
wellbeing-emotionalhealth.com Twitter: @wellbewoolston
Check out Vivienne's website, the dates of her workshops or
indeed how you can organise one for a group of friends or at
your place of work.

Gill Bescoby BSc (hons), Lic Ac, MBAcC – Acupuncturist
Based in Chichester, West Sussex.
www.maihealing.co.uk Tel: 01243 514606 Mobile: 07515709405
email: gill@maihealing.co.uk

Jeff Brazier – Life coach, NLP practitioner, TV presenter
www.jeffbraziercoaching.com

Judith Cocking – Resilience and performance coach
Mobile: 07947 353653 Email: judithc@unwindyourminduk.co.uk
Facebook: @unwindyourmind

**Dionne Curtis DipIPch – Hypnotherapist, NLP practitioner
and TFT practitioner**
www.whatiftherapy.co.uk Email: dionne@whatiftherapy.co.uk
Tel: 07533149242

Dr Ian Drever MB ChB, MRCPsych
Founder Director, Academy of Mental Fitness at Esher Groves
www.eshergroves.com Tel: 0345 1122300

Kate Guest – Registered general nurse, Mindset coach, trainer, speaker
Also trained as a: hypnotherapist, NLP Master Practitioner, EMDR practitioner, Auricular Acupressure and Acupuncture practitioner, PsyTaP practitioner, Reiki practitioner, SleepTalk – Children's Resilience practitioner, Further Education teacher
www.kate-guest.co.uk Email: info@kate-guest.co.uk
Tel: 07790303806 and 01626 833306

Jay Hurley – Personal trainer at Body Fusion Fitnesss
www.bodyfusion.fitness Email: jayhurley@hotmail.co.uk
Tel: 07774320855

Catherine Kell
Helping women and mothers connect deeply with their authentic self, and parents connect deeply with their children. Mindfulness / Self-Compassion / Connection Online coaching and programmes.
www.catherinekell.com Email: info@catherinekell.com
Instagram: @catherinekell

Rachel Kelly
www.rachel-kelly.net Twitter: @rachelkellynet
Rachel's books include her memoir *Black Rainbow* about her expression of depression and three subsequent books about her recovery and how to stay calm and well: *Walking on Sunshine: 52 Small Steps to Happiness*, *The Happy Kitchen: Good Mood Food*; and *Singing in the Rain: An inspirational workbook* published in January 2019.

Kevin Laye DPsy psychotherapist and founder of Psy-TaP,
published author and international trainer and speaker
For training www.psy-tap.com www.kevinlaye.co.uk Email:
cameltrain@aol.com Tel: 07803 161021 Skype: Kevin.Laye1

Neil Long – Voice and confidence coach
www.becomefree.co.uk

Stephen T Mallen
Chair of The MindEd Trust: www.themindedtrust.org Email:
mallenfamily@btinternet.com Facebook: @themindedtrust
Board of Governors – Cambridgeshire & Peterborough NHS
Foundation Trust
Co-founder – Zero Suicide Alliance
www.zerosuicidealliance.com ZeroSuicideAlliance
Member: National Suicide Prevention Group – Dept of Health
& Social Care

Christina McDermid – Holistic therapist, reflexologist, Reiki
master and teacher, teacher of meditation
Tel: 07748 396642

Michele Paradise – Harley Street practitioner of NLP,
Havening techniques and clinical hypnotherapist, published
author, international trainer and speaker and personal
development coach with Deepak Chopra
www.changeyourmindforgood.com Tel: 07958607599

Debbie Pennington – Yoga and massage specialist CThA
www.holisticmeadow.co.uk Email: debcobb@hotmail.co.uk
Facebook: @holisticmeadow

Leanne Poyner – Personal performance and life coach
leannepoyner@yahoo.com Tel: 07868 650021

Tan Quddus – Personal trainer
Instagram: @tanqud

Lyndy Stanway Marsh – Health and peak performance coach, Director UKHCA
www.lyndystanwaymarsh.com Email: info@lyndystanwaymarsh.com Facebook: @MyHealthyAlternative
Twitter: @LyndyStanwayMar

Laura Whitcher – Massage therapist at Wellness Aware
lwhitcher@hotmail.com Tel: 07532202884

Nicholas Warburton – Psy-TaP practitioner
www.improvemymindset.com

Contributors

The following are all happy to be contacted.

Jamie Batt
Jamie posts support, fundraising and volunteering on his Facebook page which you can find here: www.facebook.com/jamie.batt.16

Nikki Blissett – Mental health advocate, blogger and freelance writer
www.digitalbutterfly.life Twitter: @DgtlButterfly
Pinterest: DigitalButterfly Email: nikkiblissett@gmail.com

Frank Bruno MBE
Charity www.thefrankbrunofoundation.co.uk
www.frankbruno.co.uk Twitter: Frankbrunoboxer Facebook:
Frank Bruno MBE

Bobby Davro – TV comedian, impressionist, singer, actor
Twitter: @BobbyDavro1

Jamie Day
www.adayinthelifedad.com Podcast: Man Talk – tackling
MENtal health (available on all podcast platforms) Instagram:
@adayinthelifedad

Aiden Hatfield – In Music We Trust
A music-inspired clothing brand. 50% of profits are donated to
the mental health charity MIND.
www.inmusicwetrust.co.uk Twitter: @imwtclothing and @
AidenHatfield

Me and My Mental Health Matters
meandmymentalhealthmatters.wordpress.com
Twitter: @Meandmymhmatter Facebook: facebook.
com / meandmymentalhealthmatters Instagram: @
meandmymhmatters

References

Chapter 1: What is depression?

1. Anxiety or depression affects nearly one in five UK adults. *The Guardian*. www.theguardian.com/society/2013/jun/19/anxiety-depression-office-national-statistics. [accessed 9/4/19]

2. Lisa Rapaport. Anxiety, depression tied to higher risk of heart attack, stroke. *Reuters*. https://uk.reuters.com/article/us-health-mood-heart/anxiety-depression-tied-to-higher-risk-of-heart-attack-stroke-idUKKCN1LD2GN. [accessed 04/06/2019]

3. Supporting Carers to be Healthy and Connected Research Summary for Carers Week 2018. *Carers UK*. www.carersweek.org/images/Resources/CW18_Research_Report.pdf. [accessed 9/4/19]

4. Comorbid Depression: Depression and Another Mental Illness. *Healthy Place*. www.healthyplace.com/other-info/mental-health-newsletter/comorbid-depression-depression-and-another-mental-illness. [accessed 04/06/2019]

Chapter 2: Types of depression

5. Woody CA, Ferrari AJ, Siskind DJ, Whiteford HA, et al. A systematic review and meta-regression of the prevalence and incidence of perinatal depression. *Journal of affective disorders*. 2017;219:86–92. doi: 10.1016

6. Action on Postpartum Psychosis. www.app-network.org/. [accessed 9/4/19]

Chapter 3: Recognising depression and seeking treatment

7. Hannah Perlin. Long waits for mental health treatment lead to divorce, job loss and money problems, RCPsych finds. *Royal College of Psychiatrists*. www.rcpsych.ac.uk/news-and-features/latest-news/detail/2018/10/08/long-waits-for-mental-health-treatment-lead-to-divorce-job-loss-and-money-problems-rcpsych-finds. [accessed 9/4/19]

Chapter 4: A guide to therapies

8. Apaydin EA, Maher AR, Shanman R, et al. A systematic review of St. John's wort for major depressive disorder. *Syst Rev* 2016; 5(1): 148. . doi:10.1186/s13643-016-0325-2

9. Ng QX, Venkatanarayanan N, Ho CY. Clinical use of Hypericum perforatum (St John's wort) in depression: A meta-analysis. *J Affect Disord* 2017; 210: 211-221. doi: 10.1016/j.jad.2016.12.048.

10. Depression Alliance Staff. Understanding the Truth Behind Hypnotherapy. *Depression Alliance*. www.depressionalliance.org/hypnotherapy/. [accessed 9/4/19]

11. Callahan R.J. and J. Callahan. and Chapter 18: TFT and Heart Rate Variability. *Rebprotocol* www.rebprotocol.net/heartrate.pdf. [accessed 9/4/19]

12. Luke Walton. Depression's physical source discovered; potential for new treatments. *The University or Warwick* https://warwick.ac.uk/newsandevents/news/depression146s_physical_source/. [accessed 17/6/2019]

13. Wollmer MA, de Boer C, Kalak N , Beck J, et al. Facing depression with botulinum toxin: A randomized controlled trial. *Journal of Psychiatric Research* 2012; 46: 574-581.

Chapter 5: Depression and well-being

14. Young SN. How to increase serotonin in the human brain without drugs. *J Psychiatry Neurosci* 2007; 32(6): 394-399.

15. Penedo FJ, Dahn JR. Exercise and well-being: a review of mental and physical health benefits associated with physical activity.

Current Opinion in Psychiatry 2005; 18(2): 189–193.

16. Allen JJB. Depression and acupuncture: a controlled clinical trial. *Psychiatric Times Online* 2000; 22: 3.

17. All-Party Parliamentary Group on Arts, Health and Wellbeing Inquiry Report. Creative Health: The Arts for Health and Wellbeing. *Arts Health and Wellbeing*. www.artshealthandwellbeing.org.uk/appg-inquiry/Publications/Creative_Health_Inquiry_Report_2017_-_Second_Edition.pdf. [accessed 15/04/2019]

Chapter 6: Depression and other illnesses

18. Self-harm in over 8s: long term management. Clinical Guideline 133. *The National Institute for Health and Care Excellence*. www.nice.org.uk/guidance/cg133/resources/selfharm-in-over-8s-longterm-management-35109508689349. [accessed 23/04/19].

19. Singhal A, Ross J, Seminog O, Hawton K, Goldacre MJ. Risk of self-harm and suicide in people with specific psychiatric and physical disorders: comparisons between disorders using English national record linkage. *Journal of the Royal Society of Medicine*. 2014;107: 194–204. doi: 10.1371/journal.pone.0216317

20. Hurley K. Anorexia and depression. *Psycom*. www.psycom.net/anorexia-and-depression. [accessed 17/06/2019]

21. Presnell K, Stice E, Seidel A, Madeley MC. Depression and eating pathology: prospective reciprocal relations in adolescents. *Clin Psychol Psychother*. 2009;16(4):357-65.]

22. Pallanti S, Grassi G, Sarrecchia ED, Cantisani A, Pellegrine M. Obsessive-compulsive disorder comorbidity: clinical assessment and therapeutic implications. *Front Psychiatry* 2011; 2: 70. www.ncbi.nlm.nih.gov/pmc/articles/PMC3243905/. [accessed 23/04/19]

23. Causes: Post-Traumatic Stress Disorder. *NHS*. www.nhs.uk/conditions/post-traumatic-stress-disorder-ptsd/causes/- [accessed 17/06/2019]

24. Angelakis, S., & Nixon, R. (2015). The Comorbidity of PTSD and MDD: Implications for Clinical Practice and Future Research. Behaviour Change, 32(1), 1-25. doi:10.1017/bec.2014.26

25. Matthew Toll, PHD. The Relationship Between PTSD and

Depression. *Very Well Mind*. www.verywellmind.com/ptsd-and-depression-2797533 – [accessed 17/06/2019]

26. Post-Traumatic Stress Disorder NICE Guidelines [NG116]. *The National Institute for Health and Care Excellence* www.nice.org.uk/guidance/ng116/chapter/Recommendations. [accessed 17/06/2019]

27. Josephine A Beatson and Sathya Rao. Depression and borderline personality disorder. *The Medical Journal of Australia*. www.mja.com.au/journal/2013/199/6/depression-and-borderline-personality-disorder#0_BABIBBI. [accessed 23/04/19]

28. Kristalyn Salters-Pedneault, P. A Guide to When BPD and Depression Occur Together. *Very Well Mind* www.verywellmind.com/bpd-and-depression-425421. [accessed 23/04/19].

29. Kathleen Smith, PhD, LPC. Schizophrenia and Depression Understanding The Symptoms, Risks, & Treatment Considerations. *Psycom*. www.psycom.net/schizophrenia-and-depression. [accessed 23/04/19]

30. Alcohol and Depression. *Royal College of Psychiatrists*. www.rcpsych.ac.uk/mental-health/problems-disorders/alcohol-and-depression. [accessed 23/04/19]

31. Naylor C, et al. Long-term conditions and mental health, the cost of co-morbidities. *Centre for Mental Health* The Kings Fund, February 2012.

32. Coping With Chronic Illnesses and Depression. *WebMD*. www.webmd.com/depression/depression-caused-chronic-illness#1. [accessed 23/04/19]

33. Pitman Alexandra, Suleman Sahil, Hyde Nicholas, Hodgkiss Andrew. Depression and anxiety in patients with cancer BMJ 2018; 361 :k1415.

34. Parkinson's and Depression. *Parkinson's UK*. www.parkinsons.org.uk/information-and-support/depression. [accessed 17/06/2019]

35. Dennett, Kathryn Tometich, Danielle and Duff, Kevin. Demographic Corrections for the Modified Telephone Interview for Cognitive Status. *The Clinical Neuropsychologist*, 2013. Vol. 27, Issue. 7, p. 1121.

36. Regina Castro, M.D. Diabetes and depression: Coping with the two conditions. *Mayo Clinic*. www.mayoclinic.org/diseases-

conditions/diabetes/expert-answers/diabetes-and-depression/faq-20057904. [accessed 17/6/2019]

37. Ian Johnston. Depression doubles the risk of from coronary artery diseas, research finds. *Independent.* www.independent.co.uk/life-style/health-and-families/health-news/depression-coronary-artery-disease-double-risk-research-a7864401.html. [accessed 17/6/2019]

38. Walker AK. Neuroinflammation and comorbidity of pain and depression. *American Society for Pharmacology and Experimental Therapeutics* 2013; 66(1): 80-101.

39. Outcalt SD, et al. Chronic pain and comorbid mental health conditions: independent associations of post traumatic stress disorder and depression with pain, disability, and quality of life. *Springer Science & Business* 2015; 38: 535-543.

40. Dimitriadis Z, Kapreli E, Strimpakos N, Oldham JA. Do psycholigical states associate with pain and disability in chronic neck pain patients? *Journal of Back and Musculoskeletal Rehabilitation* 2015; 28(4): 1-6.

41. Holmes A, Christelis N, Arnold C. Depression and chronic pain. *Medical Journal of Australia* 2012; 199(6): 17-20.

42. IASP, 2017. International Association for the Study of Pain. [Online] Available at: https://www.iasp-pain.org/Education/Content.aspx?ItemNumber=1698 [accessed 03 02 2019]

43. Gifford L. *Aches and Pains* 1st ed. CNS Press, 2014.

44. Polaski AM, Phelps AL, Kostek MC, Szucs KA, Kolber BJ. Exercise-induced hypoalgesia: A meta-analysis of exercise dosing for the treatment of chronic pain. Regnaux J-P, editor. PLoS One [Internet]. 2019. January 9 [cited 2019 Jan 25];14(1):e0210418

45. Hidden issues: depression. *Carers UK.* www.carersuk.org/help-and-advice/health/looking-after-your-health/stress-and-depression/hidden-issue-depression. [accessed 17/6/2019]

Chapter 7: Depression and the risk of suicide

46. Suicide Facts and Figures. *Samaritans.* www.samaritans.org/sites/default/files/suicide_statistics_report_final_dec.pdf. [accessed 21/03/2019]

47. Hawton K, Houston K, Haw C, Townsend E, Harriss L.

Comorbidity of Axis I and Axis II Disorders in Patients who attempted Suicide. *American Journal of Psychiatry* 2003; 160(8): 1494-1500

48. World Health Organization (2017). Depression and Other Common Mental Disorders. http://apps.who.int/iris/bitstream/handle/10665/254610/WHOMSD?sequence=1. [accessed 21/03/2019]

Chapter 8: Depression in the under 25s

49. Mental Health of Children and Young People in England, 2017. *NHS Digital*. https://digital.nhs.uk/news-and-events/latest-news/one-in-eight-of-five-to-19-year-olds-had-a-mental-disorder-in-2017-major-new-survey-finds. [accessed 21/03/2019]
50. One in three teachers fears harm for pupils waiting for mental health treatment. *Stem4*. https://stem4.org.uk/one-in-three-teachers-fears-harm-for-pupils-waiting-for-mental-health-treatment/. [accessed 21/03/2019]
51. Mental health statistics: poverty. *Mental Health Foundation*. www.mentalhealth.org.uk/statistics/mental-health-statistics-poverty. [accessed 10/06/2019]
52. Children and Young People with Learning Disabilities: Understanding their mental health. *Young Minds*. http://vox.mtcserver3.com/wp-content/uploads/2015/01/Children-Young-People-with-Learning-Disabilities.pdf. [accessed 10/10/2019]
53. Depression and Autism. *Autisica*. www.autistica.org.uk/what-is-autism/signs-and-symptoms/depression-and-autism. [accessed 23/04/19]
54. One in eight of five to 19 year olds had a mental disorder in 2017 major new survey finds. *NHS Digital*. https://digital.nhs.uk/news-and-events/latest-news/one-in-eight-of-five-to-19-year-olds-had-a-mental-disorder-in-2017-major-new-survey-finds. [accessed 23/04/19]
55. Vallerand IA, Lewinson RT, Parsons LM, Lowerison MW, et al. Risk of depression among patients with acne in the U.K.: a population-based cohort study. *British Journal of Dermatology* 2018; 178(3): e194-e195 DOI: 10.1111/bjd.16099

56. Tony Draper. On average three children in every class have a mental health issue: and yet funding is being cut. *TES*. www.tes.com/news/average-three-children-every-class-have-mental-health-issue-and-yet-funding-being-cut. [accessed 23/04/19]

57. FOI request by Libdems, reported Jan 2018, www.theguardian.com/education/2018/jan/11/epidemic-of-stress-blamed-for-3750-teachers-on-longterm-sick-leave. [accessed 21/03/2019]

58. *Mental Health Foundation*. Promoting Student Mental Health (January 2001)

Chapter 9: Depression in the home

59. Mental Health and Rough Sleeping report, 2016 *St Mungo's*. www.mungos.org/homelessness. [accessed 25/04/19]

Chapter 10: Depression in the workplace

60. 12 statistics to get you thinking about mental health in young people. *MQ Transforming Mental Health through Research*. www.mqmentalhealth.org/posts/12-statistics. [accessed 17/6/2019]

61. Mental Health at Work Report 2017. *Business in the Community*. https://wellbeing.bitc.org.uk/system/files/research/bitcmental_health_at_work_report-2017.pdf. [accessed 17/6/2019]

62. Mental ill-health in the workplace is costing UK employers billions. *ACAS*. www.acas.org.uk/index.aspx?articleid=3915 - [accessed 17/6/2019]

63. Bullying at work *NHS*. www.nhs.uk/conditions/stress-anxiety-depression/bullying-at-work/ - [accessed 17/6/2019]

64. Suicide by occupation, England: 2011 to 2015 ONS 2017 *Office for National Statistics*. www.ons.gov.uk/peoplepopulationandcommunity/birthsdeathsandmarriages/deaths/articles/suicidebyoccupation/england2011to2015. [accessed 17/6/2019]

65. Ashleigh Webber. Hot desking affects wellbeing for eight in 10 office workers. *Personnel Today*. www.personneltoday.com/hr/hot-desking-affects-wellbeing-for-eight-in-10-office-workers/. [accessed 23/04/19]

Chapter 11: Depression and the online world

66. Michelle W Berger. Social media use increases depression and loneliness. *Penn Today*. https://penntoday.upenn.edu/news/ social-media-use-increases-depression-and-loneliness. [accessed 14/5/19]

67. Eleanor Harding. Social media does NOT harm teenagers, Oxford study says amid claims online activity only has a 'trivial' effect on their happiness. *Mail Online*. www.dailymail.co.uk/ news/article-6999807/Social-media-does-not-harm-teenagers-Oxford-study-says.html. [accessed 14/5/19]

68. Children and Parents: Media Use and Attitudes Report. *OFCOM*. www.ofcom.org.uk/__data/assets/pdf_file/0020/108182/ children-parents-media-use-attitudes-2017.pdf. [accessed 14/5/19]

69. Social Media Use Associated With Depression Among U.S. Young Adults. *UPMC Life Changing Medicine*. www.upmc.com/media/ news/lin-primack-sm-depression. [accessed 14/5/19]

70. #StatusOfMind. In May 2017, RSPH and the Young Health Movement published a report examining the positive and negative effects of social media on young people's health. *Royal Society for Public Health*. www.rsph.org.uk/our-work/ campaigns/status-of-mind.html. [accessed 14/5/19]

Index

Index

Index

Also from Lynn Crilly

Hope with OCD

www.hammersmithbooks.co.uk/product/hope-with-ocd

Hope with Eating Disorders

www.hammersmithbooks.co.uk/product/
hope-with-eating-disorders